Molecular Structure and the Properties of Liquid Crystals

Molecular Structure and the Properties of Liquid Crystals

G. W. GRAY

Department of Chemistry
The University of Hull, England

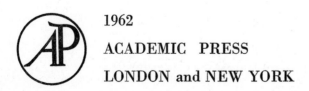

1962
ACADEMIC PRESS
LONDON and NEW YORK

ACADEMIC PRESS INC. (LONDON) LTD.
BERKELEY SQUARE HOUSE
BERKELEY SQUARE
LONDON, W.1

U.S. Edition published by

ACADEMIC PRESS INC.
111 FIFTH AVENUE
NEW YORK 3, NEW YORK

Library of Congress Catalog Card Number 61:18803

PRINTED IN GREAT BRITAIN BY THE WHITEFRIARS PRESS LTD.
LONDON AND TONBRIDGE

ƆNULP

PREFACE

THE first liquid crystalline compound was discovered in 1888, and during the intervening seventy-three years both physicists and chemists have worked towards obtaining a better understanding of these unique states of matter variously described as liquid crystalline or mesomorphic. The physicist has studied their singular physical properties, and the chemist has sought to establish the structural features which a compound should possess in order that it may exhibit liquid crystalline properties. Knowledge relating to the physical and chemical aspects of mesomorphic systems has expanded rapidly indeed, and the study of liquid crystals no longer constitutes a small, specialist topic.

In recent years organic chemists have directed their efforts away from the synthesis of larger numbers of more obscure mesomorphic compounds, and towards making systematic modifications to the structures of known liquid crystalline compounds, with a view to rationalizing knowledge concerning molecular structure and mesomorphic behaviour. This book has been written primarily to describe developments in this particular field, and to correlate material contained in very many individual publications.

Secondly, however, it is hoped that " Molecular Structure and the Properties of Liquid Crystals " fills what is felt to be a gap; for, apart from review articles, no text on liquid crystals has been written in English, and twenty years have elapsed since the last book of note on this subject was published in Germany. The book would not have served this last purpose had an adequate description and review of the physical properties of mesophases not been included. The first chapters have therefore been devoted to this end, emphasizing in particular those studies of physical behaviour which have made possible the assignment of molecular orientations to the different liquid crystalline states.

Whilst the book will appeal primarily to those who are engaged in research on liquid crystals, it is hoped that its content will be of value to all students of chemistry and physics, to those interested in the part played by intermolecular forces in determining the properties of matter in general, and to organic chemists, who should be familiar with any abnormal melting phenomena which may be confused with the effects of contamination of a compound with impurity.

Such is the extent of present-day knowledge of thermotropic liquid crystalline systems, that in a book of this size no attempt has been made to cover lyotropic liquid crystalline systems or the liquid crystal line properties of biological systems.

I wish to express my thanks to Dr. Brynmor Jones, Vice-Chancellor of Hull University, who first stimulated my interest in the study of liquid crystals, and to those who have collaborated with me at different times in research on mesomorphic systems—Dr. A. Ibbotson, Dr. B. M. Worrall, Dr. D. J. Byron, Mr. J. B. Hartley, Mr. F. Marson, and Mr. P. Culling. I also thank Dr. Byron for reading the manuscript and making many useful and constructive criticisms of it, and for compiling the index.

November, 1961   G. W. Gray

CONTENTS

CHAPTER I

INTRODUCTION

SINCE the very early days of science, it has been recognized that, under appropriate conditions of temperature and pressure, matter may exist in three possible states of aggregation—the solid, the isotropic liquid, and the gas. The solid state may be either crystalline—when the solid is comprised of a regular, three-dimensional array of molecules or ions— or amorphous. In the latter case, the regular geometric arrangement is absent, and there exists a random, though well-knit, arrangement of the units in the solid state. The majority of organic and inorganic compounds give rise to solid states which are crystalline, and indeed these crystalline characteristics and properties are often present even although the solid may appear on casual inspection to be an amorphous powder. The regular, repeating pattern of the lattice units for a given compound may sometimes alter with changing conditions of temperature and pressure. This change from one crystal form to another is known as dimorphism, trimorphism, or polymorphism, dependent upon the number of different crystal modifications which are manifested. These changes of the polymorphic type are frequently encountered when organic compounds are heated, but are seldom visible when the melting point of the compound is determined using a small sample of the material contained in a capillary tube. The crystalline solid may therefore be regarded as the most highly ordered state of aggregation in which matter exists.

When the crystal lattice is heated, the thermal vibrations increase with increasing temperature, until the molecules are no longer able to maintain themselves in their regular arrangement. At a given temperature therefore, the crystal begins to melt, and the state of aggregation changes to that of the isotropic liquid. The intermolecular cohesions have now been weakened to such an extent that individual molecules or groups of molecules possess freedom of movement and assume a generally disorganized arrangement. Dependent upon the degree to which the liquid is heated above the melting point, some molecular order doubtless persists within groups of molecules, but these ordered regions are unable to confer crystalline properties—i.e. anistropy, etc.—upon the bulk of the liquid, nor are they able to prevent the characteristic flowing properties of liquids. In inorganic systems, the melting points are usually high—a rough range would be $500 \pm 200°C$—since the strong interionic attractions in the crystals are difficult to overcome. In organic compounds, the weaker intermolecular cohesions give rise to lower melting points—in very many cases well below 250°C. Despite the profound changes in the state of aggregation which occur at the melting point, this change is usually exceedingly sharp for an organic compound, and is normally a characteristic property of the system. The melting point of an organic compound is therefore a criterion which may be used for its identification and as a means of assessing its purity, since impurity normally depresses the melting point and protracts the melting process over a range of temperature. It should of course be remembered that these are generalizations, that certain organic compounds undergo chemical decomposition before or during the melting process, and that others may sublime, i.e. pass into the gas phase without giving the intermediate liquid state.

At still higher temperatures, the remaining intermolecular or inter-ionic attractions are unable to maintain the units in the condensed liquid state, and vaporization proceeds rapidly. The liquid then boils, and in the case of an organic compound, the molecules pass into the freedom of the gas phase. Here they lead an independent existence, separated from and uninfluenced by other molecules. Provided that no thermal decomposition occurs, the change from the isotropic liquid to the gas again occurs at a well-defined temperature, the boiling point.

On passing from the crystal to the isotropic liquid to the gas phase, the degree of molecular order therefore decreases, and the transitions from crystal to liquid and from liquid to gas occur, particularly in the case of organic compounds, at well-defined temperatures which are characteristic of a particular compound.

However, towards the end of the nineteenth century, in 1888, Reinitzer[1] prepared a number of esters of cholesterol in which he observed a new and peculiar melting phenomenon. In the case of cholesteryl benzoate, the crystals melted perfectly sharply at 145·5°, but the melt was quite definitely opaque. Not until the temperature was increased to 178·5° did the opacity disappear suddenly, giving the true isotropic liquid. Although Reinitzer is generally regarded as the first to have observed such behaviour, Lehmann[2] claimed to have noticed similar properties with silver iodide between the temperatures 146° and 450°. Although this " plastic " behaviour of silver iodide is no longer classed with the type of phenomenon observed by Reinitzer, Lehmann did report in 1890[3] that ammonium oleate and p-azoxyphenetole exhibit these turbid states between the truly crystalline and truly liquid conditions. The literature at this time contains a number of papers by Reinitzer[4] and Lehmann[5] in which their relative claims for priority in observing these phenomena are contested, at times quite acrimoniously. In fact, credit belongs to both Reinitzer and Lehmann for their observations and for their initial work in establishing some of the characteristic properties of these states. Thus, it became clear that, whilst these turbid states were fluid to a greater or lesser extent, they also exhibited anisotropic properties when viewed in thin section between crossed polaroids. Their characteristics were therefore partly those of the crystalline solid and partly those of the liquid. To describe this apparent anomaly, Lehmann used the terms " Fliessende Krystalle " or " Flüssige Krystalle "—i.e. flowing or fluid crystals—for these states, and this terminology persists today in the terms liquid crystals, crystalline liquids, and liquid crystalline behaviour.

Terminology too was the subject of several papers in subsequent years, the relative merits and disadvantages of different types of nomenclature being hotly debated. Thus, as more of the properties of these liquid crystals became known, it was obvious that here indeed was a new state of matter, and Friedel[6] in particular stressed that, although these states did exhibit some of the properties of crystalline matter and some of the properties of an isotropic liquid, they were neither genuinely crystalline nor liquid. To quote Friedel from the *Annales de Physique*— " Quelque répugnance que l'on puisse éprouver pour l'introduction de termes nouveaux, on voit qu'il est de toute nécessité, s'il en est ainsi, de disposer d'un adjectif pour désigner sans ambiguité de ces formes, au même titre que les adjectifs cristallisé (ou cristallin) et amorphe servent à désigner les formes, substances, phases, etc. appartenant aux deux types antérieurement connus." In this way he criticized the nomenclature based on the term liquid crystal, and proposed that it would be preferable to refer to a liquid crystalline state as a *mesophase*. This term, derived from the Greek, *mesos*, between or intermediate, and *phasis*, a state or phase, does stress the intermediate nature of these states of matter. This term and the associated terms mesomorph, mesomorphism, mesomorphic, and mesoform are indeed widely used today, although references to liquid crystals are still frequently encountered in the literature. The persistence of the older nomenclature may well stem from the inherent attractiveness of using the apparently contradictory terms liquid and crystal in conjunction. More recently, Rinne[7] criticized both terminologies on the basis that they had no structural meaning. Rinne classified matter as exhibiting either ataxy (a disordered or amorphous structure) or eutaxy (an ordered structure). The mesomorphic and crystalline states will belong to the class of eutactites, since they possess ordered structures. To subdivide this class, Rinne suggested the term paracrystalline to describe the mesomorphic state. This term includes the word crystalline in order to emphasize the natural proximity of the state to the crystalline condition, and the prefix para- to remind us that many of the organic compounds which possess this type of eutaxy are *para*-substituted benzene derivatives. Thus, the classification is:

(1) Atactites—isotropic liquids, gases, and amorphous matter.
(2) Eutactites—(a) crystals—three-dimensional order
                (b) paracrystals—one- or two-dimensional order.

Rinne's nomenclature has not been adopted to any significant extent.

The discovery of these mesomorphic states attracted the attention of a number of chemists in the early twentieth century. Notable amongst these were Lehmann and Vörlander who, in a short number of years, prepared over 250 compounds which exhibited this type of behaviour. The increased availability of compounds manifesting these properties then led to more detailed physical studies of the mesophases themselves, and Friedel is particularly noted for his optical studies which are described and beautifully illustrated in his lengthy article in the *Annales de Physique* of 1922.[6] Despite the number of cases of mesomorphic behaviour which were soon reported, a number of years elapsed before it was universally accepted that a mesomorphic state is a true state of matter intermediate between the solid and the isotropic liquid. The writings of Tamman, Nernst, and Quincke[8] described these melting phenomena as stemming from the colloidal effect of small crystals suspended in the isotropic liquid, or from the presence of impurities in the compounds, giving an emulsion of two liquids. Eventually, however, mesomorphic behaviour was observed in so many compounds, often of quite simple chemical constitution, that attempts to explain the origin of the mesophases in terms of impurity became untenable, and were ultimately abandoned when it was found that a mesophase gives a clear field of view in the ultramicroscope. Furthermore, the transitions between the solid and a given mesophase, and between the mesophase and the isotropic liquid are perfectly well-defined and reproducible, features which would be unlikely to characterize " transitions " arising from impurity or colloidal effects.

As a result of his detailed optical studies, Friedel[6] was able to distinguish clearly three different types of mesophase. These will be considered in more detail in a subsequent chapter, but it is important to record now the names which Friedel used to describe these mesophases. They were:

(a) *The smectic mesophase*—a turbid, viscous state, with certain properties reminiscent of those found for soaps. The term smectic is in fact derived from the Greek, *smectos*—soap-like, and replaces now the older names such as " Fliessende Krystalle," " Schleimig flüssige Krystalle," or " cristaux liquides pâteaux."

(b) *The nematic mesophase*—a turbid but mobile state. On surfaces such as glass, the mesophase frequently adopts a characteristic " threaded " texture, clearly visible between crossed polaroids, and the word nematic again stems from the Greek, *nematos*—thread-like. Terms such as " Flüssige Krystalle," " Tropfbar flüssige Krystalle," and " liquides à fils " are now rarely used to describe this mesophase type.

(c) *The cholesteric mesophase*—a turbid and mobile mesophase, exhibiting some unique optical characteristics, quite different from those of the smectic and nematic mesophases. The majority of compounds exhibiting this type of mesophase are derived from cholesterol or other sterol systems.

Mesophases are most commonly observed when a suitable compound is heated to a temperature above that at which the crystal lattice is stable. This type of mesomorphism is called *thermotropic*, and the majority of liquid crystalline compounds fall into this category. Let us consider first the normal capillary method for determining a melting point. A small quantity of the solid is introduced into the sealed end of a small, thin-walled, glass capillary tube. The capillary is clipped to a thermometer immersed in an oil bath which is heated and stirred. A normal organic compound will melt suddenly over a range of say 1° and give the clear isotropic liquid, which will flow and exhibit a meniscus. If however the compound is *smectogenic*, i.e. is capable of giving a smectic mesophase, then the crystals will collapse at the melting point and give a turbid, viscous melt which adheres to the capillary walls. At a higher temperature, this smectic mesophase will flow and become clear, giving the isotropic liquid. If the compound under consideration is *nematogenic*, i.e. able to produce a nematic mesophase, then, at the melting point, the crystals will again collapse, but in this case flowing will occur to produce a turbid fluid, which is mobile and possesses a meniscus. Only at a higher temperature does the turbidity suddenly disappear and give rise to the isotropic liquid. In many cases a compound will exhibit both a smectic and a nematic mesophase, the former always occurring at the lower temperatures. The smectic-nematic transition would therefore be observed as a flowing of the viscous, turbid smectic mesophase to give the turbid, mobile nematic mesophase. The sequence of changes would then be as illustrated below, where the drawings represent the appearance of the sample in each of the four conditions (Fig. I.1).

$$\text{Crystals} \xrightarrow{\text{T}_1} \begin{array}{c}\text{Smectic} \\ \text{mesophase}\end{array} \xrightarrow{\text{T}_2} \begin{array}{c}\text{Nematic} \\ \text{mesophase}\end{array} \xrightarrow{\text{T}_3} \begin{array}{c}\text{Isotropic} \\ \text{liquid}\end{array}$$

Transitions T_1, T_2 and T_3 are reversible, but the reversal of the smectic mesophase (or the nematic mesophase) to the crystalline state is usually accompanied by supercooling. The transitions T_2 and T_3 are, in the author's experience, always reversible at the same temperatures as those at which the transitions occur on heating. That is, there is no detectable supercooling, and in fact, when the heating and cooling temperatures for smectic-nematic, smectic-isotropic, or nematic-isotropic transitions are not the same, the purity of the specimen is suspect. The isotropic-nematic or isotropic-smectic reversal is readily noted by the returning opacity, but in a capillary tube, the nematic-smectic change is marked by only a slight increase in the turbidity. It will be obvious of course that when only one mesophase occurs, the appropriate change is omitted from the above diagram.

In a capillary tube, the cholesteric mesophase resembles the nematic mesophase. The cholesteric mesophase may occur on its own or together with a smectic mesophase, as is the case with certain fatty esters

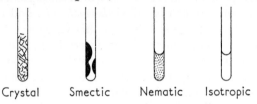

Crystal   Smectic   Nematic   Isotropic

FIG. I.1. The appearances of the crystalline, smectic, nematic, and isotropic states in glass capillary tubes.

of cholesterol. When both mesophases occur, then the sequence of changes in Fig. I.1 is again observed, except that the characteristic iridescent colours, which will be discussed later, may be observed in the cholesteric mesophase. Smectic-cholesteric and cholesteric-isotropic transitions should again be exactly reversible on cooling.

The mesomorphic transitions which have been discussed so far occur on heating the sample, and reverse in the opposite order on cooling, and such changes are associated with enantiotropic mesomorphic states.

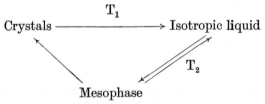

FIG. I.2. The sequence of changes of state for a compound which exhibits a monotropic mesophase.

Quite frequently, however, a mesophase may be monotropic with respect to the crystalline solid or to another mesophase. For example, the crystals may melt normally to give the isotropic liquid at T_1, but when the isotropic liquid is cooled, supercooling may occur, and the temperature may fall to considerably less than T_1 before crystallization occurs. If a mesophase has a stable range of existence just below the melting point, then, under these conditions, the mesophase may appear before crystallization occurs. From Fig. I.2, it is clear that this reversal would occur at T_2. Such a mesophase is therefore observed only on cooling, but if the temperature can be raised before crystallization occurs, the isotropic liquid will be obtained at T_2.

In some cases of course, one mesophase (nematic or cholesteric) is enantiotropic, whilst the smectic mesophase is monotropic, and in a few instances where marked supercooling of the isotropic liquid occurs before the onset of crystallization, both mesophases may exist as monotropic states.

A few examples of compounds which illustrate the above types of behaviour are given below.

4′-Methoxybiphenyl-4-carboxylic Acid[9]

    258°   300°

Solid $\rightleftarrows$ Nematic $\rightleftarrows$ Isotropic

    One enantiotropic nematic mesophase

MeO⟨◯⟩—⟨◯⟩CO₂H

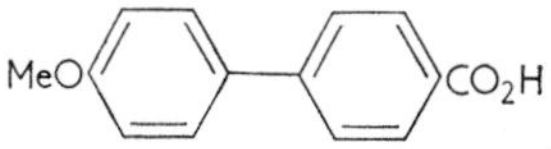

n-Propyl 4′-ethoxybiphenyl-4-carboxylate[9]

    102°   103°

Solid $\rightleftarrows$ Smectic $\rightleftarrows$ Isotropic

    One enantiotropic smectic mesophase

EtO⟨◯⟩—⟨◯⟩CO₂Pr-n

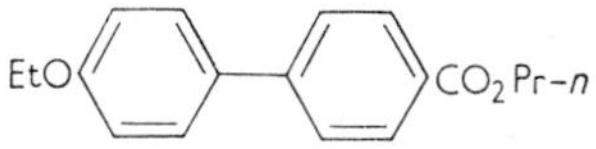

5-Chloro-6-n-heptyloxy-2-naphthoic Acid[10]

  165·5°   176·5°   201°

Solid $\rightleftarrows$ Smectic $\rightleftarrows$ Nematic $\rightleftarrows$ Isotropic

    Both mesophases enantiotropic

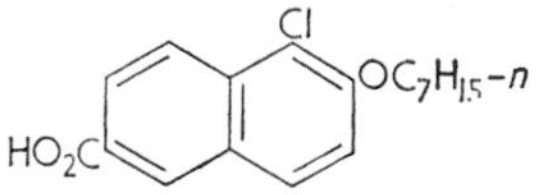

HO₂C⟨◯◯⟩OC₇H₁₅-n (Cl)

5-Chloro-6-n-propyloxy-2-naphthoic Acid[10]

        220·5°

Solid ——————→ Isotropic

             217°

        Nematic

    Monotropic nematic mesophase

HO₂C⟨◯◯⟩OC₃H₇-n (Cl)

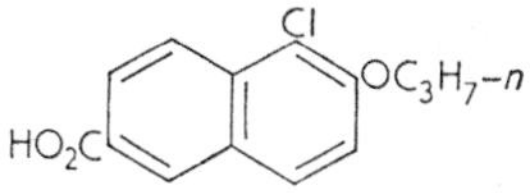

5-Iodo-6-n-nonyloxy-2-naphthoic Acid[10]

    163°   182°

Solid ——————→ Nematic $\rightleftarrows$ Isotropic

       157·5°

    Smectic

HO₂C⟨◯◯⟩OC₉H₁₉-n (I)

Enantiotropic nematic mesophase and monotropic smectic mesophase

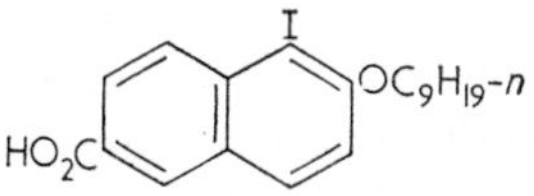

Cholesteryl Propionate[11]

$C_{27}H_{45}O.CO.C_2H_5$

102°   116°
Solid ⇌ Cholesteric ⇌ Isotropic
Enantiotropic cholesteric mesophase

Cholesteryl Acetate[11]

$C_{27}H_{45}O.CO.CH_3$

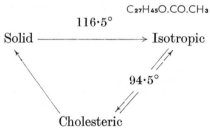

116·5°

Solid ─────────────→ Isotropic

94·5°

Cholesteric
Monotropic cholesteric mesophase

Cholesteryl Octanoate[11]

$C_{27}H_{45}O.CO.C_7H_{15}\text{-}n$

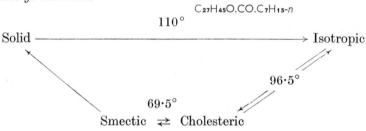

110°
Solid ──────────────────────────────────→ Isotropic

96·5°

69·5°
Smectic ⇌ Cholesteric
Both mesophases monotropic

Certain authors refer to the mesomorphic-isotropic transition temperature as the melting point, and this may cause some confusion on reading the literature on mesomorphism. In this book, the term melting point is reserved for a transition from the solid to the mesophase or the isotropic liquid. The other transitions are described as smectic-nematic, cholesteric-isotropic, etc.

It can now be seen that, in the case of mesomorphic compounds, we are dealing with a melting process which takes place in stages. Instead of passing from the three-dimensional order of the crystal lattice to the disorder of the isotropic liquid at one precise temperature—the melting point—the change from the order of the crystal to the state of disorder occurs via one or more intermediate states (the mesophases), each of which has a particular temperature range within which it is stable. As will be discussed in a subsequent chapter, we may regard the smectic mesophase as a two-dimensional solid and the nematic as a one-dimensional solid. Therefore, when a compound exhibits a smectic and a nematic mesophase, both of which are enantiotropic, the over-all melting process involves changes at *precise temperatures* from three to two to one to zero dimensional order.

It is convenient to mention at this stage that polymesomorphism is now a well-established phenomenon, although it was not accepted by Friedel.[6] Thus, it is possible to observe more than one modification of a particular mesophase type for a given compound. A given type of mesophase may of course adopt different appearances when it is mounted on different types of surface (glass, mica, etc.), or if it is disturbed when it is mounted on a particular surface. In these cases, the " texture " of the mesophase, to use the term employed by Friedel,[6] is altered as a result of changes in the mechanical stresses imposed on the mesophase by the surface or by external influences. This type of behaviour should not be confused with polymesomorphism, which again involves a change in the texture of the mesophase, but a change which occurs at a *definite temperature*, both on heating and cooling the sample, without any alteration in the type of the mesophase. The literature appears to contain no authenticated examples of polymesomorphism of nematic mesophases, but numerous examples are known of polymesomorphic smectic mesophases. For example, two smectic mesophases and one nematic mesophase occur in the case of ethyl *p*-(4-ethoxybenzylideneamino)cinnamate, for which the transitions are:

$$\begin{array}{ccccc} 78° & 110° & 154° & 158° \\ \text{Crystal} \rightleftarrows \text{Smectic I} \rightleftarrows & \text{Smectic II} & \rightleftarrows \text{Nematic} & \rightleftarrows \text{Isotropic} \end{array}$$

The 4'-n-alkoxy-3'-nitrobiphenyl-4-carboxylic acids[12] provide further very good examples of polymesomorphism, involving up to three smectic mesophases, all separated by well-defined transitions which are reversible on cooling the sample. Some examples from this series of compounds are summarized below:

n-Alkyl group	Smectic I	Smectic II	Smectic III	Nematic	Isotropic
Pentyl	—	—	157°	208°	219°
Hexyl	—	136°	158	213·5	218
Octyl	—	173·5	179·5	—	214
Hexadecyl	116·5°	161	193·5	—	198·5

Despite the very rapid development of numerous physical techniques which are now at the disposal of the organic chemist, and which assist him in elucidating the structure and assessing the purity of his materials, the melting point of a solid organic compound still remains his preliminary and frequently his final means of identifying a compound and of assessing its purity. Whether he employs an electrically heated block in conjunction with a microscope, or the ordinary capillary method for his melting point determinations, a well-defined change from the solid state to the isotropic liquid, occurring at a particular temperature, is regarded as the criterion of purity. The organic chemist should therefore be aware that factors other than impurity can lead to departures from the usual well-defined solid-isotropic liquid transition.   For example, the phenomena already described for mesomorphic systems could lead one to conclude, quite wrongly, that a compound was impure. Thus, on casual inspection, a nematic mesophase could be confused with a suspension of finely divided particles of high-melting impurity in the isotropic liquid of the lower-melting material.   The two cases are of course readily distinguished from each other, for the nematic-isotropic transition which occurs at a higher temperature will be sharp and precisely reversible, whereas the solution of the suspended solid will occur gradually, and the recrystallization of the impurity from the melt will usually involve some supercooling.   However, the author has on record several instances in which *pure* compounds were about to be discarded as inseparable mixtures, simply because they exhibited mesomorphic properties with which the operators were not familiar. It is therefore quite important that the organic chemist should be familiar with the changes which occur on heating a mesomorphic compound, and that he should know something about the general molecular characteristics which are most likely to lead to mesophase formation. The relationships between molecular constitution and mesomorphic behaviour will be discussed fully in subsequent chapters, but it is worthwhile to draw attention now to a simple means whereby a suspected instance of mesomorphism may be verified. A small sample of the compound is heated on a microscope slide, until the crystals pass to the isotropic liquid. A cover slip is then pressed down upon the liquid drop, to give a thin section of the material. The cold cover slip frequently causes rapid solidification of the melt, and the crystals may have to be remelted and the cover slip pressed down again to obtain a section of the isotropic liquid free from air bubbles.   When a satisfactory section of the isotropic liquid is obtained, it is allowed to cool slowly, when the mesophase or mesophases will be seen to pass across the preparation as successive, well-defined, opaque regions, followed finally by the crystals. Similarly, if the solid section is heated gently over a small flame, the solid-mesomorphic, mesomorphic-mesomorphic, and mesomorphic-isotropic changes will be observed as they pass back across the preparation as distinct fronts. The changes which may be observed are shown diagrammatically in Fig. I.3.

If high-melting impurity were the cause of the turbidity occurring in the melt, no definite fronts, as shown in Fig. I.3, would be observed on heating or cooling the sample, and the change from the solid to the molten state would simply be ill-defined. Further, if the mesophases were observed under a microscope, using crossed polaroids, each one would be anisotropic over its entire area, except for any

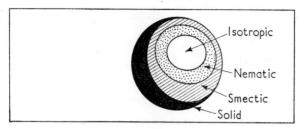

Fɪɢ. I.3. A thin section of isotropic liquid cooling between a glass slide and a cover slip.

regions which were in a position of optical extinction, or which exhibited homœotropic properties (see p. 19). A suspension of solid material in an isotropic melt would have quite a different appearance. The isotropic melt would give a black, optically extinct background, and the solid impurity would be seen as anisotropic dots, patches, or crystals, depending on its concentration in the melt.

One may ask how frequently an organic chemist is likely to encounter compounds which behave in this way. Naturally a great deal depends on the types of compound with which he is working, but on average, one in every two hundred organic compounds is liquid crystalline. The incidence of such compounds in day-to-day organic research is not therefore high, but the following examples of mesomorphic compounds should serve to illustrate that the phenomena occur with a wide range of molecule types, and that mesomorphic compounds do not necessarily have highly complex molecular structures.

Compound	Structure	Comments
6-Methoxy-2-naphthoic acid	MeO—[naphthalene]—CO_2H	Nematic mesophase
Trans-p-methoxy-cinnamic acid	MeO—[ring]—$CH{=}CH{\cdot}CO_2H$	Nematic mesophase
p-n-Propoxybenzoic acid	$n{-}PrO$—[ring]—CO_2H	Nematic mesophase
p-n-Hexylbenzoic acid	C_6H_{13}—[ring]—CO_2H	Nematic mesophase
4,4′-Di-(benzylidene-amino)biphenyl	[ring]—$CH{=}N$—[ring]—[ring]—$N{=}CH$—[ring]	Nematic mesophase

Compound	Structure	Comments
4-p-Methoxybenzyl-ideneaminobiphenyl	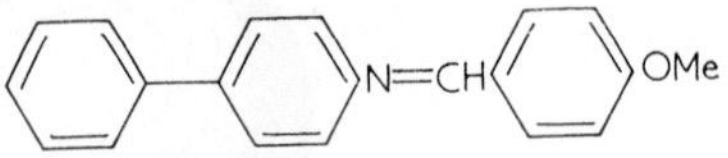	Nematic mesophase
p-Azoxyanisole	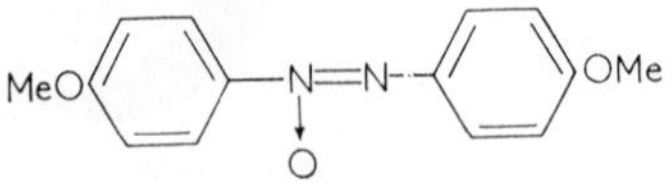	Nematic mesophase
4-Methoxy-4″-nitro-p-terphenyl	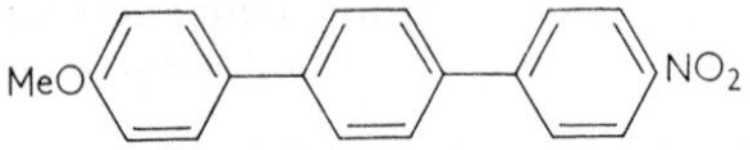	Nematic mesophase
2-p-Methoxybenzyl-ideneamino-phenanthrene	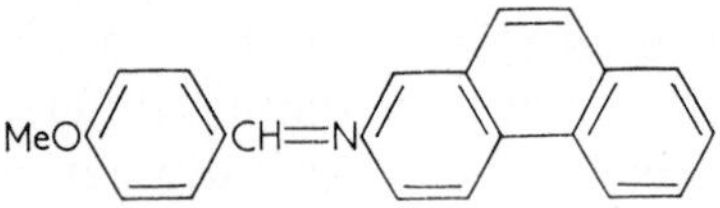	Nematic mesophase
2,7-Di-(benzylidene-amino)fluorene	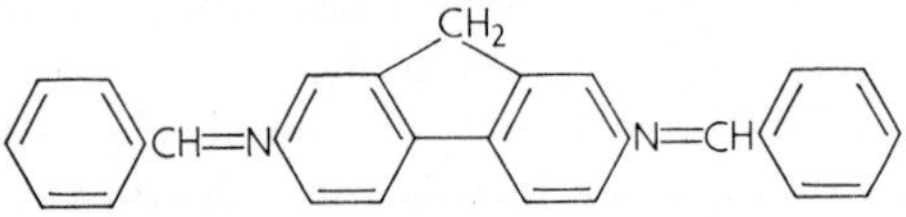	Nematic mesophase
2,5-Di-(p-ethoxy-benzylidene) cyclopentanone	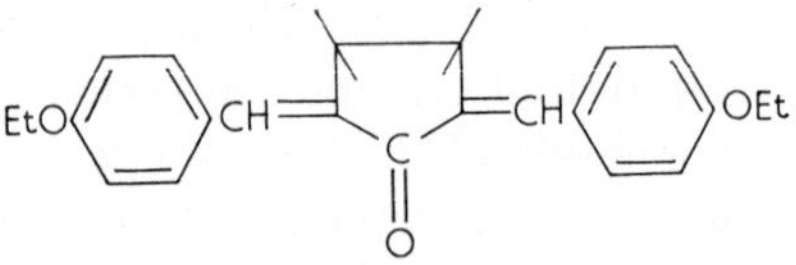	Nematic mesophase
Ethyl-p-azoxycinnamate	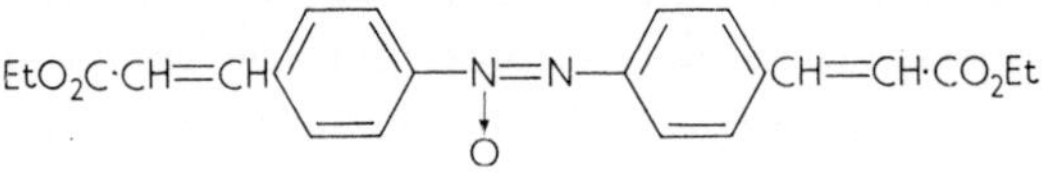	Smectic mesophase
Ethyl p-azoxy-benzoate	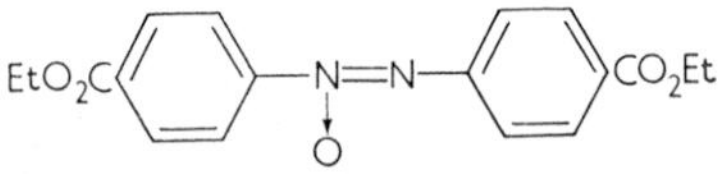	Smectic mesophase
Amyl p-(4-cyano-benzylidene-amino)cinnamate	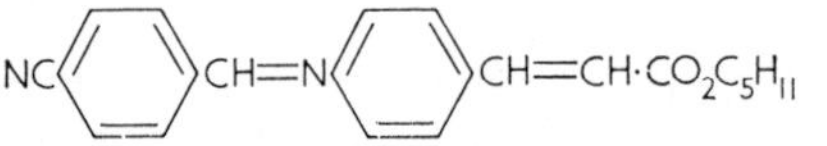	Cholesteric mesophase
Cholesteryl acetate	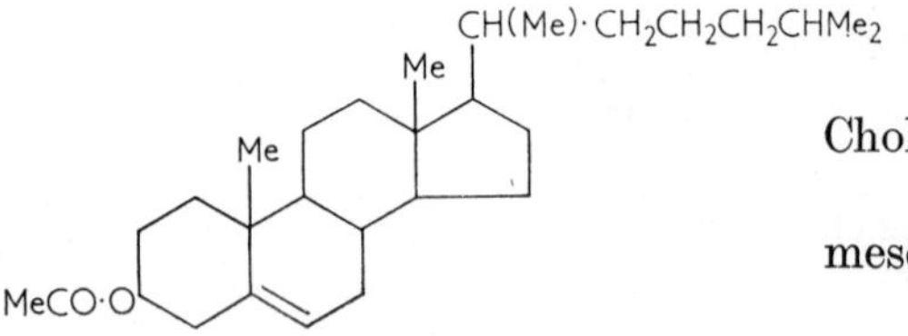	Cholesteric mesophase
4,4′-Dimethoxy-stilbene	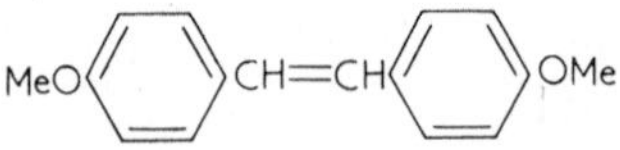	Nematic mesophase

Compound	Structure	Comments
Potassium oleate	$Me(CH_2)_7CH=CH(CH_2)_7.CO_2K$	Smectic mesophase
Ammonium oleate	$Me(CH_2)_7CH=CH(CH_2)_7.CO_2NH_4$	Smectic mesophase
Nona-2,4-dienoic acid	$Me(CH_2)_3.CH=CH—CH=CH.CO_2H$	Nematic mesophase
Undeca-2,4-dienoic acid	$Me(CH_2)_5.CH=CH—CH=CH.CO_2H$	Nematic mesophase

LYOTROPIC MESOMORPHISM

Up to this point, thermotropic mesomorphism alone has been discussed. In this case, the crystal lattice is disrupted in stages by thermal vibrations, so giving the successive transitions between the solid, the mesophases, and the isotropic liquid, with rising temperature. The action of a solvent upon a solid also involves a disruption of the crystal lattice, in this case, by an attraction of solute molecules from the ordered crystal lattice into the disordered state of solution. The majority of compounds pass quite normally into solution, whether assisted by heat or not, just as most compounds melt normally. Very early in the history of the study of liquid crystalline properties, it was, however, observed that when certain compounds are treated with solvent they give states which are neither true solids nor true solutions, but which are intermediate in character between these two extremes. Such states are in fact liquid crystalline or mesomorphic in their properties, and since the effect of a solvent was responsible for their occurrence, the phenomenon is referred to as lyotropic mesomorphism. An excess of solvent will of course cause a lyotropic mesophase to pass over to a true solution, and the evaporation of such a solution will give first the liquid crystalline state, followed by the solid. Similarly, if a hot saturated solution of a compound capable of exhibiting lyotropic mesomorphism is cooled, the deposition of liquid crystalline states is frequently observed. Lyotropic mesophases are always strongly birefringent, although their physical nature may vary widely from that of a waxy substance to that of a clear gel.

Simple examples of substances which behave in this way, employing water as the solvent, are 9-chloro- and 9-bromo-phenanthrene-3-sulphonic acid[13] and certain naphthylamine disulphonic acids.[14] Alcoholic solutions of these compounds do not generally show anisotropic behaviour, and a high degree of hydration appears to be a necessary prerequisite for the occurrence of many lyotropic mesophases. Many alkali metal and ammonium salts of long chain aliphatic acids exhibit lyotropic mesophases with controlled amounts of water,[15-23] as do a number of well-known dyes such as the potassium salt of methyl orange,[24] naphthol yellow S,[25] and p-aminoazotoluene.[26] Some of the soap systems have been studied with solvents other than water, e.g. liquid paraffin,[27] glycerol, isopropanol, and diethylene glycol,[28] and with these solvents too, the lyotropic mesophases are found to occur. A number of cationic and non-ionic detergents have also been shown to give anisotropic phases when they are treated with solvents, and in particular with water.[29-34] A close relationship obviously exists between these liquid crystalline states and the truly colloidal states, and this has been discussed by Ostwald.[35]

Lyotropic liquid crystalline states analogous to the smectic and nematic thermotropic mesophases have been clearly demonstrated, the change from the smectic to the nematic state being brought about by the addition of further solvent.

More recently, Robinson[36] has reported the interesting observation that viscous solutions of poly-γ-benzyl-L-glutamate in certain organic solvents are anisotropic, and show a number of the characteristic properties which we associate with the thermotropic cholesteric mesophase. Although these extremely interesting birefringent solutions exhibit other features which are not common to the thermotropic cholesteric mesophase, they do appear to constitute the lyotropic analogue of the cholesteric liquid crystalline state.

BIOLOGICAL SYSTEMS

It has been recognized for many years that several biological systems exhibit liquid crystalline properties, and that others have properties analogous to those observed in liquid crystalline systems. The literature on this subject is exceedingly chaotic, and is difficult to summarize in a general way. However, it may be useful to mention a few representative examples of the types of system which show these properties. For example, living tissue, such as muscles, nerves, and tendons exhibit double refraction under different conditions, the degree of double refraction in such fibrous systems increasing on stretching, and decreasing on contraction. This behaviour is compatible with an increased ordering of the structural units of the fibres when they are stretched, and is similar to the appearance of crystalline properties in stretched rubbers or drawn polymer fibres. Certain living sperms are known to possess a truly liquid crystalline phase, and aqueous solutions of certain viruses, e.g. the tobacco mosaic virus, exhibit lyotropic mesomorphic properties. Furthermore, many parts of the body contain considerable concentrations of mesomorphic compounds, often derived from cholesterol and other sterol systems. Much more work must be done before the true significance of liquid crystallinity in biological systems is understood, but it is conceivable that in the liquid crystalline states there is a particularly valuable balance between the cohesiveness of the system (strong attractions still operate between the molecules) and its deformability, and that this balance is a particularly suitable one for the structure of certain body parts and organs which must be strong yet flexible.

As the title implies, the principal aim of this book is to describe the development of knowledge concerning the rôle which the chemical constitution of a compound plays in determining the nature and extent of the mesomorphic properties. The vast majority of the work which has been carried out in this field has concerned thermotropic mesomorphic systems, and indeed little can be said about the significance of chemical constitution in relation to the behaviour of lyotropic systems or the liquid crystalline properties of biological systems except that, as is ordinarily the case for thermotropic systems, the molecules are frequently very long and extended. For these reasons, lyotropic mesomorphic systems and the liquid crystalline properties of biological systems, interesting as they are in their own right, will not be referred to in any further detail in this book.

The last three chapters of the book are devoted to a detailed description of the studies which have helped to throw light on the question of the significance of molecular structure in determining the thermotropic mesomorphic behaviour of a system. These chapters are prefaced by others in which the physical properties of mesophases are described, for before the reader attempts to understand the subject matter of Chapters VIII, IX, and X, it is essential that he should have a clear picture of the evidence which exists for the different types of mesomorphic state, of the physical properties which they possess, and in particular, of the reasons for associating particular types of molecular organization with the smectic, nematic, and cholesteric mesophases.

REFERENCES

1. Reinitzer, F. (1888). *Monatsh.* **9**, 421.
2. Lehmann, O. (1889). *Z. phys. Chem. (Leipzig)*. **4**, 462.
3. Lehmann, O. (1890). *Z. Krist.* **18**, 464.
4. Reinitzer, F. (1908). *Ann. Physik.* **27**, 213.
5. Lehmann, O. (1908). *Ann. Physik.* **25**, 852; **27**, 1099; (1908) *Ber.* **41**, 3774.
6. Friedel, G. (1922). *Ann. Physique* **18**, 273.
7. Rinne, F. (1933). *Trans. Faraday Soc.* **29**, 1016.
8. Tamman, G. (1901). *Ann. Physik.* **4**, 524; (1902) **8**, 103; (1906) **19**, 421.
   Nernst, W. (1906). *Z. Elektrochem.* **12**, 431.
   Quincke, F. (1894). *Annalen* **53**, 613.
9. Gray, G. W., Hartley, J. B. and Jones, B. (1955). *J. Chem. Soc.* 1412.
10. Gray, G. W. and Jones, B. (1955). *J. Chem. Soc.* 236.
11. Gray, G. W. (1956). *J. Chem. Soc.* 3733.
12. Gray, G. W., Jones, B. and Marson, F. (1957). *J. Chem. Soc.* 393.
13. Sandquist, H. (1915). *Ber.* **48**, 2054; (1916). *J. Amer. Chem. Soc.* **40**, 556; (1916) *Kolloid Z.* **19**, 113.

14. Balaban, I. E. and King, H. (1927). *J. Chem. Soc.* 3068.
15. McBain, J. W. (1926). " Colloid Chemistry ", Chemical Catalogue Co., Inc., New York. Vol. I, p. 138. (Editor: J. Alexander).
16. Lawrence, A. S. C. (1933). *Trans. Faraday Soc.* **29**, 1008.
17. Vold, R. D. (1939). *J. Phys. Chem.* **43**, 1213.
18. Vold, R. D. and Vold, M. J. (1939). *J. Amer. Chem. Soc.* **61**, 37.
19. Vold, R. D. and Ferguson, R. H. (1938). *J. Amer. Chem. Soc.* **60**, 2066.
20. McBain, J. W., Vold, R. D., and Frick, M. J. (1940). *J. Phys. Chem.* **44**, 1013.
21. Vold, R. D., Reivere, R. and McBain, J. W. (1941). *J. Amer. Chem. Soc.* **63**, 1293.
22. Gonick, E. and McBain, J. W. (1946). *J. Amer. Chem. Soc.* **68**, 683.
23. McBain, J. W., Lazarus, L. H. and Pitter, A. V. (1930). *Z. phys. Chem.* (*Leipzig*). **A147**, 87.
24. Branner, F. (1939). *Nord. Kemikermode, Forh.* **5**, 207; (1944) *Chem. Abs.* **38**, 2872.
25. Dreyer, J. F. (1948). *J. Phys. Colloid Chem.* **52**, 808.
26. Gaubert, P. (1916). *Compt. rend.* **163**, 392.
27. Lawrence, A. S. C. (1938). *Trans. Faraday Soc.* **34**, 660.
28. Vold, R. D., Leggett, C. W. and McBain, J. W. (1940). *J. Phys. Chem.* **44**, 1058.
29. Broome, F. K., Hoerr, C. W. and Harwood, H. J. (1951). *J. Amer. Chem. Soc.* **73**, 3350.
30. Marsden, S. S. and McBain, J. W. (1948). *J. Phys. Colloid Chem.* **52**, 110.
31. Bury, C. R. and Browning, J. (1953). *Trans. Faraday Soc.* **49**, 209.
32. Windsor, P. A. (1952). *J. Phys. Chem.* **56**, 391; (1954) *Nature* **173**, 81; (1955) *J. Colloid Sci.* **10**, 88 and 101.
33. Philippoff, W. and McBain, J. W. (1949). *Nature* **164**, 885.
34. Marsden, S. S. and McBain, J. W. (1948). *Acta Cryst.* **1**, 270.
35. Ostwald, W. (1931). *Z. Krist.* **79**, 222.
36. Robinson, C. (1956). *Trans. Faraday Soc.* **52**, 571; Robinson, C., Ward, J. C. and Beevers, R. B. (1958). *Faraday Soc. Discussions* **25**, 29; Robinson, C. (1961). *Tetrahedron* **13**, 219.

CHAPTER II

SMECTIC, NEMATIC, AND CHOLESTERIC MESOPHASES

WHILST it is a useful technique to heat a small sample of a compound contained in a melting point capillary tube in order to obtain a rough guide to the mesomorphic properties, the nature of a particular meso-phase may be ascertained with reasonable certainty only in the case of enantiotropic mesophases. Moreover, the transition temperatures de-termined by the capillary method may be inaccurate (see Chapter III), particularly when high temperatures are involved. In order to carry out an exact study of a mesomorphic compound, it is necessary to mount the material as a thin section between glass surfaces. This is readily achieved by melting a few crystals on a glass microscope slide, and pressing a glass cover slip onto the molten drop, to give a more or less uniformly thin section of the material. When such a section of the isotropic liquid is cooled, the mesophases pass across the preparation as successive regions of different opacity. Each transition is seen as a well-defined, usually crescent-shaped front which moves across the section, and passes back again on heating the sample. When the compound exists as one of the mesomorphic states, the cover slip may be readily displaced, since the liquid crystalline states are fluid, but when the opaque mesophase is observed under a microscope, using crossed pola-roids, the birefringent properties which relate the mesomorphic and the crystalline states are clearly manifested. However, at this stage, it should be noted that a mesophase occasionally adopts an homœotropic state which is optically extinct between crossed nicols. The absence of birefringence in such homœotropic preparations should not of course be interpreted as implying the absence of anisotropy or ordering of the molecular units, for in fact the molecules are arranged in such a way that the optic axis of the preparation is everywhere normal to the glass or other supporting surface. Homœotropy is frequently induced in a birefringent section by a cover slip displacement, but in other cases the birefringent pattern has merely been altered when the sample recovers from the mechanical movement. Friedel[1] referred to the birefringent patterns of mesophases as " textures ", a term which is preferable to structures, and demonstrated that a particular type of mesophase will adopt one of a limited number of textures which may be used to establish with certainty whether the mesophase under consideration is smectic, nematic, or cholesteric.

Compared with the use of capillary techniques for the study of meso-phases, considerably more information concerning the physical characteristics and the identity of mesophases is therefore obtained by an examination of sections of the mesophases mounted between plane glass surfaces. Such sections may also be used to determine the melting points and the mesomorphic transition temperatures with great accuracy. If a slide carrying such a thin section of a mesomorphic compound is housed in a suitably designed microscope heating block,[2] and the section is observed either under a microscope or by means of a polarizing, projection system,[3] the well-defined fronts which separate solid from mesophase, mesophase from mesophase, and mesophase from isotropic liquid are clearly visible as they move across the preparation with increasing temperature.

Friedel[1] developed his original observations on the textures of the different mesophase types into a detailed optical study upon which is based a very great deal of our present-day knowledge of these states of matter. Thus, Friedel was able to reach certain conclusions regarding the probable molecular arrangements which give rise to the textures and the optical characteristics of the mesophases.

The three mesophase types—smectic, nematic, and cholesteric—will now be discussed from the point of view of their optical properties.

THE SMECTIC MESOPHASE

Smectic mesophases may adopt three different textures dependent upon:

(1) the nature of the compound under consideration;
(2) the way in which the mesophase is produced, e.g. by heating the crystals, by cooling the isotropic liquid, or by cooling the nematic mesophase; and
(3) the nature and the cleanliness of the supporting surface employed to mount the specimen.

It is instructive to consider first the texture which Friedel called the *homogeneous structure*.* If the thin section of material mounted between the slide and the cover slip is cooled slowly in order to obtain large crystals of the solid, and the temperature is then raised just sufficiently to produce the smectic mesophase, this will be obtained as large, homogeneous, birefringent areas, which correspond exactly to the large crystalline areas from which they were derived. Now, some anisotropy or order in the molecular structure must persist in the smectic mesophase if we are to explain the birefringent properties of this otherwise fluid state of matter. It could of course be argued that, when the crystals melt, a thin pellicle adheres to the glass surface—a pellicle in which the molecular order of the crystal persists. This orientated pellicle could

* Most of the mesomorphic textures are extremely well illustrated in the article in *Annales de Physique* by G. Friedel.[1]

then possibly influence the arrangement of the molecules throughout the bulk of the thin section of the smectic mesophase, so giving rise to an anisotropic state exhibiting the same discontinuities as the original crystalline section. The inference of this point of view is that the smectic mesophase possesses no molecular order in its own right, and that in the absence of the orientating influences of the pellicle, the smectic mesophase would be nothing more than the disordered isotropic liquid. As will emerge from the subsequent discussion on the smectic mesophase, there is, however, abundant evidence to show that molecular order is an inherent property of this type of mesophase, and it is because this order is so similar to that of the three-dimensional ordering of the molecules in the crystal, that the anisotropic mesophase maintains in its texture a pattern of discontinuities apparently identical with that of the crystalline areas. Similar though the homogeneous texture may be to the crystalline section, the fluid properties of the mesophase are shown by the readiness with which a cover slip displacement may be made. Such a mechanical deformation does not necessarily destroy the homogeneous texture, and the mesophase often regains the same arrangement of the homogeneous areas. In other cases, the cover slip displacement does produce a radical change in the appearance of the mesophase, changing it from a birefringent section to one in which almost the entire field of view is optically extinct between crossed polaroids, i.e. the section is *homœotropic*. Frequently, some of the areas in the homogeneous texture manifest this property of homœotropy, without bringing it about by a cover slip movement, and occasionally an entire section will be obtained homœotropic on obtaining the smectic mesophase by cooling the isotropic liquid. The *homœotropic texture* is therefore the second of the three textures which a smectic mesophase may adopt spontaneously on glass surfaces.

Friedel[1] was able to demonstrate that, irrespective of whether the homœotropic regions were induced or spontaneous, the optic axis was uniformly perpendicular to the supporting surface. Lehmann[4] contended that these homœotropic areas corresponded to regions of molecular order, but that they were produced by the orientating influence of the supporting surface, in this case, in such a way that the optic axis was normal to the surface. Friedel was at great pains to refute Lehmann's suggestion, and contended that homœotropy in fact arises when the surface exerts no orientating effects, i.e. when contact between the mesophase and the surface is imperfect. Friedel[1] demonstrated this fact by stretching a drop of ethyl *p*-azoxybenzoate over a hole drilled in a glass surface, when the drop of smectic mesophase immediately adopted homœotropic properties, with the optic axis uniformly perpendicular to the *flat* surface of the drop. In this case, the homœotropy cannot possibly be a function of the effect of the surface, and must arise from the inherent ordering of the molecules in the mesophase. The proposal that the orientating effects of surfaces by themselves explain the anisotropy and other optical characteristics of smectic mesophases therefore becomes untenable. These properties are explained only by the occurrence of a spontaneous ordering of the molecules of the smectic mesophase.

When a drop of smectic mesophase is supported on glass (the upper surface of the drop exposed to air), perfect homœotropy is not achieved, unless the glass is scrupulously clean, so that strong attachments between the molecules and the surface are minimized. If this is not the case, the drop has an homœotropic border, and the remainder of the drop is found to have the focal-conic texture (see below), which arises as a result of the disturbing influences of surface attractions upon the smectic molecular orientation.

However, if the glass surface is rigorously clean, the drop exhibits some very important characteristics first observed by Grandjean.[5] The drop is found to have stepped edges—Grandjean described such drops as "gouttes à gradins"—but such drops are difficult to obtain on glass surfaces, which are not easy to obtain in a sufficiently clean state to reduce surface contact with the drop to a sufficient extent. Even if the glass surface is good enough to give these Grandjean terraces, and the mesophase is heated to too high a temperature, contact between the drop and the surface becomes intimate and the focal-conic texture is adopted. It is much more convenient to employ a fresh cleavage surface of mica to support the drop, although excessive heating may again give focal-conic textures. Stepped drops are probably best produced by stretching the drop of smectic fluid over a hole drilled in a glass surface. The drops are not then so sensitive to temperature, but considerable experience is necessary to achieve the manœuvre of mounting the drop over a reasonably sized hole. Hartshorne and Stuart,[6] and Lawrence[7] have described methods for preparing Grandjean terraces and other homœotropic conditions of the smectic mesophase.

The stepped drop is homœotropic, and consists of a number of flat planes which are exactly parallel to one another and to the plane of the supporting surface in which the hole is drilled. Each plane terminates in a sharp step or edge, and only on the perimeter of each plane, where a narrow chain of focal-conic groups is observed, is the homœotropy incomplete. The steps are not of equal height, but in all cases, the layers or planes slip over one another extremely easily. However, in any direction other than in the plane of the layers, the drop is extremely viscous. Figure II.1 represents a stepped drop viewed in plan and cross section.

Friedel[1] considered that a close analogy existed between these stepped drops of smectic fluid and soap films formed by evaporation.

The inner and outer surfaces of soap films or bubbles are layers in which the molecules are arranged parallel to one another, and he concluded that the stepped drops too consist of layers comprised of molecules lying parallel to one another, and with their long axes, which will be in the direction of the optic axis of the homœotropic layer, at right angles to the

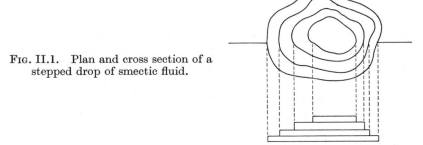

FIG. II.1.   Plan and cross section of a stepped drop of smectic fluid.

smectic plane.   All the characteristic properties of smectic mesophases are, in fact, in keeping with their having a layer molecular structure. Moreover, as will be discussed in a subsequent chapter, the characteristic features of the molecules of smectogenic compounds are such that strong attractions are likely to exist between the sides and planes of the elongated molecules, so leading to the formation of layers (Fig. II.2), between which the cohesions will be relatively weak—accounting for the characteristic layer flow observed in the stepped drops.

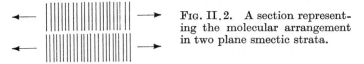

FIG. II.2.   A section representing the molecular arrangement in two plane smectic strata.

In soap films, the thickness of each layer is very small—of the order of the length of the particular molecular species involved, but frequently less than this, if the long axes of the soap molecules are not normal to the plane of the soap film.   In the stepped drops, the thicknesses of the strata are unequal, and greater than those found for soap films, but they correspond to multiples of the molecular length.   Each layer in the stepped drop must then correspond to a laminate of unimolecular smectic strata, the number of such strata in a given layer being variable and probably determined by factors such as the size of the drop and the surface tension of the fluid.

In the homogeneous texture, the layer arrangement of the molecules must be such that either the molecules are no longer perpendicular to the layers, or more likely, that the layers are no longer parallel to the glass surface.   The homogeneous areas would then be birefringent.   A disturbance of the cover slip may well alter this state of affairs so that the optic axis of the preparation and the long axes of the molecules become normal to the supporting surface, i.e. giving induced homœotropy.

The close similarity between the proposed smectic molecular structure and that in a solid layer lattice is obvious—the only difference lies in the mobility of the smectic layers in any direction parallel to their own planes. If a crystalline solid with a layer lattice is obtained when the thin section of mesophase crystallizes, it is easy to understand that the change that occurs when this solid produces the smectic layer structure may be so slight that the smectic texture may be very closely similar to the crystalline texture, i.e. the homogeneous texture. Here again then, it is unlikely that the orientating influences of the surface play a significant rôle in determining the molecular order in the smectic mesophase, and the similarity between the homogeneous texture and the crystalline state probably arises from the close similarity between the molecular arrangements in the two states of matter. These ideas would also explain:

(1) The change which often occurs from the homogeneous texture to a different texture when the temperature is raised appreciably from the solid-smectic transition temperature, since the thermal vibrations may cause the smectic layers to move, or become disturbed, so destroying the semblance of the crystalline arrangement; and

(2) the fact that the homogeneous texture is not obtained on cooling from the isotropic liquid or the nematic mesophase, since in neither of these states does any predetermining three-dimensional order exist.

In addition to the homogeneous and the homœotropic textures, there is the *focal-conic texture* of the smectic mesophase. This texture is the one most usually observed for smectic mesophases, and it is a very important fact that a detailed study of this texture leads to further strong evidence for the layer arrangement of the molecules in the smectic state. The next section is therefore devoted to these extremely interesting focal-conic arrangements.

It is, however, opportune to mention first that, irrespective of the texture adopted by a smectic mesophase, its optical characteristics are always those of a positive uniaxial crystal. In the homogeneous texture the orientation of the optic axis is constant within a particular homogeneous area, but varies from one such area to another. There is, however, no sudden discontinuity in the optic axial direction at the junction of two of these areas. Instead, the optic axial direction changes gradually in a very narrow region from that of area A to that of area B. In this very narrow region bordering the areas, the texture of the meso-phase is very confused, consisting in fact of very minute focal-conic groups.

THE FOCAL-CONIC TEXTURE

The focal-conic texture of the smectic mesophase is the most common one, and, if observed only casually, can readily be confused with a crystalline solid. When the mesophase is observed by means of a micro-scope, it is seen to be quite immobile, unlike the nematic mesophase in which particles of dust may be observed in rapid and sometimes violent motion, but the illusion that the focal-conic texture is crystalline is dispelled when it is found that a displacement of the cover slip may be made quite easily. Plate 1 (facing p. 30) illustrates an example of this smectic texture, which usually arises when the mesophase is obtained by cooling the isotropic liquid. The focal-conic texture may also invade the homogeneous texture if the temperature is raised, and it may occasion-ally arise if the cover slip is displaced on an homœotropic preparation. As

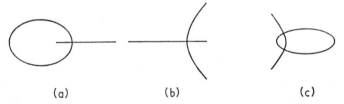

(a)   (b)   (c)

FIG. II.3 (a), (b), and (c). Three possible arrangements of the ellipses and hyper-bolas relative to the plane surface (equivalent to the page) of a smectic focal-conic preparation.

mentioned earlier, the focal-conic groups are also observed, in a very minute form at the junction of homogeneous areas, and in drops of smectic fluid mounted on glass surfaces, when homœotropy is incomplete.

When the focal-conic groups are large, it becomes evident that the preparation contains an arrangement of fine dark lines which are ob-served both between crossed polaroids and in ordinary light. Neither the shape nor the arrangement of these lines is random, and they are in fact ellipses and hyperbolas or portions of ellipses and hyperbolas. Moreover, the lines are in pairs, with an ellipse and an hyperbola in association, such that the two lines are related as focal-conics. This is made clear in Fig. II.3 (a), (b), and (c).

For an ellipse and an hyperbola to be related as focal-conics, the locus of the vertices of the cones of revolution whose bases are the ellipse must be the hyperbola which passes through the focus of the ellipse, and whose plane is at right angles to the plane of the ellipse. In Fig. II.3 (a), the ellipse is in the plane of the page, and in Fig. II.3 (b), the plane of the ellipse is at right angles to the page. Arrangements of this kind will be observed in a preparation when the ellipse and the hyperbola respectively lie in the plane of the surface of the preparation. Figure II.3 (c) corresponds to a focal-conic group within the bulk of the section of mesophase. The eccentricities of the ellipses are very variable, and when the ellipse approximates to a circle, the hyperbola, of course, approximates to a straight line passing at right angles through the centre of the plane of the circle. The focal-conic relationship of these ellipses and hyperbolas is clearly demonstrated by making a cover slip displacement in order to distort the shapes of the ellipses and hyperbolas. Every distortion of an ellipse affects the entire ellipse, making it more, or less eccentric, and does not simply cause a distortion of the ellipse at,

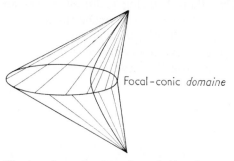

Focal-conic *domaine*

FIG. II.4. The two largest cones of revolution for an ellipse and hyperbola which are related as focal-conics.

say, the point of maximum pressure or stress. Moreover, such a distortion of an ellipse is accompanied by a change in the shape of the hyperbola, such that the focal-conic relationship is maintained.

Figure II.4 illustrates the two largest cones of revolution for an ellipse and an hyperbola related in this way, i.e. these cones having the extremes of the hyperbola as their vertices. Friedel[1] called the enclosed volume the " domaine " of the focal-conic group. In many focal-conic preparations, the ellipses and hyperbolas are of course fragmentary, and the " domaines " incomplete, but in so far as it is possible to make microscopic examinations of such preparations, the focal-conic arrangement is always maintained.

A closer inspection of a focal-conic preparation reveals a further fact about the focal-conic groups, namely that the ellipses never intersect one another, and meet only tangentially, with the result that the focal-conic " domaines " never invade one another. This tangential arrangement of the ellipses results in what Friedel described as the polygonal structure of the smectic mesophase. This should not be regarded as a further type of texture of the smectic mesophase. Under suitable conditions,[1] the surface of the preparation, e.g. underneath the cover slip, is divided into polygonal areas, which have straight or slightly curved sides and into which the ellipses are fitted, such that they are tangential to the sides of the polygons and to one another. If the lower surface of the same preparation is now examined, it too will be found to have a similar arrangement of polygonal areas and ellipses. Under these circumstances, in which the ellipses are in the planes of the two surfaces of the preparation, the hyperbolas appear as straight lines which originate from the focus of each ellipse and run in the direction of the major axis of each ellipse. In fact, of course, the hyperbolas pass into the body of the section of mesomorphic material. For each particular polygonal area, all these lines which are the hyperbolas meet at a point. Now, the polygonal areas on the lower surface of the preparation are in fact related to those on the upper surface. This is made clear in Fig. II.5 in which the polygonal areas on the lower surface are represented by

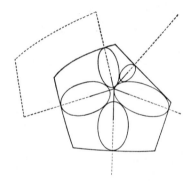

Fig. II.5. The relationship between the polygonal areas on the upper and lower surfaces of a section of a smectic focal-conic preparation.

dotted lines, and those on the upper surface by full lines. In every case, if the polygonal areas on the upper surface are projected onto those on the lower surface, the sides intersect at right angles. This relationship exists because each junction of the sides of the polygons on the lower surface is in fact the point at which the hyperbolas from a particular family of ellipses in a given polygonal area on the upper surface coincide on the lower surface. Because of the focal-conic relationship of the ellipses and hyperbolas, it follows that the polygonal areas on one surface must be matched on the other side by corresponding polygonal areas, the sides of the polygons being in pairs at right angles.

It is clear then that the section of mesophase is comprised of cones whose bases are ellipses and whose apices are the meeting points of a number of hyperbolas, the bases and apices lying on either the upper or lower surface of the preparation, and the ellipses and hyperbolas always obeying the focal-conic relationship. Such a simple case as the one described would be observed only under very favourable circumstances, and in many cases in which the polygonal structure arises, the ellipses are not in the planes of the surfaces of the preparation, and the cones lie with their bases in various planes of inclination to the surfaces. The position is then more complex, but the relationships outlined above are always maintained.

It has been said above that the section of the mesophase is comprised of cones, but it will be realized that no polygonal area can be *entirely* filled with ellipses. Even when smaller and smaller ellipses are drawn to fill in the interstitial spaces, small triangular-like areas will remain. These may be thought of as the bases of wedges or tetrahedra which are portions of focal-conics, and which together with the cones will fill an entire volume.

Friedel[1] then showed that it is possible to relate this focal-conic arrangement of the smectic mesophase to the state of molecular organization in the mesophase, and to obtain evidence for a layer arrange-

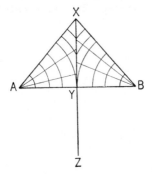

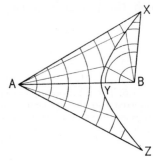

FIG. II.6. Cross section of a cone whose base is a circle (AB), showing the curved, parallel strata (Dupin cyclides).

FIG. II.7. Cross section of a cone whose base is an ellipse (AB), showing the curved, parallel strata (Dupin cyclides).

ment of the molecules, as already indicated by the nature of stepped drops of smectic fluid.

Let us consider first the simple case in which the ellipse becomes a circle, and the hyperbola is a straight line passing at right angles through the centre of the circle. In Fig. II.6, this circle is considered to lie at right angles to the plane of the page, so that it is represented by the line AB. The hyperbola is the line XYZ.

If we join any points on XYZ to either A or B, we obtain a series of lines all of which will be intersected at *right angles* by a series of arcs which are portions of circles with their centres at either A or B. If we now consider this in a three-dimensional way, it is realized that the cone, whose base is the circle, may be divided into a series of curved surfaces which intersect at right angles *all* lines drawn from any points on XYZ to *all* points on the circumference of the circle. These curved surfaces are all parallel to one another, and are known as Dupin cyclides.

The " domaine " of the cone of revolution for a circle and a line, which are related as focal-conics, may therefore be divided into a series of curved, parallel strata which will entirely fill the cone. The more complex case of an ellipse and a hyperbola is shown in Fig. II.7. Here the plane of the ellipse, which lies at right angles to the plane of the paper, is shown as the line AB, and the hyperbola as the line XYZ, the point Y being one of the foci of the ellipse. The position is essentially the same, in that the lines joining points on the hyperbola XYZ to the points A and B are cut at right angles by arcs of circles drawn with their centres at A and B. These arcs of circles are of course the contours of the series of parallel surfaces which may fill the two cones with their common base in the ellipse, and their apices at Z and X. The circular surfaces have in this case been pushed to one side, but the nature of the cyclides will remain unaltered, and all the lines joining points on the hyperbola to points on the perimeter of the ellipse will be normal to the series of parallel surfaces.

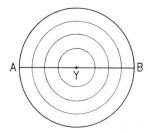

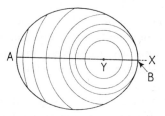

FIG. II.8. A section of Fig. II.6, at right angles to the page, through the line AYB—the circles are the contours of the curved, parallel strata.

FIG. II.9. A section through the base of a cone defined by the ellipse AB which lies in the plane of the page. The circles and arcs of circles represent the contours of curved, parallel strata similar to those in Fig. II.7.

Figures II.8 and II.9 represent sections of Figs. II.6 and II.7 and the planes of the circle and the ellipse are now in the plane of the paper. The lines in Figs. II.8 and II.9 of course represent the contours of the parallel surfaces for these particular sections.

If we now assume that the molecules in the strata lie at right angles to these curved surfaces, then we see that at any given position in the " domaine ", a molecule will lie with its major axis in the direction of a line joining a point on the ellipse to a point on the hyperbola. For the type of extended molecule which is conducive to mesophase formation, the optic axis will lie in the direction of the long axis of the molecule, and therefore in the direction of the line joining the point on the ellipse to the point on the hyperbola, e.g. along the line AX in either Fig. II.6 or II.7. Thus, whereas the direction of the optic axis is constant in a crystal, the optic axial direction must change continuously throughout the " domaine " of a focal-conic group, but must always remain normal to the strata.

These factors concerning the optic axial direction were confirmed by Friedel,[1] and readers who are interested in a more theoretical approach to the question of the changing optic axial direction in the smectic meso-phase are referred to the article which was published by Sir William Bragg in *Nature* in 1934.[8] Friedel[1] made many of his observations on the smectic mesophase of ethyl *p*-azoxybenzoate, and, using a quarter wavelength plate, was able to obtain the characteristic figures for a positive uniaxial system in which the optic axis at a given point in the preparation lay along a line joining both the conics. The optical figures that he obtained were not particularly sharp, probably because of interference from small focal-conic regions in the bulk of the preparation. He had shown earlier, however, that although the focal-conic texture of ethyl *p*-azoxybenzoate is destroyed when crystallization occurs, this is not the case with mixtures of the compound with ethyl *p*-azoxycinna-mate. When the smectic mesophases of such mixtures are cooled, the solid is obtained in a *pseudomorphic state*, in which the focal-conic arrangement is largely maintained. In fact, the larger focal-conic groups are preserved, and the smaller groups are destroyed by the crystallization. Perfect examples of large focal-conic groups are thus obtained in a rigid structure which will exist indefinitely. Friedel was therefore able to carry out more detailed and more leisurely optical studies on such specimens, and found no exceptions to the concept that the optic axial directions lie along lines joining the hyperbolas to the ellipses of the focal-conic groups. Later Friedel[1] carried out similar studies upon pseudomorphic crystalline states of pure substances, e.g. ethyl *p*-(4-methoxybenzylideneamino)cinnamate, cholesteryl stearate, and octyl *p*-azoxycinnamate, largely as a result of criticisms made by other workers on the basis that optical studies on mixtures might give results which were not applicable to pure substances. The same results were obtained using the pure compounds.

Still further evidence for the layer arrangement in the smectic meso-phase was obtained as a result of these studies of pseudomorphic crystal-line states which maintain the focal-conic texture. If a focal-conic group was obtained so that the hyperbola lay in the plane of the surface of the preparation, i.e. as though it were attached to the cover slip, and the ellipse was therefore reduced to a straight line as in Fig. II.7, then the crystalline region corresponding to this particular section of the cone of revolution is marked by fine dark lines which are the arcs of concentric circles. In other words, the section of crystalline material has a pattern equivalent to the drawing in Fig. II.7.

From what has been said about the continuously changing direction of the optic axis of a focal-conic " domaine ", it is now possible to understand why the ellipses and hyperbolas are visible in a preparation. The ellipses and hyperbolas can now be regarded as lines in the neighbourhood of which the optic axial direction changes suddenly. That is, they represent optical discontinuities, either within a " domaine ", in the case of an hyperbola, or between "domaines ", in the case of an ellipse. A ray of light passing close to such a discontinuity is deviated, and the discontinuity in optic axial direction is seen as a black line. The centres of crystalline spherulites are visible for the same reasons.

The optical properties of the focal-conic texture are therefore quite compatible with the view that each focal-conic " domaine " is filled with curved parallel strata, in which each molecule is arranged at right angles to the tangent to the surface at that given point. The molecules will therefore lie almost parallel to one another, the deviation from parallelity

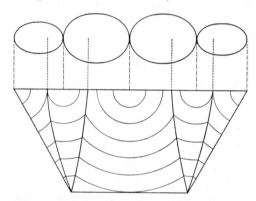

FIG. II.10. The continuum of strata for neighbouring focal-conic regions in a smectic mesophase.

becoming appreciable only in the case of curved surfaces of small radius. Now, as discussed in detail in the article by Sir William Bragg,[8] an entire volume of material can be divided into these focal-conic "domaines", the small interstitial volumes being filled by wedges and tetrahedra corresponding to portions of focal-conic "domaines". The entire volume will then be made up of a continuous series of distorted strata. Figure II.10 illustrates that the strata corresponding to neighbouring focal-conic groups may in fact be regarded as continuous.

In the special case of stepped drops, the smectic layers are *flat* as well as parallel to one another. We must therefore envisage that, when the mesophase exists between glass surfaces, the distortions imposed by expansions and contractions of the mesophase in the restricted volume and the effect of local attractions of the molecules to the glass surface give rise to such disturbing influences that the parallel layers no longer remain flat, and become curved and highly distorted, i.e. the focal-conic texture is produced. The adoption of this particular layer structure corresponding to Dupin cyclides, rather than any one of a number of other possible arrangements involving parallel strata, must stem from the fact that the potential energy of the mesophase is a minimum under these particular conditions. For example, it might be thought that a simpler arrangement of the layers in cylindrical volumes would be more likely than the focal-conic arrangement. However, a volume of material cannot be divided up into cylindrical volumes which correspond to *continuous* strata, and this fact probably explains why this particular arrangement of layers is disfavoured.

OTHER EXAMPLES OF FOCAL-CONIC ARRANGEMENTS

(A) OILY STREAKS (" STRIES HUILEUSES ")

These are often obtained when a cover slip displacement is made to a focal-conic preparation in order to induce homœotropy. It is unusual to achieve complete homœotropy by one cover slip displacement, and normally partial homœotropy results, together with birefringent bands with parallel sides. These resemble oily streaks or smears, but a closer inspection reveals that they are simply chains of small focal-conic groups.

(B) " BÂTONNETS "

When the isotropic liquid of a smectogenic compound is cooled, the smectic mesophase appears to the naked eye to pass across between the slide and the cover slip as a sharply defined front. Magnification of this front will, however, reveal that it is not in fact a clearly defined line, and that the mesophase is separating from the isotropic melt in somewhat elongated, irregularly shaped, birefringent bodies (not in spherical drops, as in the case of the nematic mesophase). Further magnification shows that these bodies differ very widely in shape, and that only rarely are they cylindrical. Their surfaces are, however, curved, and they are often symmetrical about their long axes. Drawings of some typical bâtonnets are shown in Fig. II.11, and it can be seen that they are frequently highly ornate and reminiscent of the carved legs and decorations on antique furniture. This analogy in fact led Friedel to describe them as " bâtonnets " (little batons or rods). If the magnification under which the bâtonnets are viewed is low, the detail shown in the drawings in Fig. II.11 is not of course visible, and the bâtonnets are seen simply as elongated bodies, as illustrated in Plate 2 (facing).

As the temperature falls, and the bâtonnets become more crowded together, they are seen to coalesce, just as drops of an ordinary liquid merge into one another, and the smaller of two bâtonnets will always be swallowed up by the larger bâtonnet. The surfaces of these bâtonnets are interlaced with minute focal-conic groups, and as the bâtonnets

PLATE 1. A typical focal-conic texture of a smectic mesophase.

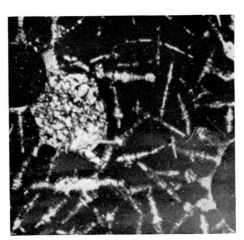

PLATE 2. Bâtonnets separating from the isotropic liquid of a smectogenic compound.

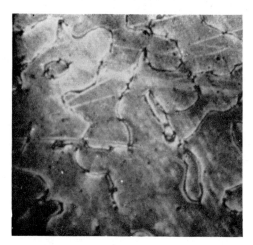

PLATE 3. A typical threaded region of a nematic mesophase.

at the side of the cover slip. When the large crystalline areas have developed, the temperature is raised just sufficiently to obtain the nematic mesophase. Each large crystalline area will then be found to be matched by an identical area in the mesophase, the preparation being strongly birefringent, and having the properties of a positive uniaxial crystal. At first sight the preparation appears to be solid, for the pattern of the areas is quite immobile and the section gives optical extinction in four positions at right angles. The illusion of crystallinity is, of course, destroyed when it is found that the cover slip may be readily displaced. In so far as this texture has been described, there is an obvious analogy with the homogeneous texture of the smectic mesophase, but in reality there are several fundamental differences between the two. For example, although the outline of the nematic homogeneous areas is static, if one observes dust particles floating in the bulk of the mesophase, these will be seen to be in intense and continuous movement. This movement, which is probably due to currents arising from temperature gradients in the hot preparation, is not observed in the analogous smectic texture, but it does not influence the optical constancy of the individual areas in the homogeneous texture. Thus, each area has its particular optic axial direction, and although the molecules or groups of molecules must be able to move freely from one such area to another— since dust particles are capable of doing this—the optic axial direction in each area remains constant. This can only mean that the molecules *suddenly* change their orientation on passing from one area to another, for there are no confused regions at the sharply defined edges of the areas, and no focal-conic bands such as occur at the borders of the smectic homogeneous areas. Then again, whilst a cover slip displacement changes the smectic homogeneous texture to the homœotropic or the focal-conic texture, a doubling of the boundaries of the nematic areas is observed in the case of the nematic homogeneous texture. This behaviour is explained by a pellicle or skin which adheres to the upper and lower glass surfaces which support the preparation. The molecules in these pellicles are considered to retain the orientation of the crystalline state which gave rise to the mesophase. This indelible pattern of the crystals is then imposed upon the bulk of the mesophase. Now, when the cover slip is displaced laterally, the upper pellicle remains attached to the cover slip, and therefore is displaced relative to the pellicle attached to the slide. This obviously explains the doubling of the boundaries of the nematic areas. The two images, one on each surface, are well-defined, and the fact that nothing can be seen of the preparation between the pellicles, except the intense movement of small particles of extraneous matter, led early workers to the conclusion that only the pellicles are orientated, and that the intervening volume of mesophase is disorganized. This idea was dispelled by Mauguin[9] who observed that a twisting movement of the cover slip about its centre conferred a twisted or helicoidal structure upon the *entire* preparation, from one surface to the other. This was clearly demonstrated by the fact that, whilst an angle of rotation of 360° would be equivalent to no rotation at all if the superficial pellicles alone were involved, sections treated in this way still had the optical properties of a helicoidal structure. Thus, the body of the preparation is twisted, and both the ordinary and extraordinary rays follow the screw-like arrangement of the structure, there being no deflection of the extraordinary ray. We must therefore accept that the entire thickness of the preparation is orientated, and this makes the intense movement which occurs in these preparations all the more surprising. The orientating pellicles are extremely permanent, and a sample may be heated to give the isotropic liquid, and cooled again to the mesomorphic state, without destroying the original pattern of homogeneous areas. Indeed, the nematic mesophase may be withdrawn from between the glass surfaces, and a fresh sample admitted, only to give the same pattern. The degree of persistence of the pellicle does of course vary from one compound to another.

Chatelain[10] has made interesting observations in connection with this tendency of the molecules of the nematic mesophase to adhere to the supporting surface. Thus, if a thoroughly clean surface is used, adhesion to the glass is weak, and an homœotropic preparation is obtained; but if such a clean surface is rubbed carefully, in one particular direction, on paper, then the nematic mesophase adopts an optic axial orientation which is in the direction in which the surface was rubbed, i.e. the molecules arrange themselves parallel to one another and to the glass surface, and with their long axes in the direction of the rubbing. This property, which was discovered by Chatelain and used to great advantage in his many optical studies, has been employed by the Americans to produce polaroid sheet.[11] A dyestuff, which exhibits strong dichroism and which gives lyotropic liquid crystalline behaviour, is used. A solution of the dye is allowed to evaporate to the nematic liquid crystalline state, which is then spread over a rubbed surface. The nematic fluid orientates itself in one direction, and on complete evaporation there is left a skin of orientated, dichroic molecules.

Frequently some of the areas in the homogeneous texture are optically extinct, and are in fact spontaneously homœotropic. Homœotropy of an induced kind is encouraged by making a cover slip displacement to the nematic preparation, and spontaneous homœotropy by cleanliness of the supporting surface. If strong attractions exist between the molecules and the glass surface, an orientated pellicle is formed, and in this the molecules are attached lengthwise to the surface. A normal, birefringent, homogeneous area is then obtained. If contact with the surface is poor, the molecules appear to become orientated perpendicular to the glass, so giving homœotropy. Thus, those compounds consisting of molecules which adhere only weakly to the surface are likely to give homœotropic nematic mesophases, and those for which the molecules become strongly attached lengthwise to the surface give nematic mesophases which exhibit the homogeneous texture.

When a drop of nematic fluid is stretched over a hole, one observes areas in which the optical extinction is constantly varying. In such a film, the two free surfaces do not behave like an orientated pellicle, and are in fact in a constant state of turbulence and movement, just like the bulk of the drop between glass surfaces. Such drops therefore give no evidence for any arrangement of plane layers, as for the smectic mesophase, and the absence of focal-conic groups from all nematic preparations is a strong indication that no stratified arrangement of any kind exists in this mesophase.

Indeed, the high degree of molecular orientation required by any kind of layer arrangement would be quite out of keeping with the generally high mobility of nematic mesophases. For example, when an homœotropic specimen is disturbed by touching the cover slip, the homœotropy is momentarily destroyed, and in parallel light, between crossed nicols, a flash of light is observed. In convergent light, the black cross is dislocated by such a movement, and forms again when the preparation settles down. This behaviour and the constant movement of dust particles in a nematic fluid emphasize the mobility of the mesophase. Indeed, homœotropy of a nematic mesophase is seldom so complete that the field of view is completely black, and one observes tiny pin points of light constantly flashing, but quite independently of one another. This type of Brownian movement implies, as suggested by Mauguin,[9] an intense degree of molecular agitation, and as would be expected, this behaviour is most marked at elevated temperatures.

THE THREADED TEXTURE (" STRUCTURE À FILS ")

The nematic mesophase does not always assume the homogeneous texture in which the direction of the optic axis varies from one area to another, but always lies parallel to the supporting surface. In fact, as mentioned earlier, some care has to be exercised in order to produce good examples of this type of nematic texture. If the nematic mesophase is produced by cooling the isotropic liquid, or if the crystalline solid is heated to give the nematic mesophase, without taking the precautions necessary to obtain the homogeneous texture, the threaded texture is obtained (Plate 3, facing p. 31). The section of mesophase between the glass surfaces is birefringent, and especially when the preparation is thick, contains numerous fine dark lines or threads, from which the texture derives its name. Unlike the lines observed in the smectic mesophase (the ellipses and hyperbolas), these lines have no definite geometric shape. When the thread is attached lengthwise to one of the surfaces, it is quite immobile, but when only one end adheres to the glass, or when both ends are free, the thread moves freely about in the melt. Frequently, a thread will be seen to disappear without leaving any trace. There seems to be little doubt that the threads are lines which represent an optical discontinuity in the anisotropic medium, but it is by no means certain what the precise nature of this discontinuity is. It will be remembered that the lines in the smectic focal-conic texture represent lines on either side of which the optic axial direction is different, and it is possible that the threads are lines from which the long axes of the molecules radiate. The thread would then be visible for the same reason that the centre of a spherulite is visible. On the other hand, the thread may be a line about which the whole medium is circulating. If we imagine circles having the thread as an axis passing through their centres, and with their planes normal to the thread, the molecules may then lie with their long axes tangential to these circles. The circles would then be equivalent to vortex rings in the circulating medium, and the molecules would be carried round the centre of the vortex, i.e. the thread, with their long axes in the direction of the circulating flow. In such a system, the thread would again be equivalent to the centre of a spherulite, and would be visible. It is of course possible that both interpretations are correct, and that the threads mark both kinds of optical discontinuity.

Sir William Bragg[8] refers to a further interesting and remarkable fact relating to nematic threads. He illuminated a threaded nematic preparation from below, such that the entrant light was not polarized, but passed through the analyzer after traversing the section of mesophase. The section was photographed twice in rapid succession, the analyzer having been rotated through 90° for the second photograph, and a particular difference was noted between the two textures. The threads which were narrow and well-defined in one photograph were blurred and distorted in the other. However, the odd feature was that all the threads in one part of the preparation were well-defined at the same time, whilst in another part they were all indistinct. Returning for a moment to the homogeneous texture, it will be remembered that the molecules are orientated from one surface of the preparation to the other, through the influence of the two pellicles which retain the molecular orientation of the crystals. In the threaded texture, this constant orientation of the optic axis within fixed areas is not observed, but this does not mean that orientated pellicles are absent. For instance, the orientations existing in the upper and lower pellicles could be quite different, but a continuous change in orientation could occur, except in the regions of the threads, on passing through the thickness of the preparation. Now the directions of the vibrations of the emergent light depend upon the molecular orientation in the pellicle adhering to the upper glass surface. Since ordinary rays vibrate at right angles to the long axes of the molecules, they will emerge undeviated with their vibrations perpendicular to the plane of the pellicle, although when they passed by a thread they would all vibrate parallel or perpendicular to the thread, dependent upon which view we hold as to the nature of the molecular arrangement about a thread. If the threads are indeed such axes about which the medium is structurally organized, then the extra-ordinary rays, vibrating at right angles to the ordinary rays, will be deviated by the curvature of the structure on passing near to a thread. Now, if the orientation of the long molecular axes in the upper pellicle is parallel to the vibration direction of the analyzer (set accordingly), then only extraordinary rays will pass, and the images of the threads will be blurred and distorted in the poorly illuminated section, because of the deviations of the extraordinary rays. If the ordinary rays are passing through, then the threads will be clearly defined in the brightly illuminated section. In the two photographs in Sir William Bragg's article,[8] it so happens that there are two distinct areas in the preparation. In these, the molecular orientations in the pellicles happen to be more or less normal to one another, so that when one part is seen by ordinary rays, the other is seen by extraordinary rays. Rotation of the analyzer through 90° will obviously reverse the positions of these areas. Phenomena of this kind have also been studied by Zocher.[12]

We can see then that the threaded texture represents a more complex arrangement of the molecules than that which occurs in the homogeneous texture. It would appear that the interior of a section of the mesophase exhibiting this texture involves vortices and intertwinings, but that the complexities of the interior gradually diminish as the supporting surfaces are approached, so that there is a continuous change from the internal arrangement to that in the pellicle where the molecules are orientated parallel to the surface in the predetermining pattern of the crystals. We can now form a picture of the nematic state in which the molecular arrangement is essentially parallel, but highly distorted and complex in the bulk of the specimen.

THE CENTRED TEXTURE ("PLAGES À NOYAUX")

When contact between the nematic mesophase and the surface is poor, homœotropy may result, but it is sometimes found that the centred texture is adopted. The centred areas are birefringent in parallel light, and the orientation of the optic axis changes in a continuous way from one position to another in the preparation. The section is crossed by black bands when viewed between crossed polaroids, and between these bands are clear areas. These black bands meet at a certain number of points which are visible as black dots, and such a dot or centre may be the meeting point of two (an incomplete centre) or four (a complete centre) of these bands. Friedel[1] has classified these bands on the basis of the direction and angle of rotation which is observed when they are viewed with only one nicol which is rotated, and of their behaviour when viewed between crossed nicols, when the microscope turntable is rotated. He concluded that the optical properties of the centred regions are similar to those of crystalline spherulites, and that the centres are none other than threads which are normal to the surfaces of the preparation. Indeed, when the cover slip is displaced, the centres can be seen as threads, with their ends attached to the two glass surfaces. The centres would appear to be the ends of axes about which the structure is unrolling, and the bands are the extinction positions about the centre. The bands would of course be accounted for either by a spherulitic arrangement of molecules radiating from the centre or thread, or by an arrangement of molecules lying tangential to the perimeters of concentric circles at right angles to the thread as axis—the two possible molecular arrangements considered above in the section dealing with the threaded texture.

NEMATIC DROPLETS

A notable difference between the smectic and nematic mesophases lies in the way in which the two mesophase types separate from the isotropic liquid. Whilst the smectic mesophase appears as bâtonnets, the nematic mesophase separates as tiny, spherical droplets which coalesce to give one of the nematic textures. Each drop (circular in section) shows a cross with arms which lie parallel to the principal planes of the nicols. If the preparation is rotated, the cross does not move, and the drop must correspond to a true sphere which is suspended freely in the bulk of the mesophase, and which is unattached to the surfaces. Again, the molecules must either radiate from the centre of the drop or be arranged in concentric circles about the centre of the drop, in order to explain the cross of extinction. When the drop grows and attaches itself to the surface, it becomes flattened and gives a centred region, as described above. However, the drops do not always exhibit one simple cross, and towards the edge of the drop, a partial cross with, say, two arms may be seen. The origin of the centred texture from such drops is now obvious. If contact with the surface is poor, the thread (represented by the centre of the cross) may continue through to the other side of the preparation, in a direction normal to the surfaces of the preparation, so giving the centred texture. If, however, contact with the glass is good, the orientating influences of the pellicle will operate, and the threaded texture will develop. The coalescence of the nematic droplets to give the homogeneous texture is much more rare, and occurs only with compounds, e.g. p-azoxyanisole and p-azoxy-phenetole, which give pellicles in which the molecules are so firmly attached to the glass in the pattern of the crystals, that they maintain this orientation even in the isotropic liquid.

A study of the textures adopted by the smectic mesophase and of the optical properties of drops of smectic fluid leaves us in little doubt that the molecular organization in this mesophase is one of parallel molecules arranged in sheets or layers which may be plane or highly crumpled and distorted. Similar studies on the nematic mesophase give us much less precise information. However, the optical properties established for the nematic mesophase by Friedel[1] indicate strongly that a parallel arrangement of the molecules still persists in the nematic mesophase, but that

FIG. II.12. An idealized representation of the probable arrangement of the molecules in a nematic melt.

this orientation is disturbed and convulsed particularly in the interiors of thick sections. There is, however, absolutely no evidence for a layer arrangement of the parallel molecules in the nematic melt, and the molecules may be assembled as shown in Fig. II.12, parallel to one another, but without any definite or regular arrangement of the ends of the molecules. It must be emphasized, however, that the representation of the molecular orientation shown in Fig. II.12 should be considered as applying only in the pellicles, in which the intense movements of the molecules in the nematic state do not disturb the suggested simple pattern.

More recent optical studies on the textures of the nematic meso-phase have been made by Zocher and his colleagues,[12] but their results confirm the earlier findings by Friedel,[1] and are consistent with an essentially parallel arrangement of the molecules. Thus, Zocher and Ungar[12] examined sections (up to 1 mm thick) of nematic melts ex-hibiting the homogeneous texture. They found no reason to dispute the view that the molecules in a given homogeneous area lie parallel to one another and to the plane glass surface used to mount the section, and that the parallel arrangement extends throughout the thickness of the section. Homœotropic sections were also examined, and the long axes of the molecules found to lie normal to the surfaces of the preparations.

Further evidence for the types of molecular organization in the smectic and nematic mesophases will be given as it emerges from the discussions in subsequent chapters of other physical properties of the mesophases. Meanwhile, to complete this section on the optical properties and textures of mesophases, the cholesteric mesophase will now be considered.

THE CHOLESTERIC MESOPHASE

The cholesteric mesophase is formed by suitable derivatives of cholesterol, e.g. cholesteryl esters derived from open-chain aliphatic acids, and the mesophase derives its name from this fact. However, compounds derived from other sterol systems do give rise to cholesteric mesophases, and in the case of active amyl p-(4-cyanobenzylideneamino)-cinnamate (I), a cholesteric substance, the molecules do not contain the sterol type of skeleton.

I

Cholesteric compounds do not necessarily exhibit only a cholesteric mesophase, although this is the case with cholesteryl benzoate, the first known example of a cholesteric substance, studied by Reinitzer.[13] Many of the open-chain aliphatic esters of cholesterol exhibit a smectic meso-phase in addition to the cholesteric mesophase. However, Friedel[1] states wrongly that cholesteryl stearate gives only a smectic mesophase, and more recent work[14] has shown that the compound exhibits both a cholesteric and a smectic mesophase, both of which are monotropic with respect to the solid. Moreover, the trends of the mesomorphic transition temperatures along the homologous series of open-chain aliphatic esters of cholesterol suggest that the cholesteric properties would not become extinct, and the compounds exclusively smectic in behaviour, until considerably longer carbon chains were employed in the ester alkyl group.

As Friedel[1] points out, however, there is no known case of a compound which gives both a cholesteric and a nematic mesophase. Since the transition from a smectic to a nematic mesophase is discontinuous and the transition from a smectic to a cholesteric mesophase is discontinuous, Friedel[1] concluded that the cholesteric mesophase should be regarded as most similar to, and indeed a special type of nematic mesophase. It should be remembered, however, that the basis of Friedel's argument was that a discontinuous transition between a smectic and a cholesteric mesophase could not occur if the cholesteric mesophase is a type of smectic mesophase. In other words, Friedel did not believe in the occurrence of polymesomorphism. However, well-established cases of polymesomorphism involving clearly defined, discontinuous transitions between different forms of the smectic mesophase are now known.[15] For example, polymesomorphism is particularly well marked in the 4'-n-alkoxy-3'-nitrobiphenyl-4-carboxylic acids, and the fact that the structural differences between the smectic modifications are not understood, does not remove the fact that transitions occur between them. On these grounds, a discontinuous transition between a smectic and a cholesteric mesophase is permissible, even though we regard the cholesteric mesophase as a particular type of smectic mesophase. Indeed, the cholesteric mesophase does exhibit certain characteristics which are similar to those of the smectic mesophase. For example, both mesophase types give rise to focal-conic textures and separate from the isotropic liquid in bâtonnets. Differences between the two mesophases do, of course, exist, and these will be discussed presently in some detail, but it does seem that Friedel,[1] in relating the cholesteric mesophase to the nematic type, was to some extent influenced by his antogonism to the concept of polymesomorphism, upheld at that time by the German school of chemists. Friedel[1] did, however, reinforce his arguments by his observation that mixtures of certain *cholesteric* substances give *nematic* mesophases, and that the addition of certain optically active compounds to the *nematic* mesophase of *p*-azoxyanisole gives rise to *cholesteric* properties. Chatelain[16] too has pointed out that the amount of light diffused by the nematic mesophase is similar to that diffused by the cholesteric mesophase, and it is also true that the mobility of the cholesteric mesophase is much greater than that of the smectic mesophase. For example, the cholesteric mesophase will flow in a melting-point capillary, giving a cloudy fluid with a meniscus. However, it is pointless to argue whether the similarities between the smectic and the cholesteric mesophase are closer than those between the nematic and the cholesteric mesophase, for, as will emerge from the following discussion, the most remarkable properties of the cholesteric mesophase are the intensely iridescent colours and the extremely high optical rotatory power exhibited by one of its textures, the Grandjean plane texture—properties which are found for neither smectic nor nematic mesophases. Moreover, whilst the smectic and nematic mesophases have the properties of positive uniaxial crystals, the optical characteristics of the cholesteric mesophase are those of a negative uniaxial crystal. In view of the conflict between these similarities and dissimilarities, it is perhaps best to regard the cholesteric mesophase as a third distinct mesophase type, and not to attempt to fit it into either the smectic or nematic category.

Let us now consider the textures adopted by cholesteric mesophases between plane glass surfaces.

THE FOCAL-CONIC TEXTURE

When a cholesteric compound is heated until the crystals pass to the cholesteric mesophase, or when the isotropic liquid is cooled to give the cholesteric mesophase, the texture adopted is focal-conic, provided that the mesophase is not disturbed by any movement of the cover slip. The focal-conic groups are frequently small and confused, but a sufficiently large number of cases in which they are well-defined, e.g. cholesteryl benzoate, have been examined in detail to demonstrate that they are identical, except in optical sign, with smectic focal-conic groups. The areas enclosed by the ellipses are birefringent, and usually silver-grey between crossed polaroids. When the focal-conic texture is obtained by cooling the isotropic liquid, Friedel[1] comments that it is not always easy to distinguish the shape of the bodies which coalesce to give the focal-conic groups. The reason, he adds, is that the mesophase frequently appears in the form of a cloud which is not birefringent and which is coloured dull purple to the naked eye. Friedel regards this cloud as a sort of veil comprised of tiny droplets which are not resolvable by the microscope. However, it has been demonstrated[14] that with cholesteryl octanoate this so-called cloud persists while the sample cools slowly through about 8°, and it is the author's view that this condition of the mesophase is more probably an "homœotropic" condition which has arisen through the *rapid* coalescing of a large number of small, indistinguishable particles. Because of the "homœotropy" the field of view is dark between crossed polaroids, and only at a lower temperature, which is variable and not reversible, does the focal-conic texture gradually develop in the preparation. The temperature at which this "homœotropic" condition appears on cooling is in fact the same as the temperature at which the focal-conic texture becomes isotropic on heating. It would seem reasonable therefore to regard this "homœotropic" condition of the mesophase as one of the textures of the cholesteric mesophase, and the focal-conic condition as another texture. The term homœotropic used in connection with the cholesteric mesophase has, however, been placed in inverted commas in the above text because, as will be mentioned later (see p. 53), it is not easy to suggest any satisfactory molecular arrangement for the cholesteric mesophase which will account for homœotropic properties. It is certain, however, that the "homœotropic" and focal-conic conditions do not represent different mesophase types, as contended by Lehmann,[17] for there is no reversible, discontinuous transition between them at a particular temperature, and at the most they represent different textures of the same mesophase. Indeed, these facts afford an explanation of Friedel's conclusion[1] that cholesteryl stearate exhibits no cholesteric mesophase. The isotropic liquid of this substance gives the monotropic, "homœotropic" condition of the cholesteric mesophase at 79·5°, and only 1° above the cholesteric-smectic transition at 75·5° do cholesteric focal-conic groups begin to appear in the "homœotropic" state. If the "homœotropic" state was not observed, it would be easy to conclude that a direct isotropic-smectic transition was occurring.

In several instances, however, the "homœotropic" condition does not arise, and the change from the isotropic liquid to the focal-conic texture can be seen to take place via bâtonnets of the same type as those involved at isotropic-smectic changes. Friedel[1] observed these particularly clearly with certain mixtures of cholesteryl benzoate and *p*-azoxyphenetole.

The focal-conic texture of the cholesteric mesophase is always optically negative and uniaxial, unlike the smectic and nematic mesophases which have the properties of positive uniaxial crystals. The optically negative character is referred to in greater detail later in this chapter (p. 50) and in Chapter VII, which deals with mixed liquid crystalline systems.

THE GRANDJEAN PLANE TEXTURE ("STRUCTURE À PLANS")

If a cover slip displacement is made to a preparation which has adopted the focal-conic texture of the cholesteric mesophase, an immediate change in texture and properties occurs. The cover slip displacement need only be very slight to destroy the focal-conic groups and give the plane texture which reflects light of beautifully iridescent colours, resembling those of a peacock's feathers, and which exhibits extremely high optical rotatory power. The change is so sudden that early workers were led to the conclusion that the slight cover slip displacement was inducing the appearance of a different mesophase type which had become supercooled, i.e. similar to the way in which a supercooled melt or solution will suddenly crystallize on touching or seeding with a crystal. However, Friedel[1] made it clear that this was not the case, and that a definite change in texture was occurring. Thus, if the isotropic melt is allowed to cool until the field of view is filled by the focal-conic groups, and the cover slip is then displaced, the entire focal-conic area will change to the plane texture. However, the plane texture does not extend over the whole preparation, and the section of the preparation which was isotropic when the displacement was made, continues to give the focal-conic texture as the temperature falls. The two textures then exist side by side, and only a second cover slip displacement will give the plane texture throughout the entire preparation. If the plane texture were really a different type of mesophase, and the focal-conic texture were metastable with respect to it, then the second focal-conic texture would hardly have continued to develop on further cooling. Moreover, in rare instances, the plane texture has been found to appear spontaneously on cooling the isotropic liquid.

The following points also demonstrate that the focal-conic texture and the plane texture are simply structural modifications of the one mesophase type. If we take a preparation with the focal-conic texture and heat it so that the temperature of the sample may be measured accurately, then the change from the focal-conic texture to the isotropic liquid will occur at a temperature, T_1. If we now cool the melt until the entire section has adopted the focal-conic texture, and then make a cover slip displacement, we obtain the plane texture. If this is now heated, the transition temperature for the change from plane texture to isotropic liquid will be found to be T_1, i.e. the same mesophase is involved in each case.

It should also be noted that, if a cover slip displacement is made to the " homœotropic " texture before the focal-conic groups appear, the entire preparation adopts the plane texture, If the " homœotropic " state were in fact a cloud of droplets, it would hardly be expected to change with such ease and through such a slight displacement of the cover slip to a uniform plane texture. As would be expected, focal-conic groups do not develop in the plane texture derived from the " homœotropic " state.

The plane texture therefore represents a further modification of the cholesteric mesophase, and the unique properties of this texture will now be discussed. Before this is done, however, it should be mentioned that the tendency in some circles to use the term cholesteric mesophase as though it applied exclusively to the Grandjean plane texture can cause confusion. This practice suggests, contrary to all findings, that the focal-conic and " homœotropic " textures of the cholesteric mesophase relate to other types of mesophase. The term cholesteric mesophase should be used to refer to the mesophase, other than the smectic mesophase, which is given by cholesteryl esters and other structurally suitable compounds, and which may adopt an "homœotropic", a focal-conic, or a Grandjean plane texture.

The plane texture is again optically negative, and derives its name from the fact that it is comprised of optically uniform areas arranged in planes or layers, the plane of each layer lying normal to the direction of the optic axis. When these uniform areas are observed by reflection in white light, they show wonderfully brilliant colours, which vary according to the angle of incidence of the light. Between crossed nicols, colours are again shown, and these do not change on rotating the microscope stage. Under good conditions, the discontinuities at the edges of the uniform areas show the presence of the cholesteric strata, and that these Grandjean planes are of equal thickness. Such conditions are best achieved by introducing the liquid specimen into a V- or wedge-shaped split between two freshly cleaved mica surfaces. Looking down at the preparation, which increases in thickness away from the junction of the two mica surfaces, the edges of the Grandjean planes are clearly visible. By studying the Newton rings obtained from such sections, Grandjean[18] found that the equidistant layers are about 1880 Å thick at the lower temperature limit for the cholesteric mesophase, increasing to 2180 Å as the temperature is increased towards the cholesteric-isotropic transition point. Friedel[1] too obtained similar thicknesses.

The stratification, the brilliant colours diffused from the preparation, and the immensely high optical rotatory power are therefore the unique properties of the plane texture—properties which are not shown by the focal-conic or " homœotropic " textures of the cholesteric mesophase.

(A) COLOURS REFLECTED BY THE PLANE TEXTURE

As soon as the plane texture is obtained (spontaneously or by a mechanical disturbance of the focal-conic texture), the iridescent colours become visible in white light. The colour observed by reflection depends upon:

(1) The angles between the incident and reflected rays and the normal to the preparation. The wavelength of the reflected light is in fact a maximum when the two rays are normal to the preparation, and decreases as the angles between the two rays and the normal to the preparation increase. A mechanical disturbance to the preparation changes the wavelength momentarily, but it gradually restores itself to the original value. The relationship between the wavelength of the reflected light and the angle of the incident beam to the normal can be explained approximately by the Bragg diffraction relationship, and this suggests a structure of layers involving large spacings. With different compounds, the spacings appear to range from 2000 Å to 80 000 Å. The coloured, reflected light is therefore a function of the structure of the texture.

(2) The temperature of the preparation and the nature of the compound. In many cases, viz. the cholesteryl esters, the colour of the reflected light is violet when the plane structure is produced at a temperature just below the transition from the isotropic liquid. As the temperature falls, the colour of the reflected light may change gradually to light blue, to blue, to green, to yellow, to red. In suitable cases, when crystallization is delayed, the colour will then vanish. Hence, the entire solar spectrum is covered, giving finally reflected light whose wavelength is in the infra red, and which is not visible. The rapidity with which these colours replace one another varies considerably, even within an homologous series of esters, and in many cases the colour remains violet until the cholesteric mesophase is invaded by the crystals. Friedel[1] maintained that he had found no case in which the Grandjean plane texture did not reflect coloured light, i.e. in the visible range of the spectrum, at some stage in its temperature range of stability. The author has not found this to be the case with cholesteryl stearate,[14] but it will be remembered that Friedel[1] failed to observe the cholesteric properties of this compound. As is shown in Table II.1, there is a

tendency for the light reflected from the plane texture to stay towards the violet end of the spectrum in the longer, aliphatic, open-chain esters of cholesterol. In the case of cholesteryl stearate, the shift in wavelength appears to have gone even further to shorter wavelengths of reflected light to such an extent that the wavelength remains sufficiently far in the ultra violet for the light to remain invisible until the smectic mesophase appears. In cholesteryl laurate, myristate, and palmitate, a very slight violet colour may be just detected in the Grandjean plane texture. However, although no colour is shown by the plane texture of

TABLE II.1

Cholesteryl Ester	Range of colours reflected from the plane texture as it is cooled until the crystalline state or the smectic mesophase appears.
Formate	No colour or a fugitive red (crystallization)
Acetate	Green-yellow-red (crystallization)
Propionate	Violet-blue-green-yellow-orange (crystallization)
Valerate Butyrate	Violet-light violet (crystallization)
Hexanoate	Violet-blue green (crystallization)
Heptanoate	Violet (crystallization*)
Octanoate Nonanoate Decanoate	Violet-(blue-green-yellow-orange-red)—the colours in parenthesis referring to a narrow rainbow just preceding the smectic state
Laurate Myristate Palmitate	Slight fugitive violet tint (smectic state)
Stearate	No colour (smectic state)

* This ester gives a smectic mesophase, which, like the cholesteric mesophase, is monotropic. The smectic mesophase is, however, only rarely seen, when the preparation is chilled rapidly.

the stearate, the texture does possess high optical rotatory power, and is therefore a genuine Grandjean plane texture.

The ranges of colours of reflected light listed in Table II.1 were observed using Grandjean plane textures which were produced in all cases by making a cover slip displacement to the cholesteric mesophase (focal-conic or " homœotropic ") immediately after the isotropic-mesomorphic transition had passed fully across the preparation as it cooled.

There is an obvious shift to shorter wavelengths of reflected light as the ester alkyl chain length is increased. Cholesteryl acetate may show some reflected violet light, but the colour range is more usually from green to red. Cholesteryl formate, the first member of the series, like cholesteryl stearate, the last member of the series studied, gives no coloured, reflected light. Friedel[1] concluded that the wavelength of the reflected light lies in the ultra violet, and is not detected by the eye. However, in view of the obvious trend to shorter wavelengths along the homologous series, it is more likely that the formate reflects light of a wavelength which is in the infra red. This is in fact confirmed by the observation of a transient red colour which appears just as crystallization occurs. The octanoate, nonanoate, and decanoate behave in an interesting way, in that the colour range of the solar spectrum from blue-violet to red is seen as a narrow band which immediately precedes the advancing front of the smectic mesophase. It seems as though the change to the focal-conic texture of the smectic mesophase causes the rapid changes in colour of the reflected light, perhaps as a result of the disturbances to the Grandjean planes.

The plane texture of cholesteryl p-nitrobenzoate is a particularly striking example, and shows extremely brilliant colours ranging from the violet to the red end of the spectrum as the temperature falls. The cholesteric mesophase of this compound is enantiotropic with respect to the solid, which melts at 186°. The cholesteric mesophase persists until 258°, when the isotropic liquid is produced, with some decomposition of the specimen.

A further instance of the variation in colour of the reflected light with change in chemical constitution is to be found with active amyl p-(4-cyanobenzylideneamino)cinnamate. The plane texture of this compound reflects yellow or red light just below the isotropic-cholesteric transition temperature, and the wavelength of the reflected light increases as the temperature falls. The colour therefore disappears and the preparation becomes dark. The behaviour of this compound and of cholesteryl formate are therefore similar. Cholesteryl 3,5-dinitrobenzoate, too, reflects only red light from the plane texture of its monotropic cholesteric mesophase.

Friedel[1] was the first to point out that the order of succession of the colours does not always correspond to a change from shorter to longer wavelengths of reflected light as the temperature falls. A mixture of 55 % of cholesteryl benzoate and 45 % of cholesteryl acetate does behave in this way, but if about a one-third portion of p-azoxyanisole is added to this mixture, the colours of the reflected light from the plane texture change from green to blue with decreasing temperature. The addition of an equal amount of p-azoxyphenetole to the original binary mixture gives a further range of colours from red to violet as the temperature falls. This behaviour, inverting the colour sequence for the open-chain aliphatic cholesteryl esters, is also found with pure compounds which involve certain sterol skeletons other than that of cholesterol.

(B) OPTICAL ROTATORY POWER

Friedel[1] has described in detail the phenomena associated with the extremely high optical rotatory power of the Grandjean plane texture. The outstanding features may be summarized as follows:

Stumpf[19] was the first to observe that the direction of rotation of the plane of polarization of the light depends upon the wavelength of the incident light. If a compound consisting of molecules with a *dextro*-structure is under consideration, then, if the wavelength of the incident light is less than that of the light scattered, at maximum intensity, normal to the surface of the preparation, the plane of polarization of the incident light is rotated to the right. If, on the other hand, the wavelength of the incident light is gradually increased, then an inversion of the direction of rotation of the plane of polarization of the light occurs, becoming to the left when the wavelength exceeds that of the light scattered at maximum intensity. For a compound consisting of *laevo*-molecules, the inversion again occurs at a given wavelength, but the direction of rotation of the plane of polarization of the incident light is opposite to that of a *dextro*-structure. The wavelength of inversion (λ) is variable from one compound to another, but it is a general rule that, starting at short wavelengths of incident light, the optical rotatory power decreases as the wavelength of light increases, becoming zero at a certain critical wavelength (λ), and then increasing again as the wavelength of the light increases still further. These points relating to the optical rotatory power were demonstrated by Mathieu,[20] who studied a number of derivatives of cholesterol. Previously, two views had been held with regard to the change in optical rotatory power:

1. Friedel[1] contended that the optical rotatory power assumed infinite values as the wavelength of the incident light increased, giving an inversion at some stage, at a particular wavelength (λ).

2. Stumpf[19] considered that an inversion of the plane of polarization occurred at a given wavelength (λ), at which the optical rotatory power assumed a value equal to that for ordinary optically active liquids.

It may be added here that the optical rotation for organic liquids is seldom greater than 300° per mm. Mathieu[20] obtained rotations of the order 1000° per mm for cholesteryl derivatives existing as plane textures, although an overall spread of rotations from 4000 to 30 000° per mm has been reported in the literature for the plane textures of cholesteric mesophases. These immensely high optical rotatory powers cannot therefore be associated simply with the fact that the molecules are optically active, but rather with the way in which these molecules are arranged in the mesophase.

The wavelength of inversion (λ) varies too with temperature and from one compound to another, and may lie anywhere from the ultra violet to the infra red.

Mathieu[20] also demonstrated that the scattered radiations from the plane texture of the cholesteric mesophase form a narrow spectral band, of width 0.02μ, which separates the two spectral regions of opposite optical rotatory sign. The mean wavelength of this band is the wavelength of inversion (λ), and at this wavelength the scattered light is circularly polarized. In this spectral band, the transmitted light is elliptically polarized, although, if the thickness of the preparation is large enough, it becomes circularly polarized.

The circularly polarized, scattered light may be either *dextro-* or *laevo*-rotatory. If a compound which scatters light of a *dextro*rotatory nature is illuminated by incident light which is circularly polarized in the same sense, i.e. *dextro-*, the light will be diffused without inversion. The absence of any inversion is quite contrary to the normal effect observed when circularly polarized light is incident upon other bodies. Moreover, if the incident light contains a vibration circularly polarized to the left, this will be *transmitted* without change of sense, and there is little diffusion.

These extremely interesting and unparallelled properties—immensely high optical rotatory power and the diffusion of coloured light—must be associated with the stratified arrangement of the Grandjean plane texture, an arrangement which in its turn must arise from a particular mode of aggregation of the molecules of the cholesteric substances. The molecular aggregation in the cholesteric layers is not completely understood, although De Vries[21] has attempted to relate the physical characteristics of the texture to the arrangement of the layers. De Vries appears to have been unaware of the work carried out by Mathieu, and regards the cholesteric mesophase, in its plane texture, as being comprised of birefringent layers of refractive index n_1 and n_2 and thickness b. He imagines that these layers are piled one above the other in such a way that the electric axes of the molecules rotate like a screw (see also p. 50) on passing through successive layers. A twisted structure is therefore envisaged, having a pitch, p. De Vries also uses a mean refractive index, $n = (n_1 + n_2)/2$ and a relative birefringence, $\alpha = (n_2 - n_1)/n$. Applying the electromagnetic theory of light, he illustrates that the observed optical properties of the texture are independent of b, provided that this is small in relation to p, and that a wavelength of light $\lambda = pn$ must exist, for which such a system will give a particularly intense, selective reflection of circularly polarized light. Moreover, he shows that this reflection will be marked in the spectral range $\lambda\,(1 - \alpha/2)$ to $\lambda\,(1 + \alpha/2)$. Outwith this range, the preparation will have a considerable optical rotatory power with regard to transmitted light.

Chatelain himself[16] points out that the calculations of De Vries are not given in detail and that they are difficult to follow. He also makes the point that De Vries appears to show that the selective reflection stems from multiple reflections arising at the surfaces of contact between the mesophase and the supporting glass surfaces, after he (De Vries) has used an approximate calculation to indicate that the selective reflection must be attributed to internal reflections at the interfaces of two successive strata. This contribution by De Vries is none the less important, and it can only be hoped that the treatment is made more rigorous in the future.

De Vries also proposed an ingenious explanation of the clearly defined appearance of the Grandjean planes, when the mesophase is contained in a fresh cleavage wedge of mica. The mica will orientate the molecules in a particular way, and the upper and lower mica surfaces should tend to impose the same orientations on the molecules. If we imagine that the first stratum is orientated by the lower mica surface, the second will, however, adopt a different orientation, in keeping with the helicoidal arrangement of the molecules in the layers. As the helix is built up, the molecular orientation at the upper mica surface will only be the same as that of the first layer on the lower surface, if the thickness, e, of the space between the surfaces is equal to $kp/2$, where k is an integer. If the separation of the surfaces is not a suitable value, the succession of layers will stop, and the intervening space will be filled by thin layers or leaves. Considering now the wedge-shaped sections, we will have a series of prisms defined by the uppermost layer, the mica surface, and the edge of the next complete layer. These birefringent wedges of mesophase, adopting the orientation imposed by the mica surface, therefore draw attention to the edges of the Grandjean planes, and so explain the clearly defined nature of the terraces under these conditions of observation.

Unlike the other two mesophase types, and particularly the smectic mesophase, the molecular orientation in the cholesteric mesophase, in any of its textures, does not follow in a straightforward manner from a knowledge of the optical properties of the system. The optical characteristics of the Grandjean plane texture are of course complex, and only by more detailed studies can we hope to achieve complete elucidation of the molecular assemblage involved.

However, it is possible to carry our ideas on the molecular arrangement in the Grandjean plane texture and in the focal-conic texture of the cholesteric mesophase somewhat further. Reference will be made in greater detail in Chapter VII to Friedel's work[1] on mixtures of compounds each of which may give a cholesteric mesophase, one rotating the plane of polarization of light in a right-handed manner, and the other in a left-handed manner. Friedel showed that within certain ranges of composition, the sense of the optical rotation changed suddenly at a temperature T, at which the Grandjean planes disappeared and were replaced by a typical centred nematic texture. The interesting observation was made that the positive optic axial directions lying parallel to the surface of the preparation of the "nematic mesophase" were normal to the negative optic axial directions of either the right- or left-handed optically rotating Grandjean plane textures occurring at temperatures above or below T, respectively.

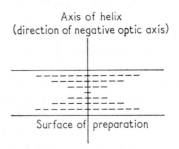

Axis of helix
(direction of negative optic axis)

Surface of preparation

Molecules represented by — — — — — — — — —

Major axes of the molecules twisted through 180° about the axis of the helix

FIG. II.13. A simple picture representing the possible nature of the torsion of the molecular structure in a Grandjean plane of a cholesteric mesophase.

This change in optic axial direction through 90° appears to be quite general, and arises when a smectic mesophase undergoes the discontinuous change to the focal-conic texture of the cholesteric mesophase, e.g. in cholesteryl esters. That is, the negative optic axial directions of the cholesteric focal-conic groups are normal to the positive optic axial directions of the smectic focal-conic groups, from which they arise on heating, or to which they give place on cooling. Friedel concluded that the negative optic axis of the uniaxial cholesteric mesophase is only an apparent optic axis arising from a very high degree of twisting of the molecular arrangement, c.f. the proposals made at a later date by De Vries.[21] The axis of the helix would be a line at right angles to the plane in which the positive optic axes of the individual molecules lie. This would explain a negative optic axis normal to the surface of the preparation. Moreover, the torsion of the molecules, as shown in Fig. II.13, is necessary in order to explain the optical rotatory power of the plane texture.

The torsion must be considerable to explain the magnitude of the optical rotation observed for the mesophase, and Friedel[1] suggests that a torsion through about 180° must exist in the system.

It seems fairly clear then that the Grandjean plane texture constitutes a twisted arrangement of the molecules, and similar conclusions have been reached by Robinson[22] to explain the cholesteric-like properties observed for solutions of certain polypeptides. It is, however, difficult to be more precise about the molecular arrangement in the Grandjean plane texture. As Friedel points out, a simple torsion would explain neither the inversion of the plane of polarization of incident light with changing wavelength of the incident light, nor the fact that the wavelength of incident light which corresponds to the inversion is exactly the wavelength of the scattered light at maximum intensity. The Grandjean planes are, however, probably equidistant discontinuities in the twisted molecular arrangement, and Friedel suggested[1] that mixtures of *dextro-* and *laevo-* rotatory substances, which become nematic at a temperature T, must have achieved these nematic properties as a result of an unwinding process which occurs in the structure at the temperature T.

Though the concept of a twisted structure fits well enough the general behaviour of the Grandjean plane texture, and explains the right- and left-handed senses which the optical rotating power may adopt, its postulation does involve a further difficulty. Thus, the negative optic axial sign of the Grandjean plane texture has been attributed to the twist of the structure, the direction of the optic axis being that of the axis of torsion, and normal to the surface of the preparation. However, the optic axial sign of the focal-conic texture of the cholesteric mesophase is also negative. Herein lies the difficulty, for if we explain the negative sign in terms of a torsion in the molecular structure, why are none of the resultant properties of the torsion observed in the focal-conic texture? That is, why is the texture lacking in optical rotatory power, and the ability to diffuse coloured light, a property which is doubtless connected with extremely high optical rotatory power of the Grandjean plane texture? These questions are difficult to answer, for we do not understand the details of the molecular arrangement which are responsible for these properties in the Grandjean plane texture. However, it is of interest to consider a spiral arrangement of molecules in a focal-conic " domaine ". It will be remembered that in a normal smectic focal-conic " domaine ", the molecules lie with their major axes in the direction of lines joining points on an ellipse to all points on the hyperbola passing through one focus of the ellipse. The optic axial directions therefore vary throughout the " domaine " and will lie along the converging lines from the ellipse onto the hyperbola. The optical properties of the focal-conic texture of the cholesteric mesophase show that the negative optic axial directions behave similarly and lie along lines joining an ellipse to an hyperbola. These lines must therefore correspond to the axes of torsion of the molecules, the direction in which the negative optic axes of each individual spiral of molecules must lie. Therefore, in the cholesteric focal-conic texture, the major axes of the molecules will lie at right angles, not parallel to the lines drawn between points on the ellipse and points on the hyperbola.

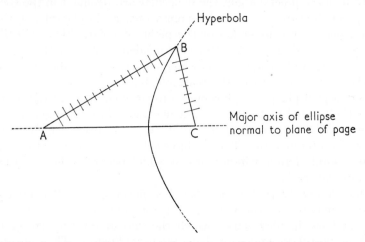

FIG. II.14. An attempt to represent the incorporation of a twisted arrangement of parallel molecules in the focal-conic " domaine " of a cholesteric mesophase.

Some arrangement as shown in Fig. II.14 would be obtained. Here an attempt has been made to represent two such spiral arrangements of the molecules. Although the twist from one surface of a *Grandjean plane* to the other is probably about 180°, it is not necessarily the case that the entire thickness of a Grandjean plane corresponds to the distance (AB) between the base and the apex of the cone, and that a torsion of 180° occurs along this line. The torsion along such a line may correspond to only a few degrees, i.e. AB may be equivalent to only a small part of the thickness of a Grandjean plane. We cannot then be certain about the degree of torsion occurring along AB, and in the absence of this knowledge it is not clear how the crowding together of the spirals at the apex of the cone is relieved. If, in fact, this is the arrangement in the cholesteric focal-conic groups, there is no real comparison with the analogous smectic arrangement in which there are curved, parallel strata running in a highly distorted manner from one focal-conic " domaine " to another, throughout the bulk of the preparation. In fact, the cholesteric focal-conic arrangement would hardly correspond to a layer structure at all. However, it will be noted that the negative optic axes lie neither parallel to one another nor at right angles to the surface of the preparation, even if only one focal-conic " domaine " is considered. When we remember that the bulk of the mesophase is comprised of an assemblage of such" domaines ", with the interstitial volumes filled by smaller cones and tetrahedra, it will be realized that the net effect is a random distribution of the negative optic axes of the system. This may well explain the absence of optical rotatory power, but, as mentioned above, such arguments cannot be carried too far, since we remain ignorant of the detailed state of molecular aggregation in the Grandjean plane texture. It is convenient to remember at this stage that torsion or twist can be imposed upon a nematic mesophase by rotating the cover slip. This does not result in any optical activity, in the true sense of the term, and therefore, although we relate the optical rotatory power of the Grandjean plane texture to a twisting of the structure, it is necessary for the molecules to possess a centre of asymmetry before the property of extremely high optical rotatory power is encountered.

Returning to the " homœotropic " texture of the cholesteric mesophase, it is difficult to imagine how this texture can possess a twisted structure and be homœotropic, without exhibiting optical rotatory power. The texture is difficult to study, as it is obtained only on cooling the isotropic liquid, and is then invaded by the cholesteric focal-conic groups when the temperature falls still further. However, the optical sign appears to be negative, the texture is not birefringent between crossed polaroids, although the naked eye detects a dull purple coloration, and there is no detectable optical rotatory power. The " homœotropic " texture and the molecular structure involved remain problematical.

In the section of Friedel's paper[1] which deals with mixed liquid crystalline systems, the claim is reiterated that the cholesteric mesophase is nematic in nature. In this connection, Friedel adds to his earlier arguments the fact that the change from the Grandjean plane texture to the centred nematic texture of the mixed mesophase is continuous. However, the relevancy of such arguments as to whether the cholesteric mesophase is a modified smectic or a modified nematic mesophase seems doubtful, when we remember that the details concerning the molecular arrangement in the Grandjean plane texture itself remain uncertain.

Further attention will be given in subsequent chapters to other physical properties of the three mesophase types, and particular emphasis will be laid upon characteristics which throw further light upon the molecular orientation in the mesophases. It is, however, convenient to follow this chapter, which has been concerned mainly with the optical properties and the textures of the three mesophase types, by one which deals with the practical application of a knowledge of these textures to the identification of mesophases and the accurate determination of mesomorphic transition temperatures.

REFERENCES

1. Friedel, G. (1922). *Ann. Physique* **18**, 273.
2. Gray, G. W. (1953). *Nature* **172**, 1137.
3. Gray, G. W. and Ibbotson, A. (1955). *Nature* **176**, 1160.
4. Lehmann, O. (1921). "Flüssige Kristalle und ihr scheinbares Leben", Leopold Voss, Leipzig.
5. Grandjean, F. (1917). *Compt. rend.* **166**, 165.
6. Hartshorne, N. H. and Stuart, A. (1950). "Crystals and the Polarizing Microscope", 2nd Edition. Edward Arnold & Co., London, 329.
7. Lawrence, A. S. C. (1938). *J. Roy. Microscop. Soc.* **58**, 30.
8. Bragg, Sir W. (1934). *Nature* **133**, 445.
9. Mauguin, C. (1911). *Phys. Z.* **12**, 1011.
10. Chatelain, P. (1943). *Bull. Soc. franç. Minéral. Crist.* **66**, 105.
11. Dreyer, J. F. (1951). U.S. patent 2,524,286. *Chem. Abs.* **45**, 3534.
12. Zocher, H. and Birstein, V. (1929). *Z. phys. Chem.* (*Leipzig*) **A142**, 113; Zocher, H. and Ungar, C. (1938). *Z. Physik.* **110**, 529.
13. Reinitzer, F. (1888). *Monatsh.* **9**, 421.
14. Gray, G. W. (1956). *J. Chem. Soc.* 3733.
15. Gray, G. W., Jones, B. and Marson, F. (1957). *J. Chem. Soc.* 393.
16. Chatelain, P. (1954). *Bull. Soc. franç. Minéral. Crist.* **77**, 323.
17. Lehmann, O. (1906). *Z. phys. Chem.* (*Leipzig*). **56**, 750.
18. Grandjean, F. (1921). *Compt. rend.* **172**, 71.
19. Stumpf, F. (1910). *Phys. Z.* **11**, 780.
20. Mathieu, J. (1939). *Bull. Soc. franç. Minéral. Crist.* **62**, 174.
21. Vries, HL. DE (1951). *Acta Cryst.* **4**, 219.
22. Robinson, C. (1956). *Trans. Faraday Soc.* **52**, 571; Robinson, C., Ward, J. C. and Beevers, R. B. (1958). *Faraday Soc. Discussions* **25**, 29; Robinson, C. (1961). *Tetrahedron* **13**, 219.

CHAPTER III

THE IDENTIFICATION OF MESOPHASES AND THE DETERMINATION OF MESOMORPHIC TRANSITION TEMPERATURES

THE IDENTIFICATION OF MESOPHASES

SINCE the cholesteric and nematic mesophases flow to give a turbid fluid when the sample is contained in a melting point capillary tube, it is easy to distinguish them from the more viscous smectic mesophase, which adheres to the walls of the tube. Moreover, it is sometimes possible to distinguish between a nematic and a cholesteric mesophase when the sample is contained in such a tube, by means of the iridescent colours which may be displayed by the cholesteric mesophase at some stage in its thermal stability range. However, we cannot use the viscous characteristics of a mesophase as a means of identifying it, when the mesophase is monotropic, e.g. when the liquid crystalline state is obtained only on cooling the isotropic liquid to a temperature below the melting point of the solid. In such cases, the mesophase type must be identified by examining the textures given when the liquid crystalline sample is mounted as a film between a glass slide and a cover slip. Such a preparation may then be viewed under a microscope, either between crossed polaroids or in ordinary light, as it is cooled from the isotropic liquid. It is usually advisable to retard the cooling process by resting the slide on a small, electrically heated hot plate with a hole of a suitable diameter drilled in the centre, the area of the preparation to be examined being placed over the hole. In this way, the observer can readily inspect the texture without the crystalline solid or another mesophase appearing too rapidly. Even in the case of enantiotropic mesophases, which can be identified by their characteristic appearances in melting point capillary tubes, it is advisable to check the identity of *any* mesophase by examining under the microscope the textures that it adopts when it is mounted between a slide and a cover slip.

(A) THE NEMATIC MESOPHASE

On cooling from the isotropic liquid, the nematic mesophase appears as small, spherical droplets, which, viewed from above, are circular in appearance and exhibit a cross of extinction. If the magnification and resolution of the microscope are good enough, and these droplets are seen clearly, their identification constitutes positive proof that the mesophase is nematic. Moreover, when these droplets coalesce, they generally give a threaded texture which is readily identified. As pointed out in Chapter II, the homogeneous texture, which arises as a result of the orientation of the molecules in the nematic melt by molecules adhering to the glass, in the pattern laid down by the crystals, is produced at its best only by heating the crystalline preparation very carefully to the solid-nematic transition. When the molecules adhere strongly to the glass surfaces, even when the isotropic liquid has been formed, then, on cooling the isotropic liquid, some orientation in the pattern of the crystals will be observed in the nematic mesophase. The pattern is never perfect, however, and threaded regions are always visible. The identification of the mesophase is a greater problem if the nematic mesophase gives rise to spontaneous homœotropy on separating from the isotropic melt, particularly if the mesophase happens to be monotropic, and one cannot identify it by means of its fluid behaviour in a melting point capillary tube. Fortunately, however, homœotropy is seldom complete, and traces of threaded areas are usually visible. Moreover, the nematic droplets may be visible before they coalesce to the homœotropic state, and so lead one to the identity of the mesophase. A completely homœotropic nematic mesophase may be distinguished from a completely homœotropic smectic mesophase by the fact that the intense movement in the nematic mesophase gives rise to tiny flashes of light where the homœotropy is momentarily destroyed by the thermal agitation in the mesophase. A fairly high magnification is usually required to reveal these pin points of light.

(B) THE SMECTIC MESOPHASE AND THE CHOLESTERIC MESOPHASE

The identification of bâtonnets at the isotropic-mesomorphic transition is usually a strong indication that the mesophase is smectic, although the cholesteric mesophase may in some cases separate from the isotropic melt in well-defined bâtonnets. The production of a focal-conic texture does not permit one to distinguish between the smectic and the cholesteric mesophase, although, if the focal-conic groups are large, the indications are again strong that the mesophase is smectic. However, the distinction between the two mesophase types is usually straightforward, for the cholesteric focal-conic texture is changed to the Grandjean plane texture by a slight cover slip displacement. In the vast majority of cases, this plane texture exhibits the beautifully iridescent colours referred to in Chapter II, and in only a few instances, e.g. the long chain fatty esters of cholesterol, such as cholesteryl palmitate and stearate, does the plane texture remain colourless. On the other hand, a cover slip displacement to the focal-conic texture of the smectic mesophase merely alters the focal-conic arrangement, or at the most induces homœotropy. There is therefore a possibility of confusing a homœotropic smectic mesophase, produced by a cover slip displacement, with a Grandjean plane texture for which the wavelength of the diffused light is outwith the visible range of the spectrum. If the mesophase is enantiotropic, the viscosity of the system will determine whether it will flow or not in a melting point capillary tube. Thus, flow will be observed if the mesophase is cholesteric, and adherence to the capillary walls if it is smectic. If the mesophase is monotropic, this evidence for its identity cannot be obtained, and in such a case, one would require to determine whether the mesophase was optically positive (smectic) or negative (cholesteric). One may add, of course, that the chemical constitution of the compound would give one a very strong lead as to whether the mesophase was likely to be smectic or cholesteric.

Determination of Mesomorphic Transition Temperatures

For enantiotropic mesophases, transition temperatures for the changes solid to smectic, nematic, or cholesteric, from smectic to nematic or cholesteric, and from smectic, nematic, or cholesteric to isotropic may be obtained by melting point capillary methods as described in Chapter I. That is, the solid and the isotropic liquid are readily distinguished from the viscous smectic mesophase which clings in opaque drops to the capillary walls, and from the nematic and cholesteric mesophases which are fluid, but turbid. Since nematic and cholesteric mesophases never occur in the same compound, a transition between these mesophases does not arise.

The change from the isotropic liquid to a monotropic smectic, nematic, or cholesteric mesophase may also be determined by noting the temperature at which the turbidity of the mesophase reappears.

However, there are several limitations connected with the determination of mesomorphic transition temperatures by melting point capillary methods.

(a) The transition from the solid to the smectic mesophase is difficult to obtain with accuracy. For example, there may be a slight softening and lattice breakdown on approaching the melting point of even a very pure compound, and, although the transition to the smectic mesophase occurs very sharply, it may be difficult to distinguish the softening solid from the viscous smectic mesophase. This is particularly true with compounds containing long alkyl groups such as dodecyl, hexadecyl, and octadecyl, for the compounds are becoming so predominantly paraffinic that they adopt wax-like characteristics.

(b) The measurement of smectic-nematic or -cholesteric transition temperatures is subject to error, since the temperature taken is that at which the smectic mesophase flows. This flowing is in fact determined to some extent by external factors. Thus, if the capillary tube is wide, and the amount of sample used is small, the more mobile nematic mesophase may simply form a thin film on the walls of the tube and be unable to flow to any bulk of " liquid ". Abrasions on the surface of the glass capillary walls are also liable to prevent immediate flowing at the transition point. Erroneous results have also been observed in the case of the 4'-n-alkoxybiphenyl-4-carboxylic acids,[1] for which the smectic-nematic transitions occur at high temperatures (240–260°). At these elevated temperatures, the viscosity of the smectic mesophase has decreased to such an extent that flowing begins to take place before the sample has adopted nematic properties.

(c) Polymesomorphic transitions between one viscous smectic mesophase and another cannot be detected.

(d) The transition from a monotropic nematic mesophase to a monotropic smectic mesophase must normally be obtained by cooling the sample. If the sample is observed carefully, a slight increase in the turbidity of the nematic melt should be seen at the transition, but, when the sample is contained in a melting point capillary tube, the change is difficult to detect.

(e) Solid-solid, polymorphic transitions pass unobserved when the crystals are contained in a capillary tube.

In fact, the only completely reliable transition temperatures obtained by capillary methods are those involving the mesophase and the isotropic liquid.

Attempts to overcome these difficulties were made by Bennett and Jones,[2] when carrying out their studies on the mesomorphic p-n-alkoxybenzoic acids and the trans-p-n-alkoxycinnamic acids. The substance being examined was melted on a small strip of microscope slide (3 cm × 1 cm) and covered with a cover slip. The mounted specimen was lowered by means of a thread into a test-tube, serving as an inner air bath, surrounded by a heated oil bath. The bulb of a thermometer was arranged next to the specimen, and the upper end of the test-tube was closed with a plug of cotton wool. The temperature of the oil bath was slowly raised, and the specimen from time to time was quickly removed, placed on a cold slab, and examined to see if any transitions occurred. The actual transition temperature for a given change could be determined by finding two adjacent temperatures between which the observable transition just ceased to be detected. The authors claimed to be able to determine mesomorphic and polymorphic transition temperatures with an accuracy of ± 1°.

The repeated removal and insertion of the specimen which is involved in this method is a disadvantage, and there is a danger that the cooled specimen does not attain the internal temperature in the test-tube before being withdrawn again.

A means was therefore required for heating thin sections of material, obtained by melting a solid between a glass slide and a cover slip, so that the temperature could be measured accurately and controlled easily, while the sample was observed in some detail, preferably between crossed polaroids. In this way, solid-solid changes would be visible, and the mesomorphic transitions would be seen as changes in the characteristic textures of the mesophases. An instrument was therefore designed by the author, in 1952, to meet these requirements. The instrument was made in the workshops at Hull University by Mr. N. Taylor, and was

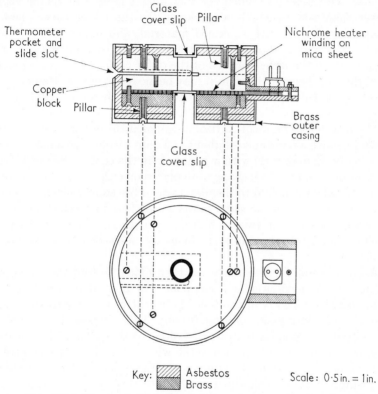

FIG. III.1. Plan and side section of the microscope heating block
(Gray, G. W. (1953), *Nature* **172**, 1137).

originally designed for use in conjunction with a polarizing microscope, i.e. as a microscope heating block. Details of the construction of this instrument have been published,[3] but it is worth recording here the essential features of its design.

The heating block, shown in side section and in plan in Fig. III.1, is about $4\frac{1}{4}$ in. in diameter and $1\frac{1}{4}$ in. thick, and was constructed of high-conductivity copper in order to reduce temperature gradients within the block. The block was made in two parts, to make it easy to cut the slide slot, and the two parts were securely bolted together. The thermometer pocket at the side of the slide slot, and the $\frac{1}{2}$-in. hole passing from top to bottom of the block were then drilled. The $\frac{1}{2}$-in. diameter hole is closed above and below by glass cover slips which are held in place by spring clips, and these minimize air currents which would give localized cooling of the section being examined under the microscope. Since it is necessary to measure the temperature of the cylinder of air enclosed by the cover slips, the tip of the thermometer just protrudes into the air space above the slide. When the instrument is used at temperatures greater than 200°, there is a tendency for the upper cover glass to become filmed over with sublimed material, and under these circumstances, it is best to replace the upper cover slip by a microscope slide which rests on the upper surface of the outer casing of the instrument. When the slide becomes opaque, it may be moved over to a clean portion, so making continuous observation possible even when rapid sublimation occurs.

The heater was made of 22 ft of 36 gauge nichrome wire of diameter 0·0076 in., with a resistance of about 250 ohms, wound on a disc of mica sheet ($3\frac{3}{4}$ in. in diameter) with a $\frac{3}{4}$-in. hole in the centre. Slightly larger sheets of mica of the same shape were placed on either side of the heater, and the whole was bolted to the underside of the copper block by means of two brass plates of the same shape as the base of the heating block. The heater wires were taken off from beneath the block to the plug, which is attached to the side of the block by means of an L-shaped brass plate.

A brass casing for the block was then made, so that the whole was well insulated. Two circular brass plates, 5 in. in diameter and $\frac{1}{8}$-in. thick, and with a $\frac{3}{4}$-in. diameter hole in the centre of each, were supported $2\frac{3}{8}$ in. apart by four pillars of brass tubing. A thin brass outer casing was bent round the circular plates and bolted to the pillars. The heating block is housed within this casing, the whole block being packed round with asbestos insulation. The plug mounting protrudes from the side of the casing, and two brass tubes are let into the top and bottom of the outer case, and meet the heating block beside the spring clips which secure the upper and lower cover glasses. Asbestos board ($\frac{1}{4}$ in. thick) was used to insulate the block above (one layer) and below (two layers), and the space round the sides was filled with asbestos cement. The upper plate of this outer case is bolted through to the heating block itself.

The heating block sits on a $\frac{1}{4}$-in. thick piece of asbestos sheet placed on the rotating stage of an old model of a Baker polarizing microscope. In order to obtain focus on the slide and a reasonable clearance (0·6 in.) between the objective ($1\frac{1}{2}$ in.) and the insulated top of the casing, it was necessary to cut through the back, supporting bracket of the microscope, and to insert a $4\frac{1}{4}$-in. brass column. In this way, the barrel of the microscope and the focusing assembly were raised to a suitable height.

A sliding potentiometer (850 ohms) in the heater circuit gave a wide range of rates of temperature increase for the heating block. For example, the temperature could be raised from room temperature (say 18°) to 320°, using no resistance in the circuit, or from room temperature to only 57°, using the full resistance, in a time of 1 hour. The accuracy of the instrument was established by determining the melting points of a range of organic compounds varying in melting point from 40° to 360°. When these melting points were corrected for exposed stem, and compared with the corrected melting points obtained using the normal capillary tube method, the agreement was within ± 0·25°, provided that the temperature was not allowed to rise at a rate greater than 2° per min in the region of the melting point. The thermometer used for the measurements is frequently calibrated in this way, to avoid obtaining erroneous results through any change in the thermometer as a result of its being subjected to high temperatures for lengthy periods of time.

Polymorphic and mesomorphic transition temperatures were determined as follows. The thin section of material between the slide and the cover slip (mounted at one end of the microscope slide) was cooled thoroughly, to ensure reversal to the stable crystal form. The slide was pushed into the slide slot and the temperature raised fairly rapidly (about 5° per min) in order to obtain rough solid-solid transition temperatures. The temperature was then allowed to fall until the stable solid reappeared, when it was raised again at an optimum rate of 2° per min from 10° below the approximate transition temperature. Mesomorphic transition temperatures were first determined approximately using normal capillary methods. The temperature of the block was then raised rapidly to within 10° of a given transition temperature, when the rate of increase of temperature was reduced to 2° per min, until the transition had occurred. The changes in texture were seen as fronts passing slowly across the field of view. Most changes were readily visible using crossed polaroids, but occasionally a change was more readily detected in ordinary light. The transition from the solid to the mesophase often proves to be the most troublesome to detect, particularly when the mesophase adopts a pseudomorphic texture closely resembling the crystal pattern. However, close observation of cleavage cracks in the crystalline preparation makes the determination of even the most difficult transition possible, for these cleavage cracks disappear when the mesophase is produced. The change from the mesophase to the isotropic liquid, on the other hand, is very easily observed using crossed polaroids, since the change involved is that from the birefringent mesophase to the optically extinct isotropic liquid. Only when the mesophase contains large homœotropic areas is the observation of this transition made difficult, but it is usually possible to detect the disappearance of even very small birefringent regions at the transition temperature.

The slide slot in the casing of the instrument causes a very slight temperature gradient across the plane of the thin section on the slide. A given transition or melting process therefore begins on the side of the slide farthest from the opening, and passes across the specimen as a well-defined front, at a rate dependent upon the rate of temperature increase in the block. Such a clearly defined, moving front is readily visible, whilst a change occurring uniformly throughout the field of view would be difficult to detect. The temperature of a given transition is recorded when the front has passed completely across the field of view.

For mesomorphic-mesomorphic transitions and mesomorphic-isotropic transitions, the reverse changes occur at the same temperature on cooling the specimen. As an added check therefore, the block was always allowed to cool slowly after obtaining a transition temperature, and the temperature of reversal of the transition was taken as that temperature at which the first sign of the mesophase appeared in the field of view. For pure compounds, the two temperatures agree within at the most $\pm 0.2°$, and are usually identical. Only when the pure compound decomposes on heating is any substantial difference ever recorded between the two temperatures for a given transition. Impurity affects the exact reversal of these transitions very markedly, and also makes the front which passes across the field of view much less well-defined. Indeed, precise reversibility of such transitions is a very rigid criterion of purity for mesomorphic compounds—in fact a much more sensitive indication of purity than is given by, say, combustion analyses or ordinary melting point determinations. A melting point may be constant after two crystallizations, whilst up to four crystallizations may be required in order that a smectic-nematic, smectic-cholesteric, or mesomorphic-isotropic transition becomes reversible at the same temperature on heating and cooling the sample.

Reversals of cholesteric-isotropic transitions usually pass undetected when the sample is observed under a microscope. It will be remembered that the cholesteric mesophase often appears from the isotropic liquid in an " homœotropic " form, and only at a lower temperature, which is variable, do birefringent focal-conic groups become visible. This could lead one to conclude that the reversal to the mesophase involves super-cooling. In fact, on cooling the isotropic liquid, the mesophase reappears at the same temperature as that at which the focal-conic groups of the cholesteric mesophase pass to the isotropic liquid on heating. The mesophase reappears as a dull purple or grey front which may be seen by the naked eye, but which readily escapes detection under a microscope. The reversals of these transitions were determined[4] by removing the barrel of the microscope and observing the sample by eye through the upper cover glass on the block. The reappearance of the mesophase was then clearly visible.

The heating instrument was used in conjunction with the microscope for about 2 years, but the eye strain involved in making the determinations is very considerable. As the number of mesomorphic compounds to be examined increased, a simple optical system was designed to replace the microscope, so that an image of the preparation was projected onto a screen. This projection system, developed in collaboration with Dr. A. Ibbotson, has been described fully in the literature.[5] Briefly, the heating block is mounted on a platform, and light is projected from above, through a condenser, a heat-absorbent glass sheet, a circular sheet of polaroid which may be rotated through 360°, the mounted sample, a fixed sheet of polaroid, and a projection lens. The image of the sample is projected onto a vertical screen by means of a mirror, set at an angle of 45°, below the projection lens. The circular image has a diameter of about $3\frac{1}{2}$ in., i.e. a magnification of about seven times is obtained. The image can be observed without discomfort from the heat radiated upwards from the block itself, and without eyestrain.

The magnification is of course smaller than that obtained using the microscope, and the detail that can be seen in the image is very much less. However, it has been found that the polymorphic and mesomorphic transitions can be observed with equal facility and without sacrifice in accuracy. The latter point was established by carrying out a series of duplicate determinations over a range of transition temperatures, using the heating block in conjunction with the projection system and the microscope in turn for each measurement.

The mesomorphic-isotropic transition is taken as the temperature at which the last trace of anisotropic mesophase disappears from the image, using crossed polaroids. Similarly, a smectic-nematic or smectic-cholesteric transition is measured as that temperature at which the last trace of the more opaque smectic mesophase vanishes. Again, such mesomorphic transition temperatures are reproduced on cooling. Melting points are given by the temperature at which the last traces of crystalline material cease to be visible, and polymorphic transitions are marked by the disappearance of one solid modification in another.

The fact that less detail can be seen using the projection system, which gives a smaller magnification than that obtained using the microscope, means that the characteristics of a particular texture, e.g. focalconic groups, threads, etc. are not visible unless they are large and well-defined. However, the boundary between the two mesophases is always so sharp as it passes across the image, that the absence of detail in the image is of little importance. Mesomorphic-isotropic changes are of course clearly seen, and the only real difficulty is encountered with certain solid-smectic and occasionally solid-nematic transitions, particularly when the mesophase adopts a pseudomorphic texture closely similar to that of the solid. When this arises, it is necessary to use the microscope in order to pick out the details of the texture which change slightly at the transition point.

In one or two instances, smectic-nematic transitions have proved to be difficult to detect, when for instance, both mesophases adopt a largely homœotropic texture. Some anisotropic patches usually persist in the smectic mesophase, but these may be so small that the microscope has to be employed to magnify them sufficiently for observation. The smectic-nematic transition would then be given by the temperature at which these traces of birefringent smectic mesophase become homœotropic. A particular instance of this kind is found with the 4-p-n-alkoxy-benzylideneamino-2-fluorobiphenyls,[6] for which it is difficult to obtain any anisotropic areas in the smectic mesophases.

Despite these limitations connected with the use of the projection system, it can be employed for determining at least 90% of the meso-morphic transitions that are usually encountered.

One disadvantage of the heating block is that it is hardly adaptable for use in determining transition temperatures which lie below room temperature. For example, with the 4-p-n-alkoxybenzylideneamino-2- and 2'-iodobiphenyls,[6] the transition temperatures recorded in Table III.1 were determined by ordinary capillary methods, using a paraffin bath cooled externally, when necessary, by a freezing mixture. In the case of the transitions which are greater than 20°, it was possible to repeat the determinations using the heating block. In fact, no differences between the two values for a given transition were found, and it may be assumed that the four transition temperatures lying below 20° in Table III.1 are in fact accurate, and comparable with other transitions determined using the heating block.

The projection system which has been described above, with the heating block in position on the platform, is shown in Plate 4 (facing). It

TABLE III.1. *4-p-n-Alkoxybenzylideneamino-2- and 2'-iodobiphenyls*

2-Iodo-		2'-Iodo-	
n-Alkyl group	Nematic-isotropic	n-Alkyl group	Nematic-isotropic
Heptyl	(3·5°)	Heptyl	(10·5°)
Octyl	(17·5)	Octyl	(22)
Nonyl	(16)	Nonyl	(22·5)
Decyl	(22·5)	Decyl	(29·5)

The above transition temperatures are recorded in parenthesis, a convention usually adopted for monotropic transitions, i.e. for transition temperatures which lie below the melting points of the compounds.

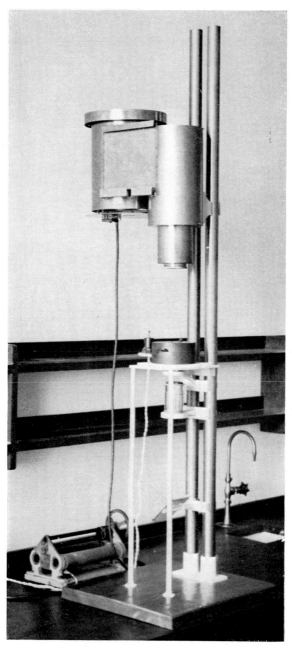

PLATE 4. The microscope heating block mounted on the platform of the projection system which is used to obtain an image of the section of crystalline solid or mesophase.

[To face p. 64.

may be mentioned here that a simpler form of this projection system, arranged so that a beam of light is projected horizontally through a sample mounted on a slide which is situated between two sheets of polaroid, one of which may be rotated, may be used very effectively for lecture demonstrations. The sample may be heated in a flame to obtain the isotropic liquid, and then quickly inserted in a suitable holder placed in the light path. The image is then projected onto a large screen so that the audience may see the actual phase changes as the sample cools, and the beautifully birefringent, coloured textures of the mesophases and the crystalline sections.   The late Dr. G. M. Bennett used such an optical bench particularly effectively to illustrate lectures on " Liquid Crystals " which he delivered at many Universities throughout the country.

REFERENCES

1. Gray, G. W., Hartley, J. B., and Jones, B. (1955). *J. Chem. Soc.* 1412.
2. Bennett, G. M., and Jones, B. (1939). *J. Chem. Soc.* 420.
3. Gray, G. W. (1953). *Nature* **172,** 1137.
4. Gray, G. W. (1956). *J. Chem. Soc.* 3733.
5. Gray, G. W., and Ibbotson, A. (1955). *Nature* **176,** 1160.
6. Worrall, B. M. (1959). Ph.D. Thesis, Hull University.

CHAPTER IV

MOLECULAR ARRANGEMENT AND ORDER IN THE NEMATIC MESOPHASE—THE SWARM THEORY AND THE DISTORTION HYPOTHESIS

THE anisotropic properties of the smectic, nematic, and cholesteric mesophases mean that an ordered arrangement of the molecules must exist in these states. The optical studies carried out by Friedel[1] on the textures of the mesophases give a fairly detailed picture of the molecular arrangement in the smectic mesophase. Here we have an arrangement of the molecules in layers or strata which may be flat or extremely distorted, dependent upon the forces acting upon the mesophase and imposed by the mounting surfaces. Apart from these optical studies, X-ray work on the smectic mesophase confirms the stratified arrangement, showing that the molecules lie parallel to one another, with their ends in line. These X-ray studies are referred to in more detail in Chapter V.

Much less is known, however, about the more complex molecular

FIG. IV.1. An idealized representation of the molecular arrangement in the nematic mesophase.

arrangement in the cholesteric mesophase, and Friedel's optical studies did not lead to a detailed and definite understanding of the molecular arrangement in the nematic mesophase, as they did for the smectic mesophase. The optical properties of the nematic mesophase suggested that the molecules remained parallel to one another to some extent at least, but there was no evidence for any stratification. The arrangement of the molecules in the nematic mesophase is usually envisaged as one in which the molecules are parallel to one another, but with no regular organization of the ends of the molecules. This arrangement is often referred to as an imbricated structure (Fig. IV.1), and some confirmation of this has been obtained from the X-ray work of Bernal and Crowfoot[2] on the molecular arrangements in the crystalline states of nematogenic compounds. This X-ray work will also be discussed further in Chapter V.

Whilst the arrangement of the smectic layers appears to extend continuously from one surface of a preparation to another, at least for fairly thin sections between glass surfaces, it has never been implied that the imbricated structure of the nematic mesophase extends uniformly throughout any bulk of the mesophase. Indeed, to postulate this would be quite out of keeping with the observed optical properties of the nematic mesophase, in which it appears that the molecules are in a constant state of movement, such that any parallel arrangement must become distorted and twisted, particularly in parts of the mesophase which are free from the orientating influences of surfaces.

In fact, a considerable body of experimental evidence points to the view that, away from the orientating influences of surfaces, the arrangement of parallel molecules in the nematic mesophase persists only in groups of some 100 000 molecules. These groups are referred to as swarms, and the theory, now known as the Swarm Theory, was first proposed by E. Bose,[3] in 1909. The first exact mathematical treatment of the Swarm Theory was not published until 1918, when Ornstein and Zernicke[4] studied systems in the neighbourhood of the critical point. Briefly, it was shown that density deviations in the region of the critical point became large, and it was possible to propose a formula for the opalescence of the system up to the critical point. Unlike the Einstein-Smoluchowski formula, this does not give the opalescence as infinite at the critical point. Other mathematical interpretations of the Swarm Hypothesis have been given by authors such as Oseen,[5] Ornstein,[6] Ornstein and Kast,[7] and Tzvetkov,[8] but none of these has in fact explained all the various properties of the nematic mesophase.

A qualitative account of the Swarm Theory will therefore be given, together with experimental observations on the nematic mesophase which support the theory.

The majority of mesomorphic compounds are comprised of long, rod-shaped or lath-shaped molecules, frequently carrying dipolar groups, which may be either centrally or terminally situated in the molecule. Because of the elongated molecular shape and the rotation moments existing between neighbouring dipolar molecules, there will be a tendency for the molecules to arrange themselves parallel to one another. Since the attractive and repulsive forces which operate between dipoles are effective only over small distances, it was suggested by Ornstein and Kast[7] that there will be a tendency for the molecules to accumulate end to end, rather than side by side. This, they proposed, would mean that the swarm itself will be elongated, the major axis of the group of parallel molecules coinciding with the major axes of the elongated molecules. For a given fluid system, they considered that the swarms will be of more or less equal size, but that the uniform direction of the major molecular axes within a given swarm will not extend throughout the entire medium.   In other words, the major axes of the swarms are disordered throughout the bulk of the mesophase, and there exists a position which is analogous to that of a random grouping of crystallites.   In the regions of different axial orientation between the swarms, the molecules will be arranged in such a way that their orientation gradually changes from that of one swarm to that of the next.

The swarms may in fact be considered as the basic particles used to build up the nematic mesophase, particles which are capable of changing their axial directions, and which are therefore subject to orientation effects and even Brownian movement.

The Swarm Hypothesis accounts satisfactorily for the turbidity which is associated with the nematic mesophase, the light-scattering properties of the swarms explaining the opalescence. On the basis of the measurements of the double refraction of the mesophase made by Riwlin,[9] it would appear that, as the temperature of the nematic mesophase is increased, thermal effects cause molecules to break away from the swarms, which therefore decrease somewhat in size. It has been suggested that a point will be reached at which the swarm is insufficiently large to scatter light, and that at this stage the nematic-isotropic transition will occur. On this supposition, it may be argued that, if the nematic-isotropic transition temperature is determined by the magnitude of the swarms and their ability to scatter light, then the nematic-isotropic transition should be observed at different temperatures when the sample is illuminated with different wavelengths of light. This is not found to be the case, but this fact can hardly be used as an argument against the Swarm Theory. The molecules must be held in position in the swarm by intermolecular attractions, and whilst temperature increases must have some effect in loosening these attractions and increasing the tendency for molecules to break away from the swarms, it is not difficult to imagine that, at a critical temperature which will increase with increasing intermolecular attractions, the breakaway will proceed very rapidly indeed. At this temperature, the nematic-isotropic transition temperature, the size of the swarm may decrease exceedingly rapidly—at least as rapidly as a crystal lattice is disrupted at the melting point of a compound—so giving a very sharp transition to the isotropic liquid. The effect could occur so rapidly that observations carried out using different wavelengths of illuminating light would detect no difference in the transition temperature.

However, Ornstein and Kast[7] point out that the nematic-isotropic transition probably does not involve simply a change from the randomly arranged swarms containing 10^5 parallel molecules in the nematic mesophase to the random *molecular* arrangement of the isotropic liquid. The work of Stewart,[10] using X-ray methods on liquids, shows the probable existence of cybotactic groups or swarms of a few hundred to a few thousand molecules in the isotropic liquid itself. These groups of molecules, like the nematic swarms, appear to be irregular in shape, and elongated. Apart from considerations of size, the difference between the two swarm types would appear to lie in the molecular arrangements within the swarms, such that in the nematic swarms, the molecules lie parallel, whilst in the isotropic swarms, the molecular arrangement is less well-defined. The change involved at the nematic-isotropic transition would therefore be from a system of nematic swarms comprised of parallel molecules, to a system of smaller swarms, in which the molecules have a less regular arrangement. The nematic-isotropic transition would not therefore depend solely upon the decrease in the swarm size and the rate at which this occurs, but also upon the strength of the intermolecular forces which prevent the molecules from deviating from the parallel orientation within the swarm. If, at a precise temperature, these intermolecular forces weaken to such an extent that they are unable to maintain the parallel orientation against the increasing thermal movement of the molecules with rising temperature, then a sudden nematic-isotropic transition will occur. It is quite reasonable to propose that this will be the case, particularly when it is remembered that weakening of intermolecular cohesions also determines the temperature at which a compound melts. Now, melting points are usually well-defined, and yet the change in the state of molecular aggregation which occurs at the melting point of a compound is much more profound than that proposed above for the nematic-isotropic transition.

Ornstein and Kast[7] have discussed the thermodynamic aspects of the change from the nematic mesophase to the isotropic liquid, in which the internal potential energy is higher. These authors show that a true phase change is to be expected between the two states of matter, and point out that any arguments which claim that the Swarm Theory cannot account for a well-defined transition between the nematic mesophase and the isotropic liquid, arise through misunderstanding of phase theory, c.f. Chapter X, p. 297.

The preciseness of the reversal of the nematic-isotropic change can now be understood, to some extent at least. Since the nematic swarm does not necessarily completely disintegrate in order that the isotropic liquid be produced, and need only decrease in size and lose its regular, parallel molecular arrangement, the changes involved are, as pointed out above, less involved than those occurring at the melting point of a compound. When an isotropic melt is cooled, there is usually a temperature range of supercooling before recrystallization occurs, i.e. the temperature falls below the melting point while the molecules become reorientated in the molecular arrangement of the crystal. Less time should, however, be necessary in order that the cybotactic group in the iso-tropic liquid becomes reorganized and large enough to have the charac-teristics of a nematic swarm. Less pronounced supercooling of the melts at isotropic-nematic transitions would therefore be expected, and the only surprising feature is that, for pure compounds, no detectable super-cooling occurs at all. The molecular organization, which is disrupted very rapidly at the nematic-isotropic transition, must therefore be restored equally rapidly on cooling.

If the molecules are indeed arranged in such swarms in the nematic mesophase, then some ordering of the dipole moments of the molecules must exist, and we would expect a magnification of the magnetic and electric anisotropies. In the isotropic swarms or cybotactic groups, the anisotropic properties of the molecules would of course cancel out and not reinforce, because of the disordered molecular arrangement. Ex-ternally applied electric and magnetic fields do indeed produce very marked orientating effects on the nematic mesophase, and these effects constitute evidence for the existence of swarms. These orientating effects are of course much more pronounced than any that would arise if the molecules were being acted upon individually by the applied fields, since the swarm will be orientated as a unit, i.e. the effect of the magnetic and electric fields will be increased due to the fact that the swarm moment (length × charge) will be much greater than that of a single molecule. From the extents of the effects of magnetic fields upon nematic mesophases, Ornstein and Kast[7] have calculated an average swarm diameter of about 10^{-6} cm, equivalent to a population of 10^5 molecules/swarm.

It is instructive to consider the work of Ornstein and his collabora-tors in greater detail, referring first to the turbidity of mesophases. Ornstein and Zernicke[4] have calculated the amount of light which is scattered by a system in which there occur arbitrary gradients in the refractive index, and they have shown that the transparency of the system depends upon $\omega^2 d$ (where d = the thickness of a layer, and ω^2 = the mean square of the scattering angle/unit length of path, which is proportional to the square of the double refraction (n)). The work was developed by Riwlin,[9] who studied layers of nematic mesophase of different thicknesses and the influence of changing the wavelength of the incident light. This work revealed that, for the same transparency, $(n_1 - n_2)^2/d$ was constant within less than 1% and suggested that the nematic mesophase consists of an agglomeration of randomly orientated, doubly refracting units, i.e. the swarms. Further observations by Riwlin showed that the thickness of a layer calculated from the observed transparency did not always agree with the actual thickness. For example, if two layers of nematic mesophase of identical thickness are obtained, one by melting the crystals to obtain the mesophase, and the other by cooling the isotropic liquid to give the mesophase, it is found that the transparency of the specimen obtained by the first of the two procedures always corresponds to a smaller thickness, by about 0·04 mm. This difference is explained by the existence of two orientated layers, 0·02 mm thick, on each glass surface. In these layers, the swarms are considered to be orientated in a regular manner, so that the majority of the light is allowed to pass through. Here then we have a quantitative assessment of the orientating effects observed by Friedel[1] and brought about by the pellicle of molecules arranged as in the crystalline state. Presumably, the nematic swarms, so readily orientated by small magnetic and electric effects, are also sensitive to orientation by small electrical double layer or capillary effects at surfaces. As would be expected from Friedel's observations, the orientating effects would be much less and the thickness calculated would be greater when the mesophase is obtained by cooling the isotropic liquid, in which orientating pellicles or layers are more readily destroyed by thermal effects.

However, Moll and Ornstein[11] have shown that some orientating effects arise in nematic mesophases obtained from the isotropic melt. A strong magnetic field applied to a specimen of the nematic mesophase contained in a glass bulb greatly increases the transparency, x, of the original specimen, measured in the same direction as that of the applied field. When the orientating influence of the field is removed, the transparency decreases, but finally reaches a value less than x, the original transparency. These observations clearly demonstrate that the original specimen was not completely orientated from one surface to the other, but that some orientation did exist. That is, the magnetic field has increased the transparency by orientating the original sample more extensively, but on removing the field, the system adopts a more disorganized state than it originally possessed. However, this very opaque state gradually increases in transparency on standing, as the surfaces slowly begin to reorientate the swarms, and the transparency x is regained. The swarm orientation imposed by the applied field must therefore have altered an existing, but *different*, orientation of the swarms imposed by the glass walls of the bulb. When the magnetic field is applied and the transparency is measured at right angles to the direction of the field, there is found to be a smaller increase in the transparency, and on removing the field, the transparency remains constant. The swarms will be orientated with their major axes parallel to the direction of the magnetic field, and it follows from the above observations that the arrangement in the orientated surface layers must be such that the swarms are attached lengthwise to the glass surface. This conclusion was also reached by Friedel,[1] although he considered that individual molecules, not swarms, were arranged with their major axes parallel to the supporting surfaces.

It is clear then, that for any appreciable bulk of mesophase, only in the vicinity of the surfaces does there exist any extensive, regular molecular arrangement. In very thin sections, mounted between surfaces, the regular arrangement may extend throughout the specimen, and in such cases, no turbidity is observed.

Even under the influence of very strong magnetic fields applied perpendicular to plane surfaces, the degree of orientation of the swarm axes never becomes high enough to give rise to a perfect optic axial picture.[12] This has been explained by considering that the original specimen does not become completely orientated by the field, and that the surface layers adopt a mean orientation between that of the interior of the sample—dictated by the field—and that originally conferred on the swarms by the surface films. This is made clear in Fig. IV.2.

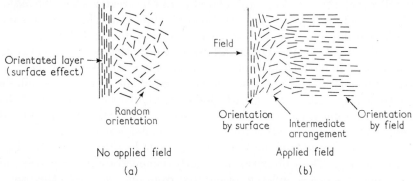

FIG. IV.2. The orientating effect of a surface in (a) the absence and (b) the presence of a magnetic field applied at right angles to the surface.

Naggiar[13] attempted to exclude the influence of surfaces from studies of orientational effects on the optical properties, by using a film of the nematic melt of p-azoxyanisole stretched over a hole. Applying the field parallel to the free surface of the film, extinction was obtained when one of the nicols was parallel to the direction of the magnetic field. The molecular or swarm axes must then lie parallel to the film surface, whereas we know that, in the absence of the field, homœotropy arises and the molecular axes are perpendicular to the free surface.

Measurements of the dielectric properties of the nematic mesophase in magnetic fields allowed Ornstein and Kast[7] to determine the magnetic rotation moment of the swarm, and made it possible to calculate the average swarm diameter and molecular population referred to earlier in this chapter.

Moll and Ornstein[11] and Miesowicz and Jezewski[14] have studied a subsidiary effect of orientating nematic melts by externally applied magnetic fields. This subsidiary effect is the temperature change which occurs through the reorientation of the swarms in the nematic melt.

When the applied field acts at right angles to the direction of the major axes of the swarms, in an already orientated nematic melt, the swarms will turn through 90° to lie with their long axes parallel to the field. Miesowicz and Jezewski showed that this rotation of the swarms causes a temperature increase of 1° per 2300 G of the applied field. As would be expected, a magnetic field applied parallel to the swarm axes causes no such temperature change.

No change in volume appears to accompany the orientating effects of magnetic fields on the nematic melt. This was established by Beneschevich[15] for p-azoxyanisole and 4,4'-di-(benzylideneamino)biphenyl, using magnetic fields from 3000 to 17000 G, under experimental conditions which would detect a volume change of 3 parts in 10 million.

Kast[16] and Ornstein and Kast[7] have also made valuable contributions to our knowledge about swarms by their studies of the effects of continuous and alternating electric fields of increasing frequency upon the X-ray diffraction photographs obtained from the nematic mesophase of p-azoxyanisole. A continuous field of 500 V/cm gave an orientation of the molecules parallel to the direction of the field, this orientation becoming more well-defined, as judged by the diffraction photographs, at 7200 V/cm. Alternating fields were found to have much more marked orientating effects than continuous fields of the same intensities. On increasing the frequency of oscillation, no very marked changes in the diffraction photographs were obtained until the frequency reached some 25 000 oscillations/sec, when the fibre characteristics became much more pronounced. The relaxation time of the particles appeared to be therefore 1/25 000 sec. At greater frequencies of oscillation, the particles did not appear to respond immediately, and by 300 000 oscillations/sec, the fibre characteristics had disappeared. A time of 1/300 000 sec would appear therefore to be necessary for the particles to turn through 180°. At still higher frequencies (600 000 oscillations/sec) the fibre characteristics returned, and this was explained by proposing that the molecular dipoles are no longer able to orientate themselves parallel to the field during the time for one reversal of the field. The molecules would then merely oscillate about an equilibrium position in which the induced dipoles lie in the direction of the field. The fibre direction was then, as would be expected, perpendicular to the field. The measurements gave a relaxation time of 10^{-5} sec for the fundamental particles in the nematic mesophase, as compared with 10^{-11} sec for single molecules.

Whilst this work by Ornstein and Kast provides strong evidence for the existence of swarms in the nematic melt, the arguments which were used at the time to explain the orientation of the major molecular axes parallel to the field at low alternating frequencies, and perpendicular to the field at higher frequencies, seem somewhat doubtful. Indeed, in the discussion of the paper given by Ornstein and Kast at the Faraday Society Discussion of 1933, Bernal[17] pointed out that their explanations were based upon the concept of (a) a permanent dipole acting along the major axis of the molecule of p-azoxyanisole, and (b) the fact that the polarizability of the molecule is greatest at right angles to this direction. The structure of p-azoxyanisole was in some debate at that time, but it is now accepted that the dipole acts at an angle across the major molecular axis. However, the experimental results demonstrating the fibre characteristics and the directions of the swarm axes remain undisputed, despite any weaknesses in the explanations of the results used by Ornstein and Kast.

The general position of the literature in relation to the direction of orientation of the long molecular axes of mesomorphic molecules by applied electric fields is, however, extremely confusing. A great deal of work has been carried out by different authors, and the conclusions are frequently conflicting. The above work by Ornstein and Kast, for instance, on the system of p-azoxyanisole, indicates an orientation of the long molecular axes parallel to the lines of force of the field at low frequencies, and perpendicular at high frequencies. Yet, as will be mentioned in greater detail in Chapter V, the X-ray studies of Herrmann, Krummacher, and May[18] lead to the conclusion that the long axes of *symmetrical* molecules are orientated perpendicular to an applied field, and that *unsymmetrical* molecules become arranged with their major axes parallel to the field. Zocher and Birstein[19] had earlier reached the same conclusions regarding the directions of orientation of symmetrical and unsymmetrical molecules, and Frederiks and Tzvetkov[20] consider that molecular structure is important in determining the direction of orientation of the major molecular axes. If we regard p-azoxyanisole as a symmetrical molecule, the orientation should therefore be perpendicular to the applied field. It is difficult to explain the apparent conflict with the results of Ornstein and Kast, for the work by Zocher and Birstein and by Herrmann, Krummacher, and May was not carried out with sufficiently strong fields to give the perpendicular arrangement found by Ornstein and Kast, with alternating fields of high intensity. Herrmann *et al.*, for example, worked with applied fields which were quite intense, but only in the range 900–5000 V/cm. There is, moreover, the added difficulty that the thickness of the specimen plays a part in determining the nature of the orientating phenomena. Thus, Herrmann *et al.* suggest that the applied field causes disturbances in the anisotropic melt, and that these disturbances tend to orientate the molecules parallel to the field, as observed by Ornstein and Kast at low frequencies. They consider that these effects are most marked in thick sections of mesophase. In thinner sections, the supporting surfaces to some extent prevent the turbulence in the melt, and it is then possible to obtain, with symmetrical molecules, the only true orientation effect, namely that perpendicular to the field.

It has long been known that applied electric fields increase the number of nematic threads in the texture of this mesophase. Friedel[1] considered that the optic axial directions were unrolling round the direction of the applied field, so giving rise to optical effects which were observed as threads. This explanation implies an orientation of the long molecular axes perpendicular to the applied field, and for a system such as p-azoxyanisole, regarded as molecularly symmetrical, this would agree with the proposals based on the X-ray work.[18]

More recently, Naggiar[21] has examined the influence of applied electric fields upon the optical properties of the nematic textures of p-azoxyanisole. He concluded that the threads are purely secondary in nature, and that they are created by the turbulence and conductivity of the anisotropic melt. We may note here that Tzvetkov[22] earlier claimed that the turbulent movements created by the electrical anisotropy of the nematic melt assist to a very considerable extent in orientating the specimens, and as mentioned above, Herrmann et al. explain the parallel arrangement with the field, for compounds consisting of unsymmetrical molecules, on this basis. Naggiar decided that in fields of low intensity, and even with thin sections of mesophase, the molecules of p-azoxyanisole are in fact arranged with their long axes parallel to the applied field. Whilst this agrees with the work by Ornstein and Kast at low alternating frequencies, Naggiar claims that his optical studies give no support to their proposal that the molecules of p-azoxy-anisole lie perpendicular to the electric field at high alternating frequencies, although it should be pointed out that, in 1935, Kast[16] described further work in support of his claim for a perpendicular molecular orientation under such conditions. Moreover, Naggiar does say that further work is required to confirm his inability to agree with Kast's results. Naggiar considers that it is not possible to comment upon the orientation of the optic axes of the molecules in a thick section of mesophase, since the turbulence effects from the applied field are too intense.

The nature of the orientating effects of applied electric fields is not therefore clear, and the extent of the influence of surface and turbulence effects remains obscure. Moreover, the directions in which the major axes of the molecules of different compounds become orientated with respect to the field are uncertain, and it is not possible to conclude this section by making any generalizations. An extensive programme of work is clearly necessary to resolve these many contradictions, and as pointed out by Frederiks and Zolina,[23] in their review of 1933 on orientation effects on anisotropic melts, some of the experimental discrepancies in the earlier work may well have stemmed from the non-homogeneity of the applied electric fields.

Fortunately, most authors are agreed that *magnetic* fields orientate the molecules with their long axes parallel to the direction of the applied field.

Measurements of the dielectric loss of p-azoxyanisole[7] over the temperature range in which the nematic mesophase exists have shown a much larger variation than expected. This could be explained by a large variation in swarm size with temperature increase, but it is unlikely that this is the case, for measurements of the double refraction indicate that the swarm size cannot change by a factor greater than 3 over the whole temperature range of existence of the mesophase.[9] It was proposed that the anomalous variation in the dielectric loss experiments be explained by a friction mechanism, whereby the swarms bump into one another and are deformed as they turn in the alternating field. The elastic properties of the swarm would then enter into the picture, and these vary greatly with temperature.

These experiments also revealed anomalous changes in the dielectric loss in the region just before crystallization occurred. Ornstein and Kast originally claimed that the molecules that do not belong to swarms become associated with swarms of rapidly increasing size in the neighbourhood of the setting point of the melt, and that, from the magnitude of the dielectric loss effects, the spaces between swarms must approximate in size to the dimensions of a swarm. Further experimental work by Kast[24] revealed, however, that these conclusions about the spaces between swarms had been reached on inadequate experimental data, and were not in fact legitimate.

However, the work of Ornstein and others would appear to demonstrate conclusively that the nematic mesophase is comprised of swarms, in which the molecules lie more or less parallel. On the other hand, the views of the various workers favouring the existence of swarms did not pass without criticism, and Zocher[25] in particular has questioned the validity of the deductions made by Ornstein and the experimental techniques employed. In place of the Swarm Theory, Zocher has proposed the Distortion Hypothesis, which is based on the concept of a continuum for the nematic mesophase, such that the orientation of the molecules changes in a continuous fashion throughout the bulk of the mesophase. The nature of the hypothesis appears to be rather imprecise, although the ideas have been expressed in highly mathematical terms. However, three basic assumptions seem to be made concerning the nematic mesophase:

1. The sample will tend to adopt a condition such that the axial direction of the molecules is the same throughout.

2. If any external force disturbs this condition of uniform orientation, the axial directions will change continuously until a restoring force of an elastic nature balances the external force.

3. On solid surfaces, such as glass or metal, the molecular positions originally adopted are almost unchangeable, c.f. the orientated pellicles proposed by Friedel.

Zocher claims that his concept of a continuously changing molecular orientation in the nematic mesophase explains the magnetic and electric properties of the mesophase better than does the Swarm Theory. Zocher's theory was first proposed in 1927, and both Ornstein[6] and Zocher[25] presented papers supporting their respective theories as to the nature of the nematic mesophase, at the Faraday Society Discussion of 1933 on Liquid Crystals and Anisotropic Melts.   Both papers were defended soundly in the general discussion following the reading of the actual papers. In this discussion, Bernal[26] made an important contribution, by reviewing the experimental facts and comparing the merits of the two theories. He pointed out that the orientating effects of surfaces on the nematic mesophase could be explained by either theory, and that the work by Riwlin[9] on the extinction of the nematic mesophase of p-azoxyanisole cannot be taken as conclusive evidence for the existence of swarms. Bernal agreed that the results of the experiments using alternating electric fields constituted much more significant evidence in support of the Swarm Theory, but criticized, without proposing any alternative suggestion, the idea of the knocking together and deformation of the swarms in order to explain the large changes, with increasing temperature, in the dielectric loss experiments.

Both Ornstein[27] and Zocher,[28] subsequent to the Faraday Society Discussion of 1933, have published papers in support of the Swarm Theory and the Distortion Hypothesis, respectively. There is a tendency among present-day workers to assume that the Swarm Theory has been proved to be correct. In reality, it is only true to say that a number of the many interesting properties of the nematic mesophase are readily explained on the basis of the swarm concept, but it is wrong to forget the Distortion Hypothesis of Zocher. Thus, while we may say that the Swarm Theory is today quite generally accepted, the impression should not be given that the concept of swarms is the ideal answer to the problem of the nature of the nematic mesophase. For instance, although Chatelain[29] has shown that his studies on the diffusion of light from sections of nematic mesophases indicate the existence of swarms of 10^7 molecules, he points out in his review of Liquid Crystals, in 1954,[29] that the true structure of the nematic mesophase is without doubt more continuous than indicated by Swarm Theory.

This implies that a compromise between the Swarm Theory and the Distortion Hypothesis may in fact be nearer to the truth, and it is interesting to remember that a paper published by Furth and Sitte,[30] in 1937, sought to show that the two theories are not incompatible.

It is probably wise to summarize the position at this stage by saying that, if we accept the considerable body of evidence which indicates that swarms exist, then the nematic mesophase should be regarded as comprised of these bundles of molecules, randomly arranged with respect to one another, but each possessing within itself a more or less parallel organization of the long molecular axes. The swarm size will be dependent to some extent upon the temperature of the mesophase, and a swarm should not be thought of as consisting of a fixed number of molecules. The molecular units in the swarm are probably exchanging rapidly with molecules in other swarms and in intermediate regions of the mesophase. The limits of a swarm will be very difficult to define because of the gradual change in molecular orientation from that of one swarm to another, and it may be for this reason that the results of even the more recent determinations of swarm size differ considerably. Thus, Furth and Sitte[30] and Tropper[31] arrive at a mean swarm diameter of 4×10^{-5} cm on the basis of scintillation effects, whilst Tzvetkov,[32] from the orientating effects of alternating electric fields, obtains a mean diameter of 7×10^{-5} cm. Chatelain's experiments[29] on the diffusion of light from the nematic mesophase give a mean swarm diameter of 2×10^{-5} cm.

No attempt has been made to apply the principles of Swarm Theory to the smectic mesophase, and indeed it would be inconsistent to do so, for magnetic and electric fields exert little or no orientating effects upon the smectic mesophase. As Zocher[25] points out, one of the limiting features of Swarm Theory is that it is not applicable to the smectic mesophase, and it must be assumed that the layer arrangement of the smectic state persists throughout any volume of the mesophase. It is of course difficult to see any way to prove that this is the case, for we would expect that the distortion of the layers would be very great in the depths of any bulk of smectic material.

The cholesteric mesophase does not appear to suffer any orientation effects by externally applied electric or magnetic fields, and again, no attempt is made to apply the Swarm Theory to this type of mesophase.

REFERENCES

1. Friedel, G. (1922). *Ann. Physique* **18**, 273.
2. Bernal, J. D. and Crowfoot, D. (1933). *Trans. Faraday Soc.* **29**, 1032.
3. Bose, E. (1909). *Phys. Z.* **10**, 32 and 230.
4. Ornstein, L. S. and Zernicke, F. (1917). *Proc. Acad. Sci. Amsterdam* **21**, 115; (1918). *Phys. Z.* **19**, 134.
5. Oseen, C. W. (1931). *Z. Krist.* **79**, 175; (1933). *Trans. Faraday Soc.* **29**, 883.
6. Ornstein, L. S. (1931). *Z. Krist.* **79**, 10; (1934). *Kolloid Z.* **69**, 137.
7. Ornstein, L. S. and Kast, W. (1933). *Trans. Faraday Soc.* **29**, 931.
8. Tzvetkov, V. (1942). *Acta Physicochim. U.R.S.S.* **16**, 132.
9. Riwlin, R. (1923). Dissertation, Utrecht.
10. Stewart, G. W. (1933). *Trans. Faraday Soc.* **29**, 982.

11. Moll, W. and Ornstein, L. S. (1917). *Proc. Acad. Sci. Amsterdam* **21,** 259;
    (1918). *Verslag. Acad. Wetenschappen Amsterdam* **26,** 1442; (1918). *Chem.
    Abs.* **12,** 2477.
12. Van Wyk, A. (1929). *Ann. Physik.* **3,** 879.
13. Naggiar, V. (1939). *Compt. rend.* **208,** 1916.
14. Miesowicz, M. and Jezewski, M. (1935). *Physik Z.* **36,** 107.
15. Beneschevich, D. (1936). *Acta Physicochim. U.R.S.S.* **4,** 607.
16. Kast, W. (1931). *Z. Physik.* **71,** 39; (1935). *Phys. Z.* **36,** 869.
17. Bernal, J. D. (1933). *Trans. Faraday Soc.* **29,** 1067.
18. Herrmann, K., Krummacher, A. H. and May, K. (1932). *Z. Physik.* **73,** 419.
19. Zocher, H. and Birstein, V. (1929). *Z. phys. Chem.* (*Leipzig*) **A142,** 186.
20. Frederiks, V. and Tzvetkov, V. (1934). *Compt. rend. Acad. Sci. U.R.S.S.*
    2, 528.
21. Naggiar, V. (1943). *Ann. Physik.* **18,** 5.
22. Tzvetkov, V. (1937). *Acta Physicochim. U.R.S.S.* **6,** 865.
23. Frederiks, V. and Zolina V. (1930). *J. Russ. Phys. Chem. Soc.* **62,** 457;
    (1933). *Trans. Faraday Soc.* **29,** 919.
24. Kast W. (1933). *Trans. Faraday Soc.* **29,** 1064.
25. Zocher, H. (1927). *Phys. Z.* **28,** 790; (1933). *Trans. Faraday Soc.* **29,** 945.
26. Bernal, J. D. (1933). *Trans. Faraday Soc.* **29,** 1069.
27. Ornstein, L. S. (1934). *Kolloid Z.* **69,** 137.
28. Zocher, H. (1936). *Kolloid Z.* **75,** 161; (1938). *Ann. Physik.* **31,** 570.
29. Chatelain, P. (1954). *Bull. Soc. franç. Minér. Crist.* **77,** 323.
30. Furth, R. and Sitte, K. (1937). *Ann. Physik.* **30,** 388.
31. Tropper, H. (1937). *Ann. Physik.* **30,** 371.
32. Tzvetkov, V. (1939). *Acta Physicochim. U.R.S.S.* **11,** 537.

CHAPTER V

X-RAY, ULTRA VIOLET AND INFRA RED SPECTROSCOPIC, AND PROTON MAGNETIC RESONANCE STUDIES ON THE MESOMORPHIC STATES

IN his well-known article on the mesomorphic states of matter,[1] G. Friedel briefly mentioned that de Broglie had carried out preliminary X-ray studies on the large homogeneous areas of a nematic preparation obtained by Mauguin. This work revealed no diffraction of the X-rays, and about the same time Hückel's examination[2] of nematic mesophases, using copper $K\alpha$ radiation, showed that the diffraction patterns were identical with those obtained from the isotropic liquid. G. Friedel referred to these results as confirming the idea that there is no regular, repeating spatial arrangement in the nematic state. Despite the negative results, Friedel did, however, stress that the range of compounds studied by X-ray methods should be increased, and that the results of work carried out on the smectic and nematic states should be compared. Friedel had in fact realized that the application of X-ray techniques to the smectic state—in which there is an ordering of the molecules in layers, but no regular three-dimensional order—might yield valuable confirmatory evidence for the stratification. It was perhaps fitting that the first X-ray studies on the smectic mesophase were carried out by E. Friedel[3] in collaboration with de Broglie. Later, more detailed studies by E. Friedel[4] were made on ethyl p-azoxybenzoate and ethyl p-azoxycinnamate. Below the transition to the smectic mesophase, the compounds behaved as true crystals, but between the solid-smectic and smectic-isotropic transitions, the diffraction patterns showed evidence for a regular arrangement of the molecules in layers, but differed from those obtained from the crystals, in that the characteristics of a regular reticular arrangement in three dimensions had disappeared. Above the smectic-isotropic transitions, the isotropic liquids gave no diffraction patterns. For these compounds, Friedel showed that the layer thickness in the smectic mesophase was equal to the length of the molecule, and greater than the thickness of the layers in the crystal lattice. For example, when the layers in the solid were 16·2 Å thick, the planes of the smectic layers were separated by 19·9Å, and the difference was explained by proposing that the molecules were tilted with respect to the planes of the layers in the solid, and upright in the smectic layers. It should be noted that the molecules are not perpendicular to the planes of the smectic layers in all cases, but it does seem that the angle of inclination to the planes is always greater in the smectic mesophase. Herrmann[5] demonstrated this by determining the layer thicknesses in the smectic and solid states of thallium oleate and thallium stearate. At 140°, thallium stearate gave an interplanar spacing of 36Å, but the molecular length is only 27Å. Herrmann concluded that the layers in the smectic mesophase were made up of double molecules placed end to end, and tilted at an angle of 42° to the planes of the layers. From the interplanar spacing in the solid, the double molecules are inclined at a smaller angle of 37°. For thallium oleate, the angle of inclination to the smectic planes was found to be 53°, again greater than that in the crystal lattice (34°).

For the majority of compounds studied, the molecules are, however, arranged perpendicular to the planes of the smectic layers, but the above thallium salts illustrate that G. Friedel's assumption[1] that the optic axial direction is *always* perpendicular to these planes does not hold in all cases. It is an interesting speculation that polymesomorphism of smectic mesophases may be explained in terms of changes in the angle of inclination of the molecules to the smectic planes. Thus, the angle of inclination of the long molecular axes appears to increase at the solid-smectic transition, frequently to an angle of 90°, and it is possible that this change may occur in stages. Two or more smectic mesophases could then arise, each possessing the necessary degree of stratification, but differing from the others in the angle at which the molecules are inclined to the strata, and presumably, therefore, in optical properties.

The satisfactory feature of the results of these X-ray studies on smectic mesophases is that they confirm the idea of the layer arrangement of the molecules first indicated by the optical properties. Still further evidence for the stratification in smectic mesophases has been given by the X-ray studies carried out by Bernal and Crowfoot[6] on the crystalline states of substances capable of giving mesomorphic states. Because of the difficulties in obtaining samples of smectogenic substances which gave crystals suitable for an X-ray examination, only one such substance, ethyl *p*-(4-methoxybenzylideneamino)cinnamate, was included in the study. The cell dimensions and the space group were most satisfactorily explained by a layer arrangement of parallel molecules, the molecules adopting a tilted orientation of their long axes with respect to the planes of the layers. It is interesting to note, however, that the molecules do not appear to lie in the layers in a uniform manner, with all the terminal ester groups and all the terminal ether groups side by side in a given layer. The molecules appear to be arranged with ester and ether groups alternately side by side in each layer, and with an ester and an ether group next to one another across the layer interfaces.

The article by Bernal and Crowfoot also contains details of their *optical* studies on ethyl *p*-(4-methoxybenzylideneamino)cinnamate, ethyl *p*-(4-phenylbenzylideneamino)cinnamate and the dianil obtained from ethyl *p*-aminocinnamate and terephthalaldehyde. Each of these systems has been reported to exhibit polymesomorphism, and Bernal and Crowfoot confirm these earlier findings. The textures of the different smectic mesophases are described, but no attempt is made to explain the polymesomorphism in terms of different molecular arrangements within the layers. No evidence was obtained for polymesomorphism of nematic mesophases.

X-ray studies on smectic mesophases therefore confirm and extend the conclusions reached on the basis of optical studies, regarding the layer arrangement in this type of mesophase. As might have been expected, the examination of nematic mesophases by X-ray techniques has been less fruitful, because of the much less perfect degree of molecular organization in this type of mesophase. The earliest work of this kind on the nematic mesophase has already been referred to, no essential difference being observed between the X-ray diffraction patterns of the mesophase and the isotropic liquid. Subsequent work by Kast[7] and Katz[8] confirmed these findings, although Kast does point out that a plot of the intensity against the angle of diffraction for the nematic mesophase is displaced relative to that for the isotropic liquid. Using the Debye-Scherrer method, Glamann, Herrmann and Krummacher[9] recorded the X-ray patterns of several mesomorphic states, and in the case of the nematic mesophases, they reported small differences between the X-ray patterns and those of the isotropic liquids. Stewart,[10] too, detected small differences between the diffraction-intensity curves, the intensity at the principal maximum being 5–15% greater for the nematic mesophase than for the isotropic liquid.

Herrmann[11] made a useful contribution to the X-ray studies of mesophases by examining a number of compounds (esters of substituted benzoic and cinnamic acids) in an apparatus which permitted both X-ray and optical examinations to be made at the same time, and at controlled temperatures. This work has been admirably summarized in the review on Liquid Crystals by Brown and Shaw,[12] but briefly, his findings were that the X-ray diffraction patterns for the isotropic liquids and the nematic mesophases were diffuse halos which could not be distinguished. For the smectic mesophases, two types of diffraction pattern were observed, one showing a halo and a narrow inner ring, and the other a sharp ring and an inner ring. The latter type of diffraction pattern was observed for the low temperature modifications of the smectic mesophases of three compounds which exhibited in each case two polymesomorphic smectic mesophases. The higher temperature modifications gave diffraction patterns consisting of the halo and the inner ring. Herrmann attributes the new type of interference giving the sharp inner and outer rings to a hexagonal cylindrical packing of the molecules within the smectic planes. This would give another possible explanation of polymesomorphic behaviour of smectic mesophases, for it is possible that the ordering and symmetry of arrangement within the smectic layers suffer changes with increasing temperature. A decrease in the sideways order with rising temperature might increase the flexibility of the layers and favour the adoption of a different smectic texture. If the change in order occurred at a definite temperature, a smectic-smectic transition might be explained.

Herrmann obtained normal Debye rings for the stable solid modifications of the compounds, but in each of the nine compounds, an unstable solid modification was found to form on cooling the mesophase, and this then changed to the stable crystal form. The diffraction patterns for these unstable solids consisted of either the sharp ring and the inner ring, or the halo and the inner ring observed for the smectic mesophases.

Although few conclusions as to the molecular orientation in the nematic mesophase may be drawn from these X-ray studies, they did stimulate X-ray studies on nematic melts which were orientated by magnetic and electric fields. The work of Kast[13] who employed electric fields to obtain the relaxation times of the swarms has already been referred to in the previous chapter. The general observation has been made that the diffraction halos of the nematic mesophase change and become crescent shaped perpendicular to either a magnetic or an electric field. Herrmann, Krummacher, and May[14] concluded that in certain cases (anisaldazine and p-azoxyanisole) the long molecular axes are orientated perpendicular to the applied electric field, and in others (e.g. methyl p-(4-ethoxybenzylideneamino)cinnamate) parallel to the field. Zocher[15] had earlier concluded that the orientation of the swarm with respect to an applied electric field depended on the molecular structure, such that molecules with different end groups should line up with their long axes parallel to the direction of the applied field, whilst the orientation should be perpendicular to this direction for symmetrical molecules. The above work of Herrmann et al. confirms these observations, if we regard p-azoxyanisole as a symmetrical molecule.

The conclusions regarding the effects of magnetic fields on nematic mesophases, as studied by X-ray methods, are similar, and both Kast[16] and Glamann et al. interpret the results in terms of an orientation of the long molecular axes parallel to the direction of the applied magnetic field.

Stewart[17] has made a particularly noteworthy study of the nematic mesophase and the isotropic liquid of p-azoxyanisole by X-ray methods, both in the presence and the absence of applied magnetic fields. Whilst

Stewart points out that it would be dangerous to generalize on the basis of his work on one compound, he has reached some interesting conclusions. Both his X-ray and optical studies indicate that the relatively large agglomerates of molecules (swarms) in the nematic mesophase do not persist in the isotropic liquid, but that smaller, cybotactic groups of molecules do exist in the isotropic melt (c.f. Chapter IV). He proposes that the swarms are aggregates of these cybotactic groups, but that the molecular order in a cybotactic group in the isotropic liquid is less perfect than that in a cybotactic portion of a swarm. Moreover, he concludes that the alignment of these smaller cybotactic units in the swarm is not sufficiently perfect to increase noticeably the intensity of X-ray diffraction or the sharpness of the bands compared with the isotropic liquid. The overall organization must, however, be adequate to produce optical anisotropy in the nematic melt.

X-ray studies of the nematic mesophase therefore yield no precise information regarding the arrangement of the molecules in the swarms. The work of Bernal and Crowfoot[6] upon the crystalline states of com-

FIG. V.1. The arrangement of parallel molecules in a nematogenic solid.

pounds which give nematic mesophases, without the formation of an intermediate smectic mesophase, must, however, be mentioned. These authors examined fairly thoroughly the crystalline states of three nematogenic compounds—p-azoxyanisole, p-azoxyphenetole, and 1,5-di-(p-methoxybenzylideneamino)napthalene—obtaining oscillation and Weissenberg photographs. A more qualitative study of 4,4'-di-(benzylideneamino)biphenyl was made. The mutual positions and orientations of the molecules in the crystal lattices have been determined within quite narrow limits. In the case of p-azoxyanisole, it is found that the molecules do not lie in layers, as is so often the case for crystals comprised of long, narrow, aliphatic or aromatic molecules. The molecules are in fact parallel to one another, but the ether group at the end of one molecule lies in close proximity to the azoxy- group of its near neighbour. Bernal and Crowfoot used the word imbricated—meaning overlapping, like the scales of a fish—to describe this molecular arrangement, which, using the short lines to represent the molecules, may be represented as shown in Fig. V.1.

The same state of affairs was found for the crystals of p-azoxyphenetole. In the case of the dianil obtained from anisaldehyde and 1,5-diaminonaphthalene, three polymorphic solid modifications were observed. In the stable form, the molecules are arranged parallel, and are considerably interlocked, forming in fact layers of molecules. This corresponds to the molecular arrangement found in smectogenic crystals. However, one of the metastable crystal forms obtained on cooling the nematic melt possesses an imbricated arrangement of the molecules as for the crystals of p-azoxyanisole and p-azoxyphenetole. It would appear that the stable crystalline arrangement is produced merely by a translational displacement of the molecules in the direction of their long axes, so producing the layer arrangement. 4,4'-Di-(benzylideneamino)-biphenyl, too, appears to have this imbricated arrangement of the parallel molecules in the crystal.

In view of the occurrence of imbricated molecular arrangements in the crystalline states of these typical nematogenic compounds, the inference is strong that such an imbricated arrangement of the parallel molecules will occur in the nematic mesophase itself. The arrangement of the molecules would of course be much less perfect. For example, the

Fig. V.2. The probable arrangement of molecules in the nematic mesophase or swarm, showing some deviations from a strictly parallel arrangement. Throughout a bulk of nematic mesophase or in the regions between swarms, the nematic molecular order will be much more distorted than the arrangement shown above.

ends of the molecules would be arranged randomly relative to one another, and would not be located exactly at the centre points of their parallel near neighbours, as in the crystal. Moreover, deviations from the strictly parallel arrangement would doubtless occur, giving a distorted arrangement of essentially parallel molecules throughout any bulk of mesophase, or if the Swarm Theory is accepted, an arrangement of more or less parallel molecules existing in groups of about 10^5 molecules. It seems reasonable then to visualize the arrangement of the molecules as shown in Fig. V.2, which represents a small portion of the nematic melt or of a swarm, and shows the molecules arranged essentially parallel to one another, with the positions of the ends of the molecules in a state of disorder.

Although there is no real proof of such an arrangement from physical studies, this conception of the molecular orientation in the nematic mesophase does seem to serve as a basis for discussing the relative thermal stabilities of nematic mesophases in terms of changes in the chemical constitutions of the compounds.

It will be realized of course that an imbricated arrangement of the molecules in the solid does not necessarily mean that a nematic meso-phase will be formed on melting the crystals. For instance, if the inter-molecular forces in the crystal are very strong, the melting point of the compound may be so high that the parallel orientation of the molecules does not persist when the lattice disintegrates, and the isotropic liquid may be produced. On the other hand, the melting point may be quite low, but the dimensions of the molecules and the strength of the inter-molecular attractions may be quite unsuitable for the maintenance of any molecular order. Again, therefore, the isotropic liquid would be formed.

Similarly, the occurrence of a layer arrangement of the molecules in the crystal is no guarantee that smectic properties will be observed on melt-ing the solid. For the reasons mentioned above, the isotropic liquid may be formed immediately on melting, or, on the other hand, a nematic mesophase may be produced. The latter would occur if, on melting, the cohesive forces between the ends of the molecules *and* between the sides and planes of the molecules weakened to a sufficient extent. The move-ment of the crystalline layers to give the smectic properties would then be accompanied by a translational movement of the molecules out of the layers. If the essentially parallel orientation of the molecules were main-tained, then the imbricated arrangement of the nematic mesophase would be produced. This state of affairs must arise in the case of the *layer* lattice of the stable crystal form of 1,5-di-(p-methoxybenzylidene-amino)napthalene.

The work carried out by Bernal and Crowfoot[6] is obviously valuable, although it did not concern the mesophases themselves. It has given us strong supporting evidence for the layer arrangement of the molecules in the smectic mesophase, and a definite inference that the molecules lie parallel to one another and in an imbricated arrangement in the nematic mesophase. Bernal and Crowfoot[6] also studied the crystalline states of two cholesteric systems, namely cholesteryl chloride and cholesteryl bromide. The molecules were found to be arranged paral-lel to one another, in layers. In the case of cholesteryl bromide, the molecules lay with their long axes inclined at an angle of 48° to a line drawn perpendicular to the plane interfaces. For cholesteryl chloride, the angle was 49°. Bernal and Crowfoot point out that this layer ar-rangement may give rise to a formal resemblance between the smectic mesophase and the cholesteric mesophase, but suggest that the inter-molecular forces binding the molecules side by side would be weaker than in the smectic mesophase. This proposal would explain (1) the greater fluidity of the cholesteric mesophase, which, it will be remembered, flows in a capillary tube like a nematic mesophase, and (2) the smaller, more complicated focal-conic groups which are obtained in the textures of cholesteric mesophases. That is, the less rigid layer arrangment would be more readily distorted by surface forces and would give rise to more complicated textures. However, these X-ray studies of the solid states of cholesteric substances give no more detailed picture of the molecular assemblage in the cholesteric mesophase.

In 1931, there appeared a paper by C. Herrmann[18] who attempted to classify matter (crystalline, amorphous, and mesomorphic) in terms of the possible degrees of freedom of the molecules in the system. Herrmann used four symbols to represent the different types of translatory movement, i.e. S for " statistical translations ", D for " direct translations ", P for " pseudo translations ", and R for " reciprocal translations ". The four translation types may be combined in different ways. Thus, he symbolizes a crystal as (RD)(RD)(RD)—indicating the possibility of both a reciprocal and a direct translation in each of three independent directions—and an amorphous liquid as (SSS), since in this case, every translatory and rotatory movement is possible, in all three dimensions in space. Between these extreme types, Herrmann showed that eighteen intermediate types may exist, and suggested that these could be associated with eighteen possible mesomorphic modifications. At the time of this publication by Herrmann, only the smectic, nematic, and cholesteric mesophases were recognized, but, since then, studies of polymesomorphic systems, exhibiting more than one smectic mesophase, demonstrate that in addition to the normal smectic mesophase (SSR), one or both of the types (P_0P_0R) and RD(RD) may exist. In these smectic mesophases, e.g. from diethyl terephthal-*bis*-*p*-aminocinnamate and ethyl *p*-(4-phenylbenzylideneamino)cinnamate, the sheets of molecules, but not the individual molecules themselves, appear to have two degrees of translational freedom, and possibly one of rotational freedom. Bernal and Crowfoot[6] point out that their work on 1,5-di-(*p*-methoxybenzylideneamino)naphthalene suggests the possibility of a state (RRD) in which the rows of molecules have one degree of freedom.

Herrmann's classification is valuable, but there is a danger of reading into Herrmann's work the suggestion that eighteen different mesophase *types* are possible. Eighteen different *modifications* of the three established mesophase types may one day be listed, and it is doubtful if the number of mesophase types will ever exceed three—the smectic, nematic, and cholesteric mesophases, c.f. however, Chapter VIII, p. 195. The classification proposed by Herrmann does, however, give a further possible explanation of polymesomorphism, within the scope of the accepted types of mesophase, i.e. different degrees of translational and rotational movement may be possible for one particular mesomorphic molecular arrangement, dependent upon the strengths of the intermolecular cohesions.

The review of the Mesomorphic State by Brown and Shaw[12] gives the symbols used by C. Herrmann to classify each of the twenty different combinations of the translation types. These are contained in a table of data which also gives details of the X-ray diffraction patterns obtained by K. Herrmann[11,14] for the different systems, i.e. ranging from the absence of sharp rings for the isotropic liquid and the nematic mesophase, to the presence of many sharp rings for the crystalline solid. This arrangement of the various translation types side by side with a description of the diffraction patterns for the different states of matter is particularly useful and did not appear in the articles of either K. Herrmann or C. Herrmann.

Finally, a brief mention should be made of the X-ray studies which have been carried out on the anhydrous salts of certain long-chain fatty acids. Such compounds exhibit a number of complex phase transformations between the stable solid states and the isotropic liquids. For example, sodium palmitate gives subwaxy, waxy, superwaxy, subneat, and neat states on heating the solid. Nordsieck, Ferguson, and Rosevear[19] have used X-ray methods to study the transformations. The three waxy phases exhibit two diffuse, short spacing rings, and the neat phases only one, but there is a continuous variation in the X-ray patterns within each group. Only at the transition from the waxy phases to the neat phases is a distinct change in the long spacing observed. Previously, De Bretteville and McBain[20] had studied anhydrous sodium stearate in much the same way, and, whilst they agreed that there is a long spacing change at the waxy to neat transition, they did not observe the short spacing differences found for sodium palmitate. Nordsieck *et al.* consider that the three waxy and the two neat phases correspond to mesomorphic states which are crystalline in the direction of the long spacing, and liquid in a direction across the long molecular axes, i.e. that they correspond to two smectic mesophases. De Bretteville and McBain, on the other hand, state that, for sodium palmitate, the subwaxy and waxy phases are in fact crystalline, and that the superwaxy phase is similar to the neat phases. These differences between the results of these two groups are not easy to comprehend, unless they correspond to inherent differences between the properties of the two compounds. There is no doubt, it seems, that polymesomorphism occurs with these open-chain fatty acid salts, but it is clear that X-ray methods will throw little light on their behaviour until such differences between the findings of various workers can be resolved. Transformations between the various waxy or neat phases do not appear to involve a sufficiently great change in molecular arrangement to lead to significant differences in the X-ray diffracting properties.

ULTRA VIOLET AND INFRA RED SPECTROSCOPIC STUDIES

Ultra violet and infra red spectroscopic studies of mesophases have not so far yielded any very vital information about either the molecular orientation or the degree of molecular aggregation in the mesophases. However, it should be remembered that accurate spectrophotometric work has been possible only during the last few years, dating from the advent of reliable double beam spectrophotometers on the market. Moreover, such studies have been made more difficult by the need for heated cells to contain the molten anisotropic specimens, and even with such cells available, the types of compound which may be examined are necessarily restricted to those which yield the mesophases at comparatively low temperatures. In the most recent infra red examinations of melts of p-azoxyanisole, Maier and Englert[21] have used temperatures up to 120°, and it is likely that the temperatures at which spectra may be obtained will be increased as the design and insulation of the cells is improved.

We find then that the early spectroscopic studies reported by Rawlins and Taylor[22] lead to the conclusion that the spectra of the mesophases and the isotropic liquids are more or less identical, and Vorländer[23] could detect no differences in the absorption characteristics at the mesomorphic-isotropic transitions of several esters which he examined by means of a quartz spectroscope. Similarly, a more recent examination of the Raman spectra of solid, nematic, and isotropic p-azoxyanisole by Freymann and Servant[24] revealed only one difference between the spectra of the anisotropic melt and the solid state and that of the isotropic liquid, namely the presence of a line at 1247 cm^{-1} in the spectra of the two anisotropic states.

The near infra red spectra (about 1700 to 10 000 cm^{-1}) of three mesomorphic esters have been considered in some detail by Taschek and Williams.[25] The spectra of both the mesomorphic and isotropic states were obtained, but only small shifts in the absorption bands were noted between the two states. These authors also studied the effect of temperature on the per cent transmission of the background absorption of these esters. For the solid and isotropic states, the background transmission remained practically constant with increasing temperature, the background transmission being lower for the solid state. As the temperature was raised through the stability range of the mesophase, the per cent transmission rose, and a rapid increase occurred at the clearing point of the mesophase. For the mesophases of active amyl p-(4-ethoxybenzylideneamino)cinnamate and propyl p-(4-methoxybenzylideneamino)-α-methylcinnamate, the changes in background transmission occurred in a stepwise manner, clearly defined arrests appearing in the heating curves obtained by plotting per cent transmission against temperature. However, for active amyl p-(4-ethoxybenzylideneamino)-α-methylcinnamate, the heating curves showed quite sharp maxima and minima. It has been suggested that two factors may explain the transmission effects shown by these heating curves: (1) with rising temperature unidentified polymesomorphic transitions occur and give rise to changes in the per cent transmission; and (2) the changes in per cent transmission are associated with changes in the light scattering as the refractive index and the birefringence alter with temperature, and as gradients in refractive index appear in the heated melt.

The most recent spectroscopic studies have been made by Maier and his colleagues. Maier and Saupe[26] used p-azoxyanisole to examine the ultra violet absorption characteristics of the nematic mesophase in relation to those of the isotropic liquid. Slight shifts in the absorption maxima, in the wavelength range from 2300–4000 Å, were observed on comparing the spectra of the isotropic liquid and the nematic melt. These authors also used plane polarized light to excite the spectra, and by employing orientated specimens of the mesophase, they were able to examine the effect of having the plane of polarization of the light both parallel and perpendicular to the major axes of the orientated molecules. The effect of temperature change on the ultra violet absorption characteristics of the nematic mesophase was also studied. However, the slight differences in the spectra obtained under these various experimental conditions led Maier and Saupe to the conclusion that ultra violet spectroscopy offers little hope of giving any information about the nature of the molecular interactions in the nematic melt.

Since this work, Maier and Englert[21] have published the results of their very detailed infra red studies on 4,4'-disubstituted azo- and azoxy-benzenes. The compounds used were 4,4'-dimethoxy-azo- and -azoxy-benzenes, 4,4'-dihalogeno-azo- and -azoxy-benzenes, 4,4'-dimethylmercaptoazoxybenzene, and 4,4'-diethylazobenzene. By recording the spectra of these compounds over the range 650–10 000 cm^{-1}, and comparing the absorption characteristics with those of the simpler, unsubstituted azo- and azoxy-benzenes, the authors have been able to assign most of the observed bands to particular vibrations of the phenyl ring system, of the phenyl rings linked to the azo- or azoxy- groups, or of one or both of the end groups of the molecules. This diagnostic study of the spectra has been carried out in order to facilitate the interpretation of the infra red spectra of p-azoanisole and p-azoxyanisole obtained for both the polycrystalline and the nematic states of the compounds. As in Maier's previous ultra violet spectroscopic studies of the nematic melt of p-azoxyanisole, orientated specimens of the nematic melts were used, and plane polarized light, directed both parallel and perpendicular to the major molecular axes, was employed. No pronounced shifts in the frequencies of the absorption bands were observed on passing from the spectrum of the solid to that of the anisotropic melt. However, pronounced intensity changes for the absorption maxima have been recorded, dependent upon the orientation of the plane of polarization of the incident light with respect to the molecular orientation of the nematic melt. Considering angles of 0° and 90° between the plane of polarization of the light and the direction of the long axes of the molecules, the two traces of the spectra of p-azoxyanisole cross at several points. Thus, intense absorption bands for a polarizer setting of 90° become much less intense at a setting of 0°, and vice versa. Knowing the assignment of the absorption bands, it therefore becomes possible to relate the dichroism to particular vibrations in the molecule. For intermediate polarizer settings, intermediate spectral traces were obtained, although, irrespective of this setting, the background transmission remained more or less constant. The spectra of p-azoxyanisole at various polarizer settings have been recorded at temperatures of 97° and 120°, but the only differences lay in smaller over-all absorption intensities at the higher of these temperatures. The use of plane polarized incident light to obtain the spectrum of a *crystalline* orientated specimen of 4,4'-dichloroazoxybenzene is also described, and again, large changes in intensity of the absorption maxima are found between polarizer settings of 0° and 90°. Maier and Englert have confined themselves mainly to the question of the assignment of the absorption bands shown by the compounds, but it is suggested in their paper that the work may eventually make it possible to use infra red spectroscopy to compare the molecular orientations of the crystalline and the mesomorphic states of compounds. If this becomes possible, it will be a very important step forward, and further work by Maier in this field must be awaited with interest—see also Chapter X, p. 296.

PROTON MAGNETIC RESONANCE STUDIES

In recent years, a few papers have been published on proton magnetic resonance in the mesomorphic state. The results have been no more than tentatively explained, but it is of interest to record the observations which have been made.

FIG. V.3. The proton magnetic resonance signal from the nematic melt of p-azoxyanisole (Spence, R. D., Moses, H. A. and Jain, P. L. (1953). *J. Chem. Phys.* **21**, 380).

Spence, Moses, and Jain[27] showed quite clearly that the proton resonance line changes markedly in character on passing from the isotropic liquid of p-azoxyanisole, which gives a single narrow line (width <0.1 G), to the nematic mesophase. Here, the amplitude of the signal is decreased, and the single line has broadened greatly and split into three peaks. The amplitude of the central peak is greatest, and the two satellite peaks on either side are of equal intensity. The proton resonance signal is of the form shown on p. 91 in Fig. V.3.

Later, Jain, Lee, and Spence[28] showed that the character of the signal from p-azoxyanisole remains virtually unaltered as the temperature is increased from the melting point (solid-nematic). The sole effect is a slight decrease in the total separation of the satellite peaks to about 2·2 G. This decrease occurs just before the nematic-isotropic transition temperature, at which the separation into the three peaks suddenly vanishes, and the single line characteristic of the isotropic liquid is obtained.

Spence, et al[27] attempted to explain these effects by a very strong hindering of the methyl groups in p-azoxyanisole, but about the same time, Spence, Gutowsky, and Holm[29] suggested an alternative explanation in terms of the magnetic non-equivalence of the protons of the aromatic rings in the mesophase of p-azoxyanisole.

FIG. V.4. The proton magnetic resonance signal from the nematic melt of p-azoxyphenetole, at the lowest temperature at which the mesophase is stable (Jain, P. L., Lee, J. C. and Spence, R. D. (1955). $J.$ $Chem.$ $Phys.$ **23,** 878).

Jain, Moses, Lee, and Spence[30] later extended these studies to p-azoxyphenetole and anisaldazine. Here again, the isotropic liquids gave proton resonance lines which were narrow, but on passing to the nematic melt as the temperature decreased, they split into three components. The separation of the triple peaks gradually increased as the temperature fell, and for anisaldazine, like p-azoxyanisole, the central peak remained the highest throughout the existence of the mesophase. In this paper, the authors state that the central peak for p-azoxyphenetole gradually decreases in height as the temperature decreases, until its height is equal to that of the two satellite peaks. In all three cases, the triplet structure of the line vanishes when the anisotropic melt crystallizes, and is replaced by a single spike on a broad base.

In their more recent paper, Jain et al.[28] give a modified description of the proton resonance signal of the nematic melt of p-azoxyphenetole. The change in character of the signal with decreasing temperature was again observed, but the shrinking of the central peak is now described as being accompanied by the appearance of two small satellite peaks on either side of the central peak. Further decreases in temperature cause the signal to broaden markedly, until at the lowest temperature at which the mesophase is obtainable, the signal consists of five peaks of about the same amplitude. The shape of the signal is then as shown in Fig. V.4.

Jain *et al.* also examined *p*-azoxyanisole in which the six methyl hydrogens were replaced by deuterium. The nematic mesophase now gave a triplet signal in which the central peak was much weaker than the satellites. Change in temperature did not alter this general shape, except to broaden the signal as the temperature fell, but at a temperature about 0·5° below the nematic-isotropic transition, the central peak grew quickly, becoming half as high again as the satellite peaks. At the actual transition, the satellites disappear suddenly, giving the single line of the isotropic liquid.

In the hexadeutero- compound, the only protons are those arranged in four pairs on the two aromatic rings. They must therefore be responsible for the satellite peaks, and in *p*-azoxyanisole, the central peak must be given mainly by the protons of the methyl group.

Jain *et al.* have given a theoretical discussion of these results in terms of the degree of orientation of the molecules in the nematic melt by the applied magnetic field. They propose that a certain number of the hexadeutero- molecules will be orientated with their long axes between the angles θ and $\theta + d\theta$, with respect to the field. The potential energy of these molecules will be low, and they should contribute two peaks (the satellites), whilst only the higher energy molecules which are less well orientated are free to rotate. These are thought to give rise to the weak central peak. The number of such molecules will increase near the transition to the isotropic liquid, and so the peak height should grow.

The central peaks for *p*-azoxyanisole and *p*-azoxyphenetole are therefore thought to arise from signals from the protons of the methyl and ethyl groups, together with those from all the protons in molecules that are able to rotate freely. The extra satellite peaks for *p*-azoxyphenetole are interpreted in terms of the protons of the $-CH_2$ units of the ethyl groups.

The broadening of the peak separation with decreasing temperature is explained by the increase in the degree of orientation by the magnetic field, and a separation of 5·8 G is associated by the authors with complete orientation of the liquid crystalline state. The separation for *p*-azoxyphenetole is 5·5 G, compared with 3·5 G for *p*-azoxyanisole, and 3·0 G for the hexadeutero-compound. Of the three compounds examined, *p*-azoxyphenetole is therefore considered to give the most highly orientated nematic mesophase.

Ewing and Lee[31] have reported on the proton resonance signals from the mesomorphic compounds ethyl *p*-(4-methoxybenzylideneamino)-cinnamate and ethyl *p*-(4-phenylbenzylideneamino)cinnamate, two compounds which have been the subject of considerable interest, since they exhibit three and four mesomorphic phases respectively. Presumably they were chosen by Ewing and Lee in order to find whether any marked changes in the proton resonance signals could be associated with mesomorphic transitions which had been reported for the compounds. The details published are, however, only brief; but it appears that the nematic mesophase of ethyl p-(4-methoxybenzylideneamino)cinnamate —the most thermally stable mesophase shown by the compound— gives a signal similar to that for p-azoxyanisole, i.e. a triplet. When the nematic mesophase is cooled, the authors comment that radical changes in the line shape are observed, until at the lowest temperatures at which mesomorphic properties are observed, the proton resonance signal is a single narrow line on a broad base. No comment is made, however, concerning any relationship between the temperatures at which the changes in the shape of the signal took place and the temperatures at which previous workers such as Vorländer[32] and Bernal and Crowfoot[6] noted the occurrence of transitions between the mesomorphic modifications.

Jain *et al.*[28] summarized the observations made by Moses[33] on smectogenic compounds by saying that the smectic mesophases of a limited number of systems such as sodium oleate and sodium stearate show a single structureless line intermediate in width between that of the isotropic liquid and the solid state. If one can generalize from this to all smectic mesophases, the signal obtained by Ewing and Lee for ethyl p-(4-methoxybenzylideneamino)cinnamate suggests that the mesophase which exists at the lowest temperatures is smectic in character. However, Ewing and Lee obtained less definite results from the other polymesomorphic compound, ethyl p-(4-phenylbenzylideneamino)cinnamate, which is claimed to give four mesophases. Here, the changes in line shape with decreasing temperature were much less pronounced. The authors conclude their paper with the remark that some of the changes in line shape may arise from the fact that crystalline phases coexist with the liquid crystalline phases. However, this is most unlikely, for the mesomorphic or polymesomorphic transitions are much too well defined to be explained on such a basis. Moreover, from all the microscopic studies carried out on the mesophases, there is no evidence to suggest that any of them is heterogeneous in composition.

Grant, Hedgecock, and Dunell[34] seem to have had more success in applying proton magnetic resonance techniques to a study of the various phase changes which occur on heating anhydrous sodium stearate. Indeed, the transition temperatures which they obtained agree well with those given by more usual methods. Their plot of the line width in gauss against temperature shows three distinct steps at temperatures of 114, 130 and 165°, which agree with subcurd-subwaxy, subwaxy-waxy, and waxy-superwaxy transition temperatures obtained by calorimetry[35] (114°, 134°, ——), dilatometry[36] (117°, 132°, ——), and light transmission experiments[37] (——, 132°, 165°). This work was inspired by the fact that nuclear magnetic resonance gives an indication of the extent of molecular rotation and reorientation in the solid state,[38] and was applied to anhydrous sodium stearate in the hope of confirming and extending the concept that the phase transitions for this compound involve changes in the rotation of the hydrocarbon chains and in the orientation of the polar end groups. However, the signals were not suitable for a calculation of the second moments of the line shapes, and information on the molecular motion was not obtained.

Little appears to be known about the proton magnetic resonance given by cholesteric mesophases. Jain et al. [30] state that the cholesteric mesophase of cholesteryl benzoate shows a single structureless line, as observed with smectic mesophases. Although it is dangerous to draw conclusions from the behaviour of only one compound, the cholesteric mesophase, on this basis, would appear to have a closer affinity to the smectic mesophase than to the nematic mesophase, which usually gives a triplet proton resonance signal.

REFERENCES

1. Friedel, G. (1922). *Ann. Physique* **18**, 273.
2. Hückel, E. (1921). *Phys. Z.* **22**, 561.
3. Friedel, E. and de Broglie, M. (1923). *Compt. rend.* **176**, 475 and 738.
4. Friedel, E. (1925). *Compt. rend.* **180**, 269.
5. Herrmann, K. (1933). *Trans. Faraday Soc.* **29**, 972.
6. Bernal, J. D. and Crowfoot, D. (1933). *Trans. Faraday Soc.* **29**, 1032.
7. Kast, W. (1933). *Naturwiss.* **21**, 737; (1934). *Ann. Physik* **19**, 571.
8. Katz, J. R. (1928). *Naturwiss.* **16**, 758.
9. Glamann, P., Herrmann, K. and Krummacher, A. H. (1930). *Z. Krist.* **74**, 73.
10. Stewart, G. W. (1933). *Trans. Faraday Soc.* **29**, 982; (1936). *J. Chem. Phys.* **4**, 231; and Letner, H. R. (1935). *Phys. Rev.* **47**, 332.
11. Herrmann, K. (1935). *Z. Krist.* **92**, 49.
12. Brown, G. H. and Shaw, W. G. (1957). *Chem. Rev.* **57**, 1049.
13. Kast, W. (1927). *Ann. Physik* **83**, 391; (1927). *Z. Physik* **42**, 81; (1931). *Z. Krist.* **79**, 146.
14. Herrmann, K., Krummacher, A. H. and May, K. (1932). *Z. Physik.* **73**, 419.
15. Zocher H. (1929). *Z. phys. Chem. (Leipzig)* **A142**, 186.
16. Kast, W. (1927). *Ann. Physik* **83**, 418.
17. Stewart, G. W. (1933). *Trans. Faraday Soc.* **29**, 982; (1931). *Phys. Rev.* **38**, 931.
18. Herrmann, C. (1931). *Z. Krist.* **79**, 186.
19. Nordsieck, H., Ferguson, R. H. and Rosevear, F. B. (1948). *J. Chem. Phys.* **16**, 175.
20. De Brettville, A. and McBain, J. W. (1943). *J. Chem. Phys.* **11**, 426.
21. Maier, W. and Englert, G. (1958). *Z. Elektrochem.* **62**, 1020.
22. Rawlins, F. I. G. and Taylor, A. M. (1929). " Infrared Analysis of Molecular Spectra ", Cambridge University Press, London, p. 63.
23. Vorländer, D. (1928). *Naturwiss.* **16**, 759.
24. Freymann, R. and Servant, R. (1945). *Ann. Physique* **20**, 131.
25. Taschek, R. and Williams, D. (1938). *J. Chem. Phys.* **6**, 546.
26. Maier, W. and Saupe, A. (1956). *Z. phys. Chem. (Frankfurt)* **6**, 327.
27. Spence, R. D., Moses, H. A. and Jain, P. L. (1953). *J. Chem. Phys.* **21**, 380.
28. Jain, P.L., Lee, J. C. and Spence, R. D. (1955). *J. Chem. Phys.* **23**, 878.

29. Spence, R. D., Gutowsky, H. S. and Holm, C. H. (1953). *J. Chem. Phys.* **21,** 1891.

30. Jain, P. L., Moses, H. A., Lee, J. C. and Spence, R. D. (1953). *Phys. Rev.* **92,** 844.

31. Ewing, R. and Lee, J. C. (1954). *Phys. Rev.* **94,** 1411.

32. Vorländer, D. (1908). " Kristallinisch-flüssige Substanzen ", Ferdinand Encke, Stuttgart, p. 74; (1933). *Trans. Faraday Soc.* **29,** 913.

33. Moses, H. A. (1953). M.S. Thesis, Michigan State College.

34. Grant, R. F., Hedgecock, N. and Dunell, B. A. (1956). *Canad. J. Chem.* **34,** 1514.

35. Benton, D. P., Howe, P. G. and Puddington, I. E. (1955). *Canad. J. Chem.* **33,** 1384.

36. Macomber, M., Vold, M. J. and Vold, R. D. (1941). *J. Amer. Chem. Soc.* **63,** 168.

37. Vold, R. D. (1941). *J. Amer. Chem. Soc.* **63,** 2915.

38. Andrew, E. R. (1956). " Nuclear Magnetic Resonance ", Cambridge University Press, London.

CHAPTER VI

OTHER PHYSICAL CHARACTERISTICS OF THE MESOMORPHIC STATES

1. Viscosity

ONLY 10 years elapsed between the discovery of mesomorphism by Reinitzer, in 1888, and the appearance of the first publication by Schenk[1] on the viscosity of the mesomorphic state. Schenk used the capillary flow method to determine the change of viscosity with temperature for the systems cholesteryl benzoate (cholesteric mesophase) and p-azoxyanisole (nematic mesophase). As is the case for an ordinary liquid, the viscosity of the mesophase fell off with increasing temperature, but at temperatures close to the mesomorphic-isotropic transition, there was in each case a sudden break in the viscosity against temperature curve, the viscosity rising steeply to a maximum at the transition temperature and then falling again. Once this discontinuity in the viscosity had occurred, the viscosity of the isotropic liquid fell normally and quite gently with further increases of temperature. Later, Eichwold[2] made similar observations concerning the sudden changes in viscosity of p-azoxyanisole, p-methoxycinnamic acid, and other compounds at the nematic-isotropic transitions, and still more recently, Becherer and Kast[3] have confirmed this type of behaviour for p-azoxyanisole, using the Helmholtz method for determining viscosities. The increase in viscosity just before the nematic-isotropic or cholesteric-isotropic transition always appears to be very sudden and the viscosity reaches a maximum exactly at the transition temperature. With increasing temperature above the transition point, the fall in viscosity appears to occur at a variable rate. In the case of the cholesteryl esters, the peak is very symmetrical, as illustrated in Fig. VI.1, but for p-azoxyanisole, the fall in viscosity after the maximum at $135\cdot2^\circ$ is quite gentle, as shown in Fig. VI.2, which represents Schenk's viscosity against temperature plot for this compound.

The more recent viscosity determinations made by Becherer and Kast on p-azoxyanisole agree with the sudden increase in viscosity immediately before the transition temperature, but show that before and after the sudden increase in viscosity, the rates of decrease of viscosity with temperature are the same—see Fig. VI.3.

The viscosity of the nematic melt of p-azoxyanisole is in fact quite low, only slightly greater than the viscosity of water at ordinary tem-

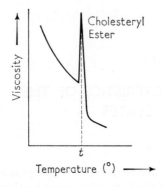

Cholesteric–isotropic transition
at $t°$

FIG. VI.1. Change of viscosity with temperature for a typical cholesteryl ester (Lawrence, A. S. C. (1933). *Trans. Faraday Soc.* **29**, 1080).

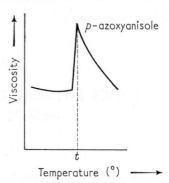

Nematic–isotropic transition
at $t°$

FIG. VI.2. Change of viscosity with temperature for p-azoxyanisole (Schenk R. (1898). *Z. phys. Chem.* (*Leipzig*) **27**, 167).

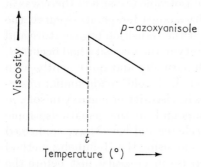

Nematic–isotropic transition
at $t°$

FIG. VI.3. Change of viscosity with temperature for p-azoxyanisole (Becherer, G. and Kast, W. (1942). *Ann. Physik* **41**, 355).

peratures, but if the nematic mesophase is orientated by magnetic or electric fields, the viscosity becomes anisotropic. Miesowicz[4] has determined the principal viscosity coefficients of nematic mesophases which were orientated either by magnetic fields or by the temperature gradients in the cooling anisotropic melts.

In contrast with the mobile cholesteric and nematic mesophases, the viscosity of the smectic mesophase is very much higher, but published work on the viscosity of this type of mesophase is much more limited. If we imagine a specimen of a smectic mesophase mounted so that the smectic layers are flat, e.g. a drop of a smectic mesophase mounted over a hole in a supporting surface, and exhibiting stepped edges—see Chapter II—the system would have two quite different viscosities in two directions at right angles (Fig. VI.4).

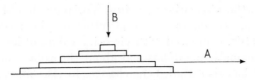

FIG. VI.4. Side section of a stepped drop of smectic fluid.

In any direction in the plane of the supporting surface, e.g. along A, the viscosity would be extremely low, since the smectic planes are free to move over one another, giving rise to the property of layer flow. In a direction B, at right angles to the smectic planes, the viscosity would be extremely high, since in this direction the system is equivalent to a section of crystalline material. Conditions such as this would never arise during any experimental determinations of a viscosity, for in even a small bulk of mesophase the smectic layers will be highly distorted, and an average, high viscosity will be obtained.

One of the few smectic systems on which viscosity data have been published involves ethyl p-azoxybenzoate, which melts at 114° and gives an enantiotropic smectic mesophase which becomes isotropic at 120°. Vorländer[5] determined the viscosity changes of the system over the temperature range 114° to about 133°, and showed that the trends were unlike those obtained with cholesteric or nematic systems. There was a very sudden fall in viscosity exactly at the smectic-isotropic transition, but no rise to a maximum preceded the transition. The viscosity against temperature plot was of the form shown in Fig. VI.5.

FIG. VI.5. Change of viscosity with temperature for ethyl p-azoxy-benzoate (Vorländer, D. (1933). *Trans. Faraday Soc.* **29**, 902).

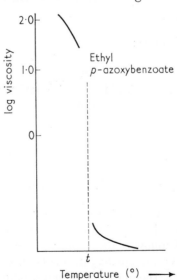

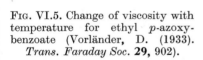

Expressing the viscosities in poises, Vorländer found that the viscosity of the smectic mesophase of ethyl p-azoxybenzoate was around 200 at about 116°, compared with viscosity values of less than 0·05 for cholesteric or nematic mesophases at about the same temperature.

Vorländer[6] has also studied the changes in viscosity with increasing temperature for systems which show mesomorphic-mesomorphic transitions, e.g. ethyl p-(4-ethoxybenzylideneamino)-α-methylcinnamate (I) and ethyl p-(4-methoxybenzylideneamino)cinnamate (II).

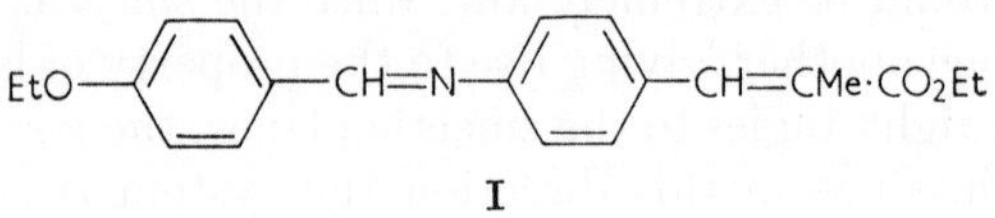

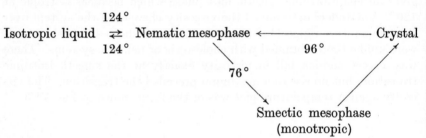

I

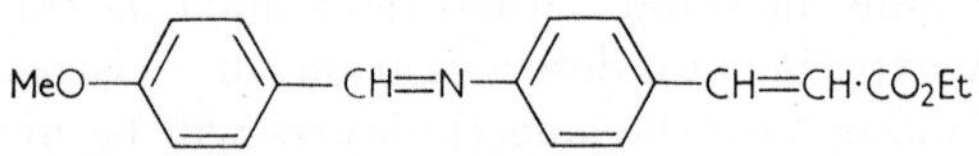

II

For I, the various transformations are:

$$\text{Isotropic liquid} \underset{124°}{\overset{124°}{\rightleftarrows}} \text{Nematic mesophase} \xleftarrow{\hspace{3cm}} \text{Crystal}$$

$$\underset{96°}{}$$

$$76° \searrow \qquad \nearrow$$

$$\text{Smectic mesophase}$$
$$\text{(monotropic)}$$

and for II:

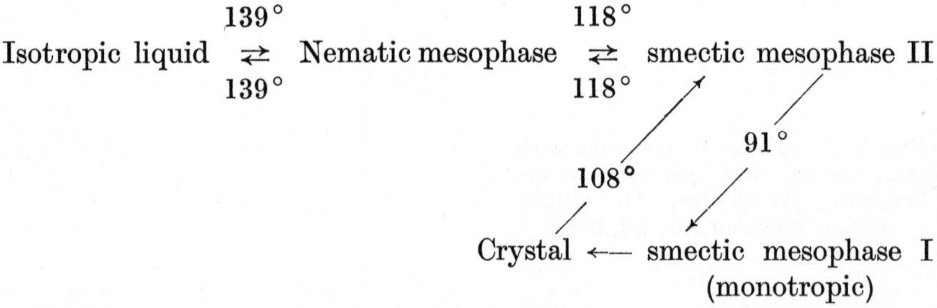

$$\text{Isotropic liquid} \underset{139°}{\overset{139°}{\rightleftarrows}} \text{Nematic mesophase} \underset{118°}{\overset{118°}{\rightleftarrows}} \text{smectic mesophase II}$$

$$\nearrow \qquad 91° \nearrow$$

$$108° \nearrow$$

$$\text{Crystal} \xleftarrow{} \text{smectic mesophase I}$$
$$\text{(monotropic)}$$

For both compounds, with rising temperature, the nematic-isotropic transition was immediately preceded by a sudden increase in viscosity, and followed by a more gradual fall in viscosity, much as illustrated above for p-azoxyanisole (Fig. VI.3). As the temperature fell from just below the isotropic-nematic points of the two compounds, sudden increases in viscosity were obtained at each of the temperatures corresponding to the transitions nematic-smectic for compound I, and nematic-smectic II and smectic II-smectic I for compound II. In the case of compound II, the plot of viscosity against temperature was of the form shown in Fig. VI.6.

Polymesomorphic changes between smectic mesophases and mesomorphic changes between different mesophase types (smectic-nematic) are therefore accompanied by sudden decreases in viscosity as the temperature rises. The viscosity changes which occur at these transitions

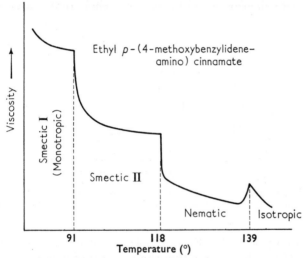

Fig. VI.6. Change of viscosity with temperature for the polymesomorphic system ethyl p-(4-methoxybenzylideneamino)cinnamate (Vorländer, D. (1930). *Phys. Z.* **31,** 428).

are therefore similar in character to those which occur at smectic-isotropic transitions.

At this stage, we should note that Powell and Puddington[7] have quite recently studied the rather complex transitions which occur on heating anhydrous sodium stearate, and by employing the capillary method for following the viscosity changes which occur with increasing temperature, have produced evidence for a new transition within the smectic, subneat phase, at 225°.

Referring back to the nematic-isotropic and cholesteric-isotropic transitions and the sudden increases in viscosity which precede the transitions and reach a maximum at the actual transition temperature, Ostwald[8] attempted to relate this behaviour to the viscosity against temperature curves which are obtained for colloidal segregating mixtures, e.g. albumen sol, starch sol, liquid mixtures of critical concentration, and molten sulphur. Such a system shows a viscosity v temperature relationship which gives rise to a curve of the general shape shown in

Fig. VI.7. The maximum, which is much less sharply defined than that which occurs at the nematic-isotropic transition or at the cholesteric-isotropic transition, corresponds to the separation of an homogeneous or finely dispersed system into an heterogeneous, coarsely dispersed system.

On this basis, Ostwald concluded that the nematic and cholesteric mesophases possess a state of dispersion which is typical of colloids. In this paper, Ostwald[8] also refers to the marked structural viscosity of the smectic and cholesteric mesophases, as shown by his experimental work on ethyl p-azoxybenzoate and the esters of cholesterol with acetic, pro-

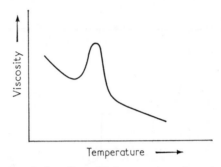

FIG. VI.7. Change of viscosity with temperature for a typical colloidal segregating mixture (Ostwald, W. (1933). *Trans. Faraday Soc.* **29,** 1002).

pionic, and butyric acids. For the isotropic melts of these compounds, the Hagen-Poiseuille law relating the velocity of flow in a capillary to the pressure is obeyed, but with the anisotropic melts, the velocity of flow is not proportional to the pressure, but is disproportionately low at small pressures. This variation in viscosity with rate of shear had been reported by earlier workers, particularly in the case of the nematic mesophase. Thus, Bose and Conrat[9] studied the nematic melt of anisaldazine and demonstrated the occurrence of the usual increase to a maximum viscosity at the nematic-isotropic transition temperature, followed by a sudden fall in viscosity with further rise in temperature, and Bose[10] showed that the mesophase of this compound disobeys the Hagen-Poiseuille relationship between viscosity and rate of shear. Since the viscosities of solvated colloids vary with rate of shear, analogies were drawn by many workers between the nematic mesophase and colloidal systems. A considerable number of papers [10,11,12] were published on this subject, some emphasizing the closeness of the analogy, and others denying that it had any significance. Ostwald supported the analogy on the basis of his work on the smectic and cholesteric mesophases, and claimed that the anomalous or structural viscosity, hitherto known only in coarsely dispersed systems, was evidence for regarding the mesophases as similar to gelatine or rubber sols. However, this suggestion did not pass without comment, and Lawrence[13] pointed out that the analogy between the viscosity behaviours of gelatine and rubber sols and of mesophases may not be as complete as Ostwald made out, and that, for instance, the change in rate of flow with distance from the capillary wall is quite different for gelatine sols and the lyotropic mesophase of ammonium oleate. Lawrence does, however, suggest that further work on the viscosity behaviour of nematic mesophases could lend support to the concept of the existence of swarms. Unfortunately, Lawrence uses the term nematic to refer to the mesophases examined by Ostwald, when in fact three of the systems were cholesteric and one smectic in behaviour. It is not clear therefore whether Lawrence refers only to the cholesteric systems, accepting the view of Friedel[14] that cholesteric mesophases are in fact modified nematic mesophases, or whether he intended his remark to apply to ethyl p-azoxybenzoate which is a smectogenic compound. If the structural viscosity of the nematic mesophase is taken as evidence for the existence of swarms in this type of anisotropic melt, then the similar viscosity properties of the cholesteric and smectic mesophases could be taken as supporting the view that swarms exist in these types of mesophase too. If this is the case, the viscosity characteristics represent one of the few indications that such molecular aggregates exist in the smectic and cholesteric states. If swarms do exist in the different types of mesophase, it is conceivable that the systems would show some of the properties of a colloid, the swarms being equivalent to the colloidal particles, and the intervening regions to the solvent. Early views that the colloidal properties of mesophases were due to the presence of impurities, which existed as a suspension of crystals in molten material, are no longer accepted. This is readily demonstrated by adding controlled quantities of non-mesomorphic impurity to a mesomorphic compound. The turbidity and other typical mesomorphic properties are diminished, not enhanced, the transition temperatures are depressed, and the mesomorphic behaviour is often eliminated at quite low concentrations of added impurity.

In his remarks on Ostwald's paper, Lawrence[13] also refers to the sudden increase in viscosity immediately before the nematic or cholesteric to isotropic transition. He stresses the point that the anomalously high viscosity can hardly be regarded as a feature of the mesophase itself, since it occurs effectively at the transition, and that the sudden viscosity changes only serve to show that fictitious viscosity values are being obtained at the transition point, probably because of turbulence in the anisotropic melt. Some support for this would appear to be given by the fact that the peak viscosity does not occur at the transition between the more viscous smectic mesophase and the isotropic liquid. Lawrence has also demonstrated that the peak height in the viscosity against temperature curve for cholesteryl propionate, i.e. at the cholesteric-isotropic transition, varies with the rate of flow, the height being greater when the rate of flow approaches Newtonian. The greater anomaly in the viscosity under these conditions would again support the idea of a turbulence effect in the anisotropic melt.

In recent years, knowledge concerning colloids has expanded rapidly but despite this, there have been no further attempts to relate the viscous properties of mesophases and those of emulsions or colloids in general. The position in this respect remains therefore vague, and from about 1935, attention seems to have been directed mainly towards the effects of magnetic and electric fields on the viscosities of mesophases. All of this work has been carried out on p-azoxyanisole or p-azoxyphenetole, i.e. on nematic mesophases. Using an oscillating-disc viscometer, Björnstähl[15] studied the effects of both alternating and direct, applied electric fields on the viscosity of the nematic mesophases of these two substances. This work and that of Björnstähl and Snellman[16] on the change of viscosity with field strength has been quite fully reviewed by Brown and Shaw,[17] and it is only necessary to say that they have concluded that their results agree with the evidence accumulated by Kast[18] —from his X-ray studies using alternating fields of low intensity—that the swarm axes lie parallel to the direction of the applied field. Mikhailor and Tzvetkov,[19] using the capillary method, verified the experimental aspects of this work, but concluded that the results were explained by the orientation of the mesophase caused by the flow of the melt under the influence of the applied field, and not by any direct orientating effect of the field. Later, however, Tzvetkov[20] decided that the molecular axes are indeed orientated by the applied electric field in a direction parallel to the field, and that the field gives rise to macroscopic movement of the melt between the electrodes. This more recent work by Tzvetkov would appear to bring his conclusions into line with those of Björnstähl. Moreover, Tzvetkov[21] has produced further evidence for the existence of swarms in the nematic melt by his examination of the effect of magnetic fields on this type of mesophase. Using a rotating magnetic field, he concluded that molecular aggregates of diameter about 7×10^{-5} cm exist in the nematic mesophase of p-azoxyanisole. Miesowicz[22] too has examined the effects of magnetic fields on the nematic mesophase, and has demonstrated that a sufficiently strong magnetic field will orientate the swarms so strongly that even the flow of the melt perpendicular to the axis of orientation does not change the orientation. Miesowicz has measured the viscosities of the nematic melts of both p-azoxyanisole and p-azoxyphenetole under conditions such that the major molecular axes are arranged (a) parallel to the direction of flow, (b) parallel to the velocity gradient, and (c) perpendicular to the direction of flow and to the velocity gradient. The results showed that the viscosities increased from condition (a) to (b) to (c), and his measurement of these three distinct viscosities explains some discrepancies reported by earlier workers for the viscosities of nematic melts measured in magnetic fields, i.e. if the required state of orientation of the swarms in the magnetic field was not reached, and if the flow in the capillary changed the orientation, intermediate viscosities would be obtained.

Such work on the influence of applied magnetic and electric fields on the viscosity of the nematic mesophase has therefore provided further confirmatory evidence for the existence of molecular groups or swarms in the anisotropic melts of p-azoxyanisole and p-azoxyphenetole. It should, however, be emphasized that these conclusions have been reached for the nematic melts of only two substances, and that it may be dangerous to generalize on this basis for all nematic melts.

2. DIELECTRIC CONSTANT

Some of the dielectric properties of mesophases have been mentioned in Chapter IV, in connection with the Swarm Theory, and indeed, studies of the dielectric characteristics of the nematic mesophase are of principal importance because of the supporting evidence which they give for the existence of swarms. The dielectric properties of the nematic mesophase, of course, become anisotropic under the orientating influence of applied magnetic and electric fields. The measurement of the dielectric constant and particularly of the dielectric anisotropy is very delicate, and there are noticeable differences in the results obtained by different authors. However, since more interest has centred around the effect of applied magnetic and electric fields upon the dielectric properties, it is possible to express results as a difference in dielectric behaviour in the presence and absence of the applied field. Such measurements are more reproducible. A similar approach was used in the experimental work by Kast,[23] who measured the changes in dielectric constant which occurred on changing the intensity of the electric field, using a constant magnetic field. From this work, Kast found a magnification of the molecular moment by 10^5, and proposed that some 10^5 molecules must aggregate in each swarm.

A body of work on dielectric properties has concerned the interpretation of the change in dielectric constant in applied magnetic and electric fields in terms of the different types of orientation and the different degrees of orientation of the major axes of the molecules or swarms with respect to the fields. With symmetrical molecules, the nematic mesophase shows a reduction in dielectric constant when the magnetic field is perpendicular to the condenser plates, and a small increase when the field is parallel. With unsymmetrical molecules, a small increase in the dielectric constant of the mesophase is found with the magnetic field parallel to the electric field. These differences in behaviour have been explained by postulating that symmetrical and unsymmetrical molecules will tend to orientate themselves respectively parallel and perpendicular to the plates. Jezewski[24] studied the effect of *electrical* field strength upon the dielectric constant of the nematic melt of *p*-azoxyanisole. In the absence of a magnetic field, and when using a magnetic field perpendicular to the electric field, the dielectric constant decreased with increasing field intensity. Kast[23] concluded that under both sets of circumstances the molecules lie parallel to the plates of the condenser and that the decrease in dielectric constant is explained by the rotation of the molecules by the electric field. In fact, the rate of decrease in dielectric constant is different with and without the applied magnetic field, and this was ascribed to turbulence effects in the mesophase. With a magnetic field parallel to the electric field, Jezewski observed an increase in the dielectric constant, which levelled off at higher field intensities, and Kast[23] interpreted this initial increase by proposing that the magnetic field had first to orientate the particles perpendicular to the plates of the condenser.

In such experiments, the extent of the dielectric change is dependent upon temperature, as well as upon the strengths of the applied electric and magnetic fields. Thus, as the magnetic field strength is increased, the orientation of the molecules or swarms becomes more nearly complete, and the dielectric constant will approach a limiting value. The temperature of the mesophase is profoundly important in determining the effectiveness of the applied fields in orientating the swarms, and a slight change in temperature will greatly alter the limiting value of the dielectric constant attained with increasing magnetic field strength. Thus, Marinin and Tzvetkov[25] examined the dielectric properties of *p*-azoxyanisole, as the nematic mesophase flowed through a capillary. An applied magnetic field was used to assist the orientation of the molecules, and the ability of the field to effect orientation should be dependent upon the rate of flow and the temperature. Thus, as would be expected, the dielectric constant should vary with magnetic field strength, with temperature, and with rate of flow. The figures in Table VI.1 illustrate these effects.

TABLE VI.1

| Temp. = 119° | Magnetic field strength | |
Flow rate (cm/sec)	1000 G	3000 G
0·17	59% orientation	20% orientation
2·12	93% orientation	87% orientation

The degree of orientation increases with flow rate, and decreases with the increase in applied field strength which operates in opposition to the orientating effect of the flow. As the temperature is increased, the degree of orientation decreases, linearly at first, up to 120°, and then rapidly to zero orientation at the nematic-isotropic transition point at about 135°.

Ornstein, Kast, and Bouma[26] have studied the dielectric properties of molten benzophenone and of the anisotropic melt of p-azoxyanisole, and they have calculated that the degree of orientation of the cybotactic groups or swarms is never perfect, reaching a maximum of 80% under their particular experimental conditions. A higher degree of orientation was found by Marinin and Tzvetkov,[25] since the flow of the specimen would assist the orientation of the swarms.

In a system of highly orientated, elongated molecules, there will be two principal dielectric constants, corresponding to directions parallel and at right angles to the long molecular axes. Maier[27] has measured the changes in these principal dielectric constants with increasing magnetic field strengths up to 5000 G (applied either longitudinally or transversely to the axes of orientation of the molecules). The ratio of the two dielectric constants, at a given temperature, differed considerably from the calculated value for the ratio, and he reached the interesting conclusion that convection currents in the mesophase give rise to added orientating effects. These effects are of course most important in experiments carried out with no magnetic field to counteract them, and Maier established that a temperature gradient of as little as 0·1°/cm produced almost complete orientation. This in itself would appear to be strong evidence in favour of the existence of swarms, since such orientating effects would hardly be expected if the molecules were present in the mesophase as individual entities.

Barth, Maier, and Wiehl[28] have also studied the two principal dielectric constants of 4,4'-dimethoxy- and 4,4'-di-n-pentyloxy-azoxybenzene,* as a function of temperature. A magnetic field of about 2000 G was used, since it was found that $\Delta\epsilon = \epsilon_{\text{transverse}} - \epsilon_{\text{longitudinal}} = \epsilon_2 - \epsilon_1$ increased rapidly with increasing field strength up to 1000 G, and was then independent of field strengths greater than 1000 G. The two dielectric constants, ϵ_2 (electric field perpendicular to the condenser plates and normal to the magnetic field (H)) and ϵ_1 (electric field parallel to the condenser plates), and ϵ_0, the dielectric constant with no applied magnetic field, were plotted against the temperature of the preparation.

The pentyl ether referred to above melts at 79°, giving a nematic melt which clears to the isotropic liquid at 121·5°. The greater of the two dielectric constants, ϵ_2, falls linearly from about 4·1 at a temperature just above the melting point, to about 3·8 just before the nematic-

* It should be noted that in two places Brown and Shaw[29] have mistakenly referred to these compounds as azo- compounds, which would not possess the strong dipole moments on the presence of which several of Maier's deductions are based.

isotropic transition. Over the same temperature range, ϵ_1 increases linearly from about 3·6 to about 3·64. At the nematic-isotropic transition (121·5°), ϵ_2 falls and ϵ_1 increases suddenly to the value of the dielectric constant (3·78–3·79) of the isotropic liquid, i.e. at the transition temperature, $\epsilon_2 - \epsilon_1$ falls sharply from just below 0·2 to 0. Thus, as would be expected, the swarm or molecular orientation is destroyed in the isotropic liquid, and the two principal dielectric constants cease to be distinguishable. When no magnetic field is applied, the dielectric constant, ϵ_0, of the mesophase falls linearly from about 4·0 to just below 3·8 over the range of temperature from slightly above the melting point to slightly below the nematic-isotropic transition. There is no sharp change in ϵ_0 at the transition point, and, at first sight, this would suggest that, in the absence of a magnetic field, the swarm or molecular orientation in both the mesophase and the isotropic liquid is random. This would contradict the results of Jezewski,[24] who showed that, without a magnetic field, the molecules are arranged parallel to the condenser plates, presumably by the orientating effect of the electric field between the plates. It is more probable therefore that both the swarms in the anisotropic melt and the cybotactic groups in the isotropic liquid are orientated to about the same extent by the electric field, so that no very sharp change in ϵ_0 occurs at the transition temperature.

Maier records very similar results for 4,4'-dimethoxyazoxybenzene. In this case, however, ϵ_0 does increase to some extent at the nematic-isotropic transition, after which $\epsilon_{\text{isotropic}}$ decreases quite rapidly. There would appear then to be an anomalous dielectric constant region in the vicinity of the mesomorphic-isotropic change (c.f. the sudden increase in viscosity for this type of transition). It is possible that turbulence effects in the neighbourhood of the transition give spurious dielectric constants over a small range of temperature, the extent of the anomaly depending perhaps on molecule size, the orientating influences of the electric field, and the actual temperature of the nematic-isotropic change. It is interesting to note that Bhide and Bhide[30] have found abrupt changes in dielectric constant at the nematic-isotropic transition, and these authors, who used a resonance frequency method for their measurements, report that the abruptness of the change depends upon the frequency being used. This suggests that external factors are influencing the extent of the anomaly in dielectric behaviour in this region.

Bhide and Bhide found similar changes in the dielectric constant at the cholesteric-isotropic transition of cholesteryl benzoate, but here, as with the nematic-isotropic change for p-azoxyanisole, the values for the dielectric constant obtained at a given temperature, on cooling from the isotropic liquid to the mesophase, did not coincide with the values obtained at the same temperature on heating from the mesophase. However, since the breakdown of the molecular order and the build-up of the molecular order need not proceed via identical, intermediate, molecular orientational changes, these differences between the two sets of results may not be altogether surprising.

Returning to the work of Maier,[28] the values for the two principal dielectric constants, ϵ_1 and ϵ_2, were used to calculate the two molecular electrical susceptibilities of the mesophase, σ_1 and σ_2, respectively, using the expression

$$\sigma = \frac{\epsilon - 1}{4\,\pi} \frac{M}{\rho}$$

where M = the molecular weight of the compound, and
$\quad$ ρ = the density of the system.

Plots of σ_2 and σ_1 against temperature of course fell and rose linearly respectively, as was the case for the plots of ϵ_2 and ϵ_1 against temperature. Maier considered that the molecular electrical susceptibility will be greatest across the long axis of the molecule of the azoxy- compound, in the direction in which the permanent dipole moment operates. If we

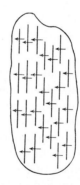

FIG. VI.8. A representation of the arrangement of dipolar molecules in a nematic swarm.

now represent each molecule in a swarm by a line, with a small arrow to indicate the dipole acting at an angle across this line, and use the imbricated molecular arrangement suggested by Bernal and Crowfoot,[31] the nematic swarm may be represented as shown in Fig. VI.8.

This arrangement would confer upon the swarm a resultant, strong dipole moment acting across the minor axis of the swarm. Tolstoi[32] argues that, *under normal conditions*, the swarm as a whole has no dipole moment, and that although dipoles will reinforce in regions within the swarm, the average picture will be one of dipole cancellation. Tolstoi considers, however, that an electrical field will tend to split up the swarm at points where the dipoles are opposed. This does not mean that the swarm size will decrease, because parts of one swarm may recombine with parts of others having reinforcing dipolar arrangements, giving a swarm with a resultant dipole moment.

Maier[33] represents the orientation of the molecules with respect to the applied magnetic field H as shown in Fig. VI. 9, where E_2 and E_1 represent the directions of the electric fields used to measure ϵ_2 and ϵ_1. The arrow in each ellipse represents the direction of the resultant permanent dipole moment of the swarm, acting across the long axes of the molecules of the azoxy- compound. This orientation of the molecules would agree with the earlier work of Jezewski[24] which suggested that the long axes of symmetrical molecules will lie parallel to the condenser plates.

It will be noted that the resultant dipole moments are not assumed to reinforce in every instance.

The decrease in ϵ_2 with increasing temperature may be explained by

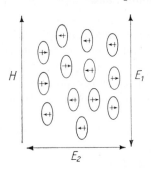

FIG.VI.9. The arrangement of swarms comprised of dipolar molecules of an azoxy- compound in a magnetic field H (Maier, W. (1947). *Z. Naturforsch.* **2a**, 457).

the increasing thermal effects which will act against the orientating effects of the applied fields, making the swarm or molecular orientation less perfect, and causing the direction of the dipoles to be displaced away from the direction in which ϵ_2 is measured. Such a rotation of the dipoles will increase the proportion of dipoles pointing in the direction in which ϵ_1 is measured, so that this lower dielectric constant, ϵ_1, will increase with temperature.

The effects of applied magnetic fields upon the microwave dielectric constants of the nematic mesophases of p-azoxyanisole and p-azoxyphenetole have been examined by Carr and Spence.[34] Contrary to Maier and Jezewski, who assume that the contribution of the permanent dipole moment of an azoxy- compound to the molecular electrical susceptibility is larger than that arising from any induced polarization in the direction of the long molecular axis, the work of Carr and Spence indicates that such induced polarizations give the larger effect. Thus it was shown that an external magnetic field orientated the nematic mesophase, a short time interval of about 1 min being necessary to achieve this orientation. If the orientation were due to permanent molecular dipoles organizing themselves in some regular way with respect to the field, then a reversal of the field should cause the molecules to turn over. In doing this, the mesophase would have to pass through a disorganized state, and no change in dielectric loss occurs to support this idea. Carr and Spence therefore conclude that for p-azoxyanisole and p-azoxyphenetole, the orientating effects occur because of induced magnetic moments. This would suggest that permanent dipoles do not play an important part in determining the molecular arrangement in the nematic mesophase, either by influencing the degree of orientation by external factors or by giving rise to strong intermolecular attractions, and this point will be referred to again in Chapters IX and X.

Similarly, if the orientating magnetic field is removed, it has been shown, from the change in dielectric loss with time, that the nematic mesophase becomes optically homogeneous in a very short time—at the most a few minutes—dependent of course upon the temperature. If the orientation had been caused by the alignment of permanent dipoles with respect to one another and to the field, it would have been expected that the orientation would have been more persistent. However, an orientation stemming from induced polarization effects could well cease to exist immediately on removal of the source of the induction.

The differences between the results arising from the work of Jezewski and of Carr and Spence may of course stem from differences in the experimental conditions, one set of results being for microwave frequencies, and one for low-frequency dielectric constants.

By evaluating the Kerr constant for the mesophase exhibited by each of a number of mesomorphic compounds, both smectic and nematic, Marinin and Tzvetkov[35] conclude that, for compounds in which the molecules have dipoles operating at right angles to the long molecular axes, these long axes will be orientated at right angles to the electric field. In these cases, the dielectric anisotropy ($\epsilon_1 - \epsilon_2$) is negative, and becomes positive only when the mesophase is comprised of molecules with dipoles which act at small angles to the long molecular axes, e.g. in 4,4′-di-(benzylideneamino)biphenyl. Tolstoi[32] has attempted to elucidate the significance of permanent molecular dipoles in relation to the electrical polarizability of the nematic mesophase. His evaluations of the Kerr constant seem to require that the dipole in p-azoxyanisole operates at 45° to the long axis, whilst Marinin and Tzvetkov assumed the dipole to be directed at 90° to this axis, in order to explain the high electrical polarizability. Indeed, attempts to relate the physical properties of mesophases to the permanent dipole moments of the molecules are always made difficult by the problem of deciding to what extent the rotation of functional groups in the molecules, or of the molecules themselves, affects the orientation of the dipole moments. It is also difficult to decide whether one can assume that, in a molecule such as p-azoxyanisole, the dipoles of the ether groups cancel out giving a net molecular dipole equivalent only to that of the azoxy- group, or whether the separation of the ether dipoles in the molecule is great enough for them to act independently in leading to attractive or repulsive forces between other molecules and to orientation phenomena by external factors.

The whole question of the interpretation of the dielectric constants, the dielectric anisotropies, and the polarizabilities of mesophases which are orientated by electric fields, by magnetic fields, or by combinations of electric and magnetic fields, in terms of the permanent and induced polarizations in the molecules, is therefore complex and at the moment imperfectly understood.* However, as referred to in an earlier chapter dealing with the elements of the Swarm Hypothesis for the nematic mesophase, studies of the dielectric properties in particular do lend considerable support to the postulate that swarms or clusters of molecules exist in this type of mesophase.

It would not be fitting to conclude this section on the dielectric behaviour of mesophases without reference to the study made by Maier[33] of the dielectric properties of the nematic mesophases of an homologous series of compounds (4,4'-di-n-alkoxyazoxybenzenes). Maier has shown that there is an alternation of the dielectric anisotropies for the orientated (magnetic field) nematic melts, and he relates this effect to the alternation of the nematic-isotropic transition temperatures which occurs along the homologous series. He has used arguments concerning the changes in polarization of the homologues to interpret his results, but it is convenient to leave a fuller discussion of his conclusions until Chapter IX which deals with the smooth curve relationships for the mesomorphic transition temperatures of homologous series of compounds.

3. DENSITY, VOLUME AND HEAT CHANGES AT MESOMORPHIC TRANSITIONS

The only detailed work that has been published on the volume change which occurs at the nematic-isotropic transition was executed over 20 years ago by Bauer and Bernamont.[36] Their studies were carried out primarily to determine whether such a transition should be regarded as a true phase change, or simply as a Curie point or second order transition. Using p-azoxyphenetole, they established that although

---

* It should be noted that, since the completion of this manuscript, a paper has been published by Maier and Meier,[52] proposing a new theory of the dielectric properties of homogeneously orientated nematic melts. In this paper, the Onsager theory of the static dielectric polarization of a dipolar liquid has been applied to the nematic mesophase, so that allowance is made for the anisotropy of the molecular polarizability, the orientation of the permanent dipole moments of the molecules, and the orientation in the nematic fluid itself. The theory is stated to explain the positive and negative dielectric anisotropies, the temperature dependence of the principal dielectric constants, ϵ_1 and ϵ_2, and the existence of a specific dispersion effect for ϵ_1. Reference is made to a forthcoming publication[53] by the same authors on the quantitative interpretation of experimental data on the dielectric properties of different nematogenic systems.

the discontinuity in volume at the nematic-isotropic transition is small, it is real, and can be associated only with a true phase change of the first order.

Bauer and Bernamont used a dilatometer which consisted of a narrow constant-bore capillary, terminating in a small bulb, each 1 cm of the capillary being equivalent to about 1% of the total volume. This thermometer-like dilatometer was immersed in a tube containing mercury, which was mechanically stirred. The tube, which also contained a thermometer, was housed in an electrically heated copper tube equipped with a small window to permit observation of the meniscus in the capillary. Care was taken to ensure that the heating windings on the copper tube were rather closer in the neighbourhood of the window, to compensate for any temperature gradients that it might cause. The

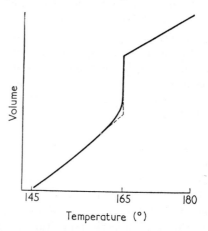

Fig. VI.10. Change of volume with temperature for the nematic melt and isotropic liquid of p-azoxy-phenetole (Bauer, E. and Berna-mont, J. (1936). *Journal Phys. Radium,* **7,** 19).

level of the molten material in the capillary was maintained about 2 mm above the level of the mercury in the heating tube. Despite the reasonable precautions taken to ensure uniformity of temperature, the authors could not eliminate temperature gradients completely, and the results of following the volume change with increasing temperature have been corrected to compensate for the small temperature fluctuations.

p-Azoxyphenetole exhibits its nematic mesophase over some 30°, giving the isotropic liquid at about 167·5°. The volumes were determined by cathotometer readings of the meniscus level, and plotted against temperature, over the range 145–180°. Figure VI.10 illustrates the general trend of increase in volume with temperature, and it is seen that the volume increases reasonably smoothly until the temperature reaches the vicinity of the nematic-isotropic transition, when a sudden increase in volume occurs. This increase was greatest (14·5–14·8 divisions) at 167·7°. The volume of the isotropic melt then continues to rise with increasing temperature, giving a straight-line plot.

The authors point out that they would have expected a more rapid change at the beginning of the sudden volume increase, as indicated by the portion of the curve drawn in broken line. However, this work clearly demonstrates that a sudden volume change does occur at the nematic-isotropic transition. The steep portion of the curve corresponds to a volume increase of about $0 \cdot 0034$ ml, i.e. to a ratio $\Delta v/v = 0 \cdot 006$, a volume increase of about $0 \cdot 6\%$.

Bauer and Bernamont measured the approximate volume change at the melting point of p-azoxyphenetole, i.e. at the solid-nematic transition, and obtained $\Delta v/v = 0 \cdot 084$. This $8 \cdot 4\%$ increase in volume on melting is therefore fourteen times greater than that occurring at the nematic-isotropic transition. The increase in molecular separation and the decrease in density which occur at the nematic-isotropic transition must therefore be much less pronounced than at the melting point, when the crystal lattice (strongly knit and possessing a close molecular packing) collapses and gives the much less well-defined molecular order of the nematic mesophase. However, the volume change is sufficiently large to imply that considerable changes in molecular organization occur at the nematic-isotropic transition.

No work appears to have been carried out on the volume changes which occur at smectic-nematic, smectic-isotropic, smectic-cholesteric, or cholesteric-isotropic transitions.

Although no extensive work has been carried out on the heat changes which occur at mesomorphic transitions, it has been established that the heats of transition for the nematic-isotropic and smectic-isotropic changes are considerably smaller than those involved at the melting points (solid-mesophase). For ethyl p-azoxybenzoate,[37] the heat change at the solid-smectic transition at $114°$ is $14 \cdot 3$ cal/g, whilst the heat change at the smectic-isotropic transition is only $3 \cdot 8$ cal/g. Even smaller heat changes were obtained by Kreutzer and Kast[38] for the nematic-isotropic transitions of p-azoxyanisole ($1 \cdot 6$ cal/g) and p-azoxyphenetole ($2 \cdot 9$ cal/g), although Kreutzer[39] subsequently published slightly higher values for these compounds—$1 \cdot 79$ cal/g and $3 \cdot 16$ cal/g respectively. These authors also obtained the differences in specific heats between the nematic mesophases and the isotropic liquids of these compounds. The isotropic liquid has the smaller specific heat, and for p-azoxyanisole $\Delta C_p = 0 \cdot 037$ cal/g, and $\Delta C_v = 0 \cdot 016$ cal/g, and for p-azoxyphenetole $\Delta C_p = 0 \cdot 11$ cal/g.

The only other determinations of the heats of transitions involving mesophases have been made by Vold[40] for the various phase changes which occur for the sodium salts of lauric, myristic, palmitic, stearic, and oleic acids. Vold does not refer specifically to the various phases of these sodium salts as liquid crystalline states, and has simply used calorimetric methods to throw light on the nature of the various transitions. A differential calorimeter was used for the measurements, and the data given below show the heat changes (ΔQ) at the transitions for sodium palmitate. However, similar heat changes have been obtained at the transitions for sodium myristate and sodium stearate, and Vold suggests that similar structural changes must be involved at the various phase changes.

TABLE VI.2 *Sodium Palmitate*

| Transition | ΔQ (cal/mole) | Transition Temp. (°) | |
		(a) Calorimetry	(b) Other Methods
Curd-subwaxy	4800±740	114	117
Subwaxy-waxy	3880±220	135	135
Waxy-superwaxy	—	—	172
Superwaxy-subneat	1850±240	209	208
Subneat-neat	1540±480	237	253
Neat-isotropic	500± 10	292	295

For sodium laurate and sodium oleate the heat changes are rather different in their relative magnitudes, and it is possible that the structural changes do not occur in the same order for these two compounds. It will be noted that the waxy-superwaxy transition for sodium palmitate gives rise to no heat change which can be detected, and other instances of this kind have been found for the other sodium salts studied.

The heat changes for the curd-subwaxy and subwaxy-waxy soap phases are large, and vary with change in alkyl chain length. For the transitions at higher temperatures, the heat changes are smaller, and are relatively independent of chain length. Vold has suggested that the low-temperature transitions, involving a large heat change, correspond to changes in the arrangement of the hydrocarbon chains, whilst the high-temperature changes involve rearrangements of the polar ends of the molecules.

Included in column (a) of Table VI.2 are the temperatures at which the sudden heat changes were observed. For comparison, the transition temperatures obtained by microscopic or dilatometric methods have been included in column (b). The two sets of transition temperatures agree well, and Vold's work shows quite conclusively that definite transitions are occurring at certain of these temperatures at least.

4. EFFECT OF PRESSURE ON
MESOMORPHIC TRANSITION TEMPERATURES

Pushin and Grebenshchikov[41] first studied the effect of pressure on the crystalline-nematic (117·3°) and nematic-isotropic (135·9°) transition temperatures of p-azoxyanisole. Two equations were obtained.

(1) For the crystalline-nematic transition, pressures up to 2645 kg/sq. cm were used, and

$$t_p = 117·3 + 0·0256\ p$$

(2) For the nematic-isotropic transition, pressures up to 1088 kg/sq. cm were used, and

$$t_p = 135·9 + 0·03949\ p$$

The melting point therefore shows less increase with pressure than the nematic-isotropic transition temperature. In more recent work, Robberecht[42] also found that the nematic-isotropic transition temperature is more sensitive to pressure than the melting point. He used pressures up to 950 kg/sq. cm, and studied a number of compounds. It was shown that $\Delta t/\Delta p$ varied from one compound to another for the melting points, but that $\Delta t/\Delta p$ for the nematic-isotropic transitions was more or less constant at 0·05. This work shows a difference from the results obtained by Pushin and Grebenshchikov, for as can be seen from the equation under (2) above, the $\Delta t/\Delta p$ ratio for p-azoxyanisole is about 0·039.

5. REFRACTIVE INDEX AND
LIGHT SCATTERING PROPERTIES OF MESOPHASES

Chatelain has undoubtedly contributed most to present-day knowledge concerning the refractivity and the light-scattering properties of the nematic mesophase in particular. The refractive index of an unorientated sample of a nematic melt cannot be measured, as the system is too opaque, but, as has been pointed out in an earlier chapter, it is possible to obtain orientated specimens of the nematic mesophase in which the optic axial direction is either perpendicular or parallel to the supporting surface. Such specimens are quite optically clear, and if the supporting surface is the glass prism of a refractometer, it is possible to measure the two indexes of refraction of the mesophase, the ordinary index (n_o) and the extraordinary index (n_e). Chatelain and Pellet[43] used such a method to determine the two indexes of refraction of p-azoxyanisole, although much earlier, Chatelain[44] had measured the indexes n_o and n_e for p-azoxyanisole and p-azoxyphenetole, using the more laborious method involving Newton rings. As illustrated below for p-azoxyanisole, these experiments showed that the difference between n_e and n_o decreases with temperature, and that at the nematic-isotropic transition there is a discontinuity in refractive index to give the value (n) for the isotropic liquid.

Temperature	n_e	n_o	$n_e - n_o$
117°	1·849	1·561	0·288
132°	1·795	1·576	0·219
136°		$n = 1·644$	

These results illustrate the extremely high birefringence of the nematic mesophase, and the rapid way in which this varies with increasing temperature.

The extraordinary index and the ordinary index of refraction of the nematic melt of p-azoxyanisole have also been measured for different wavelengths of incident light and at different temperatures, but the same general results hold under these conditions. Similarly, Falgueirettes[45] has confirmed these findings by measuring the two indexes of refraction of the nematic melt of p-n-butyloxybenzoic acid.

Chatelain[46] has given a theoretical interpretation of the values of the ordinary and extraordinary indexes of refraction of an orientated nematic melt such as that obtained from p-azoxyanisole. Assuming first that we have spherical regions in the nematic melt, and that the molecules on the surface of each sphere have a random orientation with respect to the molecule at the centre of the sphere, Chatelain shows that

$$\frac{1}{3}\left[\frac{n_e^2 - 1}{n_e^2 + 2} + 2\frac{n_o^2 - 1}{n_o^2 + 2}\right]\frac{1}{d} = \frac{4}{3}\pi\frac{N}{M}\frac{A + B + C}{3} \tag{1}$$

where N = Avogadro Number
   M = molecular weight
   d = density
   A,B,C, = principal polarizabilities of the molecule

Once more using the model of a sphere with a central molecule, but in this case with a similar orientation of the molecules on the surface of the sphere with respect to the central molecule, relationship (2) is obtained.

$$\frac{1}{3}\left[(n_e^2 - 1) + 2(n_o^2 - 1)\right]\frac{1}{d} = 4\pi\frac{N}{M}\frac{A' + B' + C'}{3} \tag{2}$$

where $A' = \dfrac{A}{1 - \dfrac{4}{3}\pi v A}$ $B' = \dfrac{B}{1 - \dfrac{4}{3}\pi v B}$ $C' = \dfrac{C}{1 - \dfrac{4}{3}\pi v C}$

and v = number of molecules/cc.

For a given temperature, it was shown that the measured values of n_e and n_o were in better accord with the theoretical expression (2) than with (1).

Expression (1) was derived from two equations, (3) and (4)

$$\frac{n_e^2 - 1}{n_e^2 + 2}\frac{1}{d} = \frac{4}{3}\,\pi\,\frac{N}{M}\left[C - \left(C - \frac{A + B}{2}\right)I_3\right] \tag{3}$$

$$\frac{n_o^2 - 1}{n_o^2 + 2}\frac{1}{d} = \frac{4}{3}\,\pi\,\frac{N}{M}\left[\frac{A + B}{2} + \frac{1}{2}\left(C - \frac{A + B}{2}\right)I_3\right] \tag{4}$$

Expression (2) was derived from two equations, (5) and (6)

$$(n_e^2 - 1)\,\frac{1}{d} = 4\,\pi\,\frac{N}{M}\left[C' - \left(C' - \frac{A' + B'}{2}\right)I_3\right] \tag{5}$$

$$(n_o^2 - 1)\,\frac{1}{d} = 4\,\pi\,\frac{N}{M}\left[\frac{A' + B'}{2} + \frac{1}{2}\left(C' - \frac{A' + B'}{2}\right)I_3\right] \tag{6}$$

where θ = the angle made between the major axes of the molecules of the orientated preparation and the isotropic axis of the preparation,

$$I_3 = \frac{1}{v}\int_0^{\pi/2} f(\theta)2\pi\sin^3\theta\,d\theta$$

and $f(\theta)2\pi\sin\theta\,d\theta = dv$ = the number of molecules/cc having their axes orientated within the limits $\theta + d\theta$ of the isotropic axis of the preparation.

Using equations (3) and (4), calculations of I_3, for different temperatures, give pairs of values which are in poor agreement, whilst excellent agreement is obtained for each pair of I_3 values obtained from equations (5) and (6).

This appears to show quite definitely that, in an optically orientated nematic melt, a given molecule may be regarded as surrounded by other molecules which have the same orientation. This work did not make it possible to calculate at what intermolecular separations two molecules may be regarded as independent of one another and free to adopt different orientations, but it was suggested that the distance is probably much greater than $\lambda/50$ (where λ = the wavelength of the illuminating light). As will be discussed presently, earlier work by Chatelain[47] had shown that the distance over which a parallel molecular orientation exists is about $0 \cdot 1\mu$.

Chatelain[46] also introduced a useful factor called the orientation factor $\varphi(t)$, given by the relation

$$\varphi(t) = 1 - 3/2\,I_3$$

For the isotropic liquid, which has no molecular orientation, $\varphi(t)$ may be taken as zero, and for the solid state of p-azoxyanisole, in which the molecules lie parallel, $\varphi(t)$ will be unity. Chatelain has calculated values of $\varphi(t)$ for p-azoxyanisole at various temperatures. $\varphi(t)$ ranges from $0 \cdot 577$ at $117°$ (just above the melting point) to $0 \cdot 445$ at $132°$, just below the nematic-isotropic transition. There is obviously a sudden decrease in the degree of orientation at the nematic-isotropic transition, i.e. a sudden disruption of the molecular organization. Similarly, at the solid-nematic change, the degree of orientation suddenly becomes less. Compared with these two effects, the decrease in $\varphi(t)$, the orientation factor, over the range of temperature in which the mesophase exists (116–$133°$), is small. This indicates that thermal agitation does decrease the degree of orientation in the nematic melt as the temperature rises but that the effect is small compared with that at the nematic-isotropic transition. That is, while there may be a continuous, small loss of orientation as we heat the nematic melt, the effect is very much greater at the nematic-isotropic transition, which should therefore be regarded as a true phase change, and not simply as the culmination of a gradual process.

However, it would obviously be of interest to obtain the spread of orientation factors, $\varphi(t)$, over a wider range of temperature, by using a substance for which the nematic mesophase persists for more than the $17°$ for p-azoxyanisole. If the thermal persistence of the mesophase were greater, it would be expected that the molecular orientation would be more difficult to disrupt, and that the orientation factors would decrease by a smaller amount/degree increase in temperature than for p-azoxyanisole. It would, however, be of value to know the over-all decrease in $\varphi(t)$ over a range of say $100°$, and to compare the $\varphi(t)$ value just below the nematic-isotropic transition, at a temperature of for example $200°$, with that for p-azoxyanisole at $132°$. One may add here that all too many physical studies of mesophases have been made on p-azoxyanisole, which happens to be one of the few mesomorphic substances which is readily obtainable on the market in a reasonable state of purity. There are, however, many other mesomorphic substances which exhibit mesophases over a range of temperature suitable for physical studies to be made on them. Such compounds are frequently quite easy to prepare, and if the trouble were taken to obtain them in sufficient quantities for physical studies to be undertaken, then the necessity of generalizing in so many instances from the properties of the nematic melt of p-azoxyanisole would be avoided. Whilst such generalizations may be quite valid, it would nonetheless be comforting to know from experimental work that this is in fact the case.

Chatelain has made a detailed study of the light-scattering properties of the nematic mesophase. The original work on p-azoxyanisole and

p-azoxyphenetole was reported in 1948,[48] but was followed in 1954[47] by a paper dealing with the theoretical implications of the earlier experimental work. These light-scattering studies were also extended by Falgueirettes[45] to the system p-n-butyloxybenzoic acid, the work being carried out in Professor Chatelain's department at the University of Montpellier, and in the light of the remarks made in the preceding paragraph, it is satisfying to see the extension of these studies at least to a system other than p-azoxyanisole. In this particular case, the results obtained on the colourless, substituted benzoic acid agreed with those obtained for p-azoxyanisole, confirming that the polarized nature of the scattered light is not due to the light-absorbing properties or the dichroism of the coloured p-azoxyanisole.

The light-scattering properties of p-azoxyanisole were studied using a thin section of the mesophase, obtained by melting the crystals between a glass slide and a cover slip. Both glass surfaces had been rubbed, and were superimposed such that the direction of rubbing was parallel for the two surfaces on either side of the anisotropic melt. The section of mesophase was therefore orientated by the glass surfaces, and behaved as a uniaxial preparation with the optic axis parallel to the glass, the birefringence in this direction being very strong. Such a section of mesophase, with a thickness of say 0·25 mm, diffuses enough light for visual photometric measurements to be made. In this way, Chatelain established that the intensity of the scattered light, measured between 10 and 50°, decreased as the angle of scattering increased, and that

$$\epsilon = \frac{K}{(\sin \phi)^{1 \cdot 6}}$$

where ϵ = intensity of the scattered light
ϕ = angle of scattering
K = constant

The effect of using plane polarized incident light was also examined, and by this means it was shown that, for small angles of diffusion, the most intense diffused vibration in fact vibrates in a plane at right angles to the original plane of vibration of the incident light. The depolarization factor was estimated to be of the order 8.

In these experiments, the temperature of the preparation was varied from the melting point of p-azoxyanisole (117°) to the nematic-isotropic transition temperature (134°), but no detectable change in intensity of the diffused light was noted. Chatelain comments that this is an unexpected result, and that the intensity of diffused light would have been thought to increase with temperature. The temperature increase, which should increase disorder and increase scattering, will, however, decrease the number of molecules in each swarm, so decreasing the light scattering.   A balance between these two effects would explain the constant light diffusion.

Chatelain considers that the large intensity of the scattered light (an orientated nematic melt, of thickness $0\cdot25$ mm, transmits only 55% of the light which is transmitted when the melt becomes isotropic, i.e. 45% of the light is diffused) can be readily explained in terms of swarms containing a large number of parallel molecules.   For instance, the results for p-azoxyanisole at $125°$ would be explained by postulating the existence of essentially spherical aggregates of radius $0\cdot1\mu$, containing $1\cdot1 \times 10^7$ molecules, the principal molecular axial direction fluctuating throughout the anisotropic medium from one swarm to another.

The state of polarization of the diffused light is less easy to explain, and necessitates the suggestion that the number of molecules contained in the swarms is not constant.   Assuming that all the swarms contain $1\cdot1$ $\times 10^7$ molecules, the calculated depolarization factor is of the order 2 instead of 8.   Chatelain has therefore proposed a simplified treatment in which he suggests that the number of molecules per swarm varies with the angle θ, the angle made between the major molecular axial direction of a swarm or of an individual molecule in a swarm and the isotropic axial direction of the preparation.   When θ lies between $0°$ and a critical angle θ_o, the swarms are considered to contain $1\cdot1 \times 10^7$ molecules, and when θ is greater than θ_o, the swarms are considered to be no more than single molecules which will of course diffuse very little light, and can be neglected from the point of view of the calculations of the intensity of light diffused.   In order to obtain a depolarization factor of 8, it is necessary that θ_o should be $36°$.

These studies by Chatelain therefore add further weight to the arguments favouring the existence of swarms in the nematic melt, but Chatelain himself points out that, in order to improve the schematic picture which this work gives of the nematic melt, it would be necessary to consider swarms shaped like ellipsoids, and containing a number of molecules which would change continuously with θ.   He considers that the theoretical difficulties in doing this are great and points out too that there is no satisfactory means of correcting experimental results for secondary diffusion.   In view of these problems, Chatelain has not considered it useful to develop his ideas further along these lines.

6. SURFACE TENSION

As is the case with the results of many of the physical studies carried out on mesophases, the data obtained from measurements of the surface tensions of mesophases are somewhat conflicting.

For example, Ferguson and Kennedy[49] concluded that the surface tension of the mesophase increases with rising temperature.   The unusual nature of this result compared with the behaviour of isotropic liquids, for which surface tension decreases with increasing temperature, led these workers to repeat their experiments several times. However, the same increase in surface tension was always obtained. It can only be pointed out that the surface tension measurements involved forcing the anisotropic melt along a capillary tube, and that under such conditions, anomalous effects may be observed. For example, the orientation of the mesophase on the capillary wall surfaces and the influence of the movement through the capillary, either assisting or opposing the surface orientation effects, could lead to extensive structural effects in the melt.

Naggiar[50] overcame such difficulties by using a thin film of the anisotropic melt stretched over a hole drilled in a supporting surface. The surfaces of the suspended film, of course, became curved under the influence of gravity, and by using a microscope, the curvature of the upper and lower surfaces of the film and its thickness were measured. From the expression given below, Naggiar then calculated the surface tension (A) of the mesophase,

$$2A \left(\frac{1}{R_1} - \frac{1}{R_2} \right) = \rho g e_o$$

where R_1 and R_2 are the radii of the curved surfaces at the centre of each of the surfaces, ρ is the density of the melt comprising the film, g is the force of gravity, and e_o the thickness of the film at its centre.

By enclosing the suspended film in an electrically heated compartment, Naggiar was able to carry out his experiments at a variety of carefully controlled temperatures. Thus, he showed that, for p-azoxyanisole, the surface tension decreased from about 39·5 dyn/cm at a temperature just above the melting point of about 116°, to just below 37·4 dyn/cm at the nematic-isotropic transition at 133–134°. The surface tension of the supercooled anisotropic melt was also measured at temperatures below the melting point, and two points are included on the plot of surface tension against temperature, for temperatures just above the nematic-isotropic transition. A very good straight-line plot is then obtained from temperatures of about 100° to 136°, and shows clearly a decrease in surface tension with temperature increase. The conflict with the results obtained by Ferguson and Kennedy is obvious, but Naggiar's results seem much more reasonable, particularly in view of the possible complicating features involved by the method used by Ferguson and Kennedy. Their results were not in fact markedly different from those obtained by Naggiar, in so far as the numerical values of the surface tensions were concerned, and the difference lies mainly in their observed increase in surface tension, particularly in the neighbourhood of the nematic-isotropic transition.

Naggiar summarized his relationship between surface tension (A) and the temperature (t) by the expression

$$A = 52 \cdot 1 - 0 \cdot 110t \text{ dyn/cm.}$$

Further doubt is cast upon the work of Ferguson and Kennedy by the fact that Schwartz and Moseley[51] have more recently confirmed Naggiar's results on p-azoxyanisole. The work was carried out using the ring method on a du Noüy tensiometer, and the study included the compounds p-azoxyphenetole (nematic) and ethyl p-azoxybenzoate (smectic). The anisole and phenetole derivatives gave a decrease in surface tension of about $0 \cdot 1$ dyn/cm/° rise in temperature, both as the nematic and isotropic melts. Ethyl p-azoxybenzoate behaved in much the same way, as far as the smectic mesophase was concerned, but the surface tension of the isotropic melt—obtained at 120°—increased up to 160°, and then fell with further increase in temperature.

The weight of evidence therefore favours a decrease in surface tension, for both smectic and nematic mesophases, with increase in temperature, with little evidence for any discontinuity in surface tension at the mesomorphic-isotropic transition, except in the case of ethyl p-azoxybenzoate, for which the surface tension gives a shallow minimum at the upper transition point. However, this last case suggests that the anomaly lies in the isotropic liquid of the ester, and not in the smectic mesophase or in the system at the exact transition between the mesophase and the isotropic liquid.

REFERENCES

1. Schenk, R. (1898). *Z. phys. Chem. (Leipzig)* **27**, 167.
2. Eichwold, E. (1923). Landolt-Bornstein, "Physikalisch-Chemische Tabellen", Julius Springer, Berlin. Vol. III, p. 64.
3. Becherer, G. and Kast, W. (1942). *Ann. Physik* **41**, 355.
4. Miesowicz, M. (1946). *Nature* **158**, 27.
5. Vorländer, D. (1933). *Trans. Faraday Soc.* **29**, 902.
6. Vorländer, D. (1930). *Phys. Z.* **31**, 428.
7. Powell, B. D. and Puddington, I. E. (1953). *Canad. J. Chem.* **31**, 828.
8. Ostwald, W. (1933) *Trans. Faraday Soc.* **29**, 1002.
9. Bose, E. and Conrat, F. (1908). *Phys. Z.* **9**, 169.
10. Bose, E. (1907). *Phys. Z.* **8**, 313 and 347; (1908). **9**, 707.
11. Bingham, E. C. and White, G. F. (1911). *J. Amer. Chem. Soc.* **33**, 1257.
12. Krüger, F. (1913). *Phys. Z.* **14**, 651.
13. Lawrence, A. S. C. (1933). *Trans. Faraday Soc.* **29**, 1080.
14. Friedel, G. (1922). *Ann. Physique* **18**, 273.
15. Björnstähl, Y. (1935). *Physics* **6**, 257.
16. Björnstähl, Y. and Snellman, O. (1939). *Kolloid Z.* **86**, 223.
17. Brown, G. H. and Shaw, W. G. (1957). *Chem. Rev.* **57**, 1097.
18. Kast, W. (1931). *Z. Physik* **71**, 39; (1935). *Phys. Z.* **36**, 869.
19. Mikhailor, G. M. and Tzvetkov, V. (1939). *Acta Physicochim. U.R.S.S.* **10**, 415.

20. Tzvetkov, V. Akad. Nauk S.S.S.R., Otdel. Tekh. Nauk, Inst. Mashino-vedeniya, Soveshchanie Vyazkosti Zhidkosteĭ i Kolloid Rastvorov (Conference on Viscosity of Liquids and Colloidal Solutions) 1941, **1**, 47 ((1946) *Chem. Abs.* **40**, 3033).
21. Tzvetkov, V. (1939). *Acta Physicochim. U.R.S.S.* **11**, 97.
22. Miesowicz, M. (1935). *Nature* **136**, 261; (1936*A*) *Bull. intern. acad. polon. sci., classe sci. math. nat.* 228 ((1937) *Chem. Abs.* **31**, 3354); (1946). *Nature* **158**, 27.
23. Kast, W. (1931). *Z. Krist.* **79**, 146.
24. Jezewski, M. (1928). *Z. Physik* **51**, 159.
25. Marinin, V. and Tzvetkov, V. (1939). *Acta. Physicochim. U.R.S.S.* **11**, 837.
26. Ornstein, L. S., Kast, W., and Bouma, P. J. (1932). *Proc. Acad. Sci. Amsterdam* **35**, 1209 ((1933) *Chem. Abs.* **27**, 2073).
27. Maier, W. (1944). *Phys. Z.* **45**, 285.
28. Barth, G., Maier, W. and Wiehl, H. E. (1954). *Z. Elektrochem.* **58**, 674.
29. Brown, G. H. and Shaw, W. G. (1957). *Chem. Rev.* **57**, 1102.
30. Bhide, B. V. and Bhide, R. D. (1938). *Rasayanam* **1**, 121 ((1939) *Chem. Abs.* **33**, 1564).
31. Bernal, J. D. and Crowfoot, D. (1933). *Trans. Faraday Soc.* **29**, 1032.
32. Tolstoi, N. A. (1949). *Zhur. eksp. teor. Fiz.* **19**, 319 ((1951) *Chem. Abs.* **45**, 9954).
33. Maier, W. (1947). *Z. Naturforsch.* **2a**, 457.
34. Carr, E. F. and Spence, R. D. (1954). *J. Chem. Phys.* **22**, 1481.
35. Marinin, V. and Tzvetkov, V. (1948). *Zhur. eksp. teor. Fiz.* **18**, 641 ((1949) *Chem. Abs.* **43**, 3675).
36. Bauer, E. and Bernamont, J. (1936). *Journal Phys. Radium* **7**, 19.
37. Spaght, M. E., Thomas, S. B. and Parks, G. S. (1932). *J. Phys. Chem.* **36**, 882.
38. Kreutzer, C. and Kast, W. (1937). *Naturwiss.* **25**, 233.
39. Kreutzer, C. (1938). *Ann. Physik* **33**, 192.
40. Vold, R. D. (1941). *J. Amer. Chem. Soc.* **63**, 2915.
41. Pushin, N. A. and Grebenshchikov, I. V. (1926). *Z. phys. Chem. (Leipzig)* **124**, 270.
42. Robberecht, J. (1938). *Bull. Soc. chim. belges* **47**, 597.
43. Chatelain, P. and Pellet, O. (1950). *Bull. soc. franç. Minér. Crist.* **73**, 154.
44. Chatelain, P. (1937). *Bull. soc. franç. Minér. Crist.* **60**, 280.
45. Falgueirettes, J. (1952). *Compt. rend.* **234**, 2619.
46. Chatelain, P. (1955). *Bull. soc. franç. Minér. Crist.* **78**, 262.
47. Chatelain, P. (1954). *Bull. soc. franç. Minér. Crist.* **77**, 353.
48. Chatelain, P. (1948). *Compt. rend.* **227**, 136.
49. Ferguson, A. and Kennedy, S. J. (1938). *Phil. Mag.* **26**, 41.
50. Naggiar, V. (1943). *Ann. Physique* **18**, 5.
51. Schwartz, W. M. and Moseley, H. W. (1947). *J. Phys. Colloid Chem.* **51**, 826.
52. Maier, W. and Meier, G. (1961). *Z. Naturforsch.* **16a**, 262.
53. Maier, W. and Meier, G. *Z. Naturforsch.* (in press).

CHAPTER VII

LIQUID CRYSTALLINE BEHAVIOUR OF MIXTURES

WHEN two mesomorphic compounds are mixed, the melting points and the mesomorphic transition temperatures are of course depressed. If both components of the mixture are capable of giving enantiotropic meso-phases, the mixture itself will probably give an enantiotropic mesophase, but this depends upon the temperature ranges over which the meso-phases of the two components are thermally stable. As will be mentioned later, binary mixtures of certain non-mesomorphic compounds with a mesomorphic compound frequently exhibit mesophases, which are sometimes enantiotropic and sometimes monotropic. Cases of liquid crystallinity in mixtures of two non-mesomorphic components have also been reported. For example, Mlodziejowski[1] claims that mixtures of cholesterol and cetyl alcohol and of cholesterol and glycerol yield mesomorphic phases, and earlier, Gaubert[2] obtained mesomorphic systems by mixing molten cholesterol with succinimide and with either malic, maleic, malonic, succinic, anisic, cinnamic, or lactic acid. Gaubert also examined the liquid crystalline mixtures obtained by heating ergosteryl acetate, propionate, or butyrate with glycollic acid, with glycerol, and with orcin, and the mesomorphic mixtures obtained on melting certain cholesterol and ergosterol derivatives with urea. Krav-chenko and Pastukhova[3] have also reported mesomorphic properties for mixtures of non-mesomorphic compounds such as the hydrocarbons indene and naphthalene.

There is nothing particularly surprising about the mesomorphic behaviour of such mixtures. If the mixture consists of a mesomorphic and a non-mesomorphic component, it is necessary only that the presence of the non-mesomorphic compound shall not destroy the parallel orien-tation of the molecules of the molten mesomorphic compound, i.e. the molecules of the non-mesomorphic component should be able to fit into the parallel distribution. Obviously then, the non-mesomorphic com-pound should consist of molecules which are structurally compatible with the mesomorphic molecular arrangement, and the most favourable conditions would arise with molecules which are long and lath-shaped. If, on the other hand, the non-mesomorphic component consisted of bulky spherical molecules, then the parallel distribution of the molecules of the mesomorphic system would be difficult to maintain, the meso-morphic-isotropic transition temperature would probably be depressed more than the melting point, and no liquid crystalline properties would be observed. Indeed, in the work of Bogojawlensky and Winogradow[4] and of Walter[5] reference is made to the latent or potential mesomorphic property of the non-mesomorphic component. Similar arguments must apply to the reported cases of liquid crystalline behaviour in mixtures of two non-mesomorphic components. Here again, an essentially parallel distribution of the mixture of molecules must exist, the melting point of the mixture having been depressed sufficiently to make possible the existence of a " liquid phase " at a low enough temperature for aniso-tropic properties to be manifested in it. It would therefore be thought that the molecules of both components should be elongated in shape, so that the latent mesomorphic character of the system would be as high as possible. However, the shapes of the molecules of several of the non-mesomorphic components which have been reported as giving meso-morphic mixtures do not seem very suitable, and, for example, in the work by Gaubert on liquid crystalline melts of cholesterol mixed with various acids, one does wonder just how much esterification of the acids might have occurred in the melt, so producing mesomorphic cholesteryl esters.

The possibility of the occurrence of liquid crystalline properties in a mixture therefore resolves itself into a question of whether the solid-liquid transition temperature of the mixture occurs at a low enough temperature for an anisotropic arrangement of suitably shaped mole-cules to persist. If this is the case, then a mixed, enantiotropic meso-phase will occur. Even if the solid mixture melts and produces the isotropic liquid, it is possible that the two-component melt may crystal-lize less readily than would the melts of either of the two pure compo-nents, i.e. quite marked supercooling of the melt may take place, and when the temperature falls, the molecules may adopt an anisotropic arrangement over a range of temperature below the melting point of the mixture. The mixture will then exhibit a monotropic liquid crystalline state. In the cases reported by Mlodziejowski,[1] one can almost think of the arrangement of cholesterol molecules being " plasticized " by the molecules of glycerol or cetyl alcohol, such that a mobile anisotropic arrangement is possible. After all, although cholesterol is non-meso-morphic, it must be considered to be potentially mesomorphic, since even cholesteryl chloride gives a monotropic cholesteric mesophase, and it is possible that the hydrogen bonding in pure cholesterol increases the intermolecular cohesions and is responsible for the high melting point. The presence of the glycerol or cetyl alcohol molecules may provide alternative sites to which the cholesterol hydroxyl group can hydrogen bond without resulting in a high melting crystal lattice, yet giving sufficiently strong intermolecular attractions to make possible the exist-ence of an anisotropic melt. Similar arguments could of course be applied to Gaubert's mixtures of cholesterol with succinimide and various acids.

The extents of the melting point depressions and the phase diagrams for mixtures showing liquid crystalline properties are well illustrated by reference to the early publications of Tamman,[6] Lehmann,[7] and Smits,[8] and to the more recent work by Vorländer and Ost.[9] Attention should be drawn here to the disagreement expressed by workers in the very early part of this century concerning the nature of the change from the anisotropic state of a mixture of a mesomorphic and a non-mesomorphic component to the true isotropic state of the mixture. Both de Kock[10] and Prins[11] maintained that Phase Rule theory did not allow a direct transition, at a fixed temperature, from the two component mesophase to the two-component isotropic melt, and that there must be a temperature range in which a series of mixtures of different composition of the two liquids (one anisotropic and one isotropic) coexist. Bogojawlensky and Winogradow[4] were quite certain, however, that the mesomorphic state of such a mixture is perfectly homogeneous, and illustrated that in several cases which they studied, the phase diagrams showed that the mesomorphic-isotropic transition temperatures changed linearly with changing composition of the mixture, and that a well-defined boundary separated the anisotropic and the isotropic liquids. Later, Walter[5] published results agreeing with Bogojawlensky and Winogradow, and indicating that perfect mixed liquid crystals are formed when both components are mesomorphic.

Much more recently, Dave and Dewar[12] have re-examined the problem by studying the behaviours of mixtures of varying composition, each mixture containing one component which is capable of giving a nematic mesophase and one which gives no anisotropic phase. One such system studied was a mixture of p-azoxyanisole (nematic) and quinol (non-mesomorphic), the two-component system for which de Kock claimed that he had obtained evidence for a range of temperature in which two liquid phases of different composition coexisted. This region is the shaded area in Fig. VII.1 (a), but Dave and Dewar found no experimental evidence for this, and obtained a phase diagram of the type shown in Fig. VII.1 (b). In this and other cases examined by Dave and Dewar, they concluded that the liquid phase, produced by heating the mixture of solids, is an homogeneous single phase, whether it be mesomorphic or not.

Dave and Dewar criticized the experimental technique used by de Kock, pointing out that because of the inefficient stirring of the melt and inadequate temperature control it was hardly surprising that the transitions obtained were not well-defined. It is possible that de Kock was influenced by the preconceived notion that the transitions should not be well-defined from a thermodynamic point of view. In this sense he was correct, for as Dave and Dewar point out, it is thermodynamically impossible for a normal first-order transition to occur in a mixed system of this kind. Thus, the possibilities are (*a*) that the transitions are not first-order—if this is the case, the heat of the transition will be zero, and the two phases must have identical compositions—or (*b*) the two-phase region is extremely small, as might well be expected in view of the small heats of transition involved at genuine mesomorphic-isotropic transitions. Dave and Dewar do not consider that their results can distinguish between the two possibilities, since the two-phase region may be too small to detect experimentally by either the optical or thermal methods used for determining the transitions. However, the authors comment that it is significant that even when the two compounds (one mesomorphic and one non-mesomorphic) are comprised of molecules of dif-

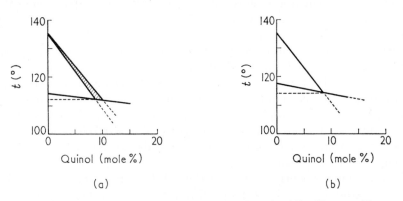

Fig. VII.1 (*a*) and (*b*). Phase diagrams for the mixed liquid crystalline system *p*-azoxyanisole (nematic) and quinol (non-mesomorphic) (de Kock, A. C.(1904).   *Z. phys. Chem.* (Leipzig) **48**, 129 ; Dave, J. S. and Dewar, M. J. S. (1954).   *J. Chem. Soc.* 4617).

ferent shape, polarity, and size (conditions which would be most likely to give two-phase liquid regions), no anomalous states between the isotropic liquids and the nematic melts are observed.

It may be mentioned here that in the writer's experience, impurity in a mesomorphic compound *does* lead to less precisely defined transition temperatures. For example, when an impure mesomorphic compound is melted between a glass slide and a cover slip and is then allowed to cool, the boundary between the isotropic liquid and the mesophase is often ragged as it moves across the specimen. Moreover, for such a compound, the transition temperature obtained on heating from the anisotropic melt to the isotropic liquid is frequently higher than that obtained on cooling from the isotropic liquid. In fact, precise reversibility of mesomorphic-isotropic transitions and clearly defined boundaries between thin sections of isotropic and anisotropic melts may be accepted as sensitive criteria of the purity of mesomorphic compounds. Although the writer has carried out very little work on mixed liquid crystal systems, these observations do seem relevant in the present context, despite the fact that Dave and Dewar claim that the nematic-isotropic transition temperatures for their mixtures were reproducible within ±0·1°, whether the bath temperature was rising or falling.

Dave and Dewar[13] extended their studies to a range of other systems involving a non-mesomorphic solute in a second component capable of giving a nematic mesophase. Dave and Dewar point out that any substance comprised of anisotropic molecules will give rise to a liquid crystalline phase if its melt can be supercooled to a sufficiently low temperature, and that for a mixture of a mesomorphic and a non-mesomorphic substance or of two non-mesomorphic substances, the probability that the anisotropy will be observed is dependent upon the extent of the melting-point depression for the mixture. Moreover, as mentioned earlier, the probability that a mixture of a mesomorphic and a non-mesomorphic substance exhibits a mesophase depends upon the suitability of the molecules of the non-mesomorphic component to fit into the anisotropic arrangement of the molecules of the mesomorphic component. If the two molecule types are similar in size and shape, then packing and steric factors should not vary much with composition of the mixture. On the other hand, since the intermolecular cohesions should change more or less linearly with composition, the plot of the nematic-isotropic temperatures against the percentage compositions of the mixtures should give a fairly straight line, as observed by Bogojawlensky and Winogradow.[4] Dave and Dewar point out that this is not in fact *always* the case, and that if the two components differ, the transition line will not be straight, but will curve concavely upwards, and may even show a maximum if the differences in shape and size of the molecules are marked, e.g. with p-azoxyanisole and p-methoxycinnamic acid.

For cases in which the transition line is linear, Dave and Dewar reasoned that the slope of the line will depend upon the latent tendency of the non-mesomorphic compound to show liquid crystalline properties. Thus, using p-azoxyanisole as the mesomorphic compound, a steep slope means a rapid decrease in nematic-isotropic transition temperature of the mixture with increasing concentration of the non-mesomorphic solute. This indicates a low tendency of the second component to be mesomorphic. Dave and Dewar obtained extremely interesting results by mixing p-azoxyanisole with various non-mesomorphic components of the type:

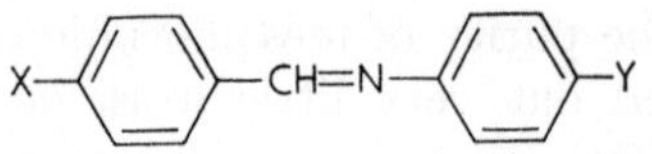

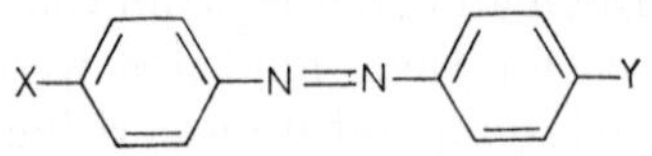

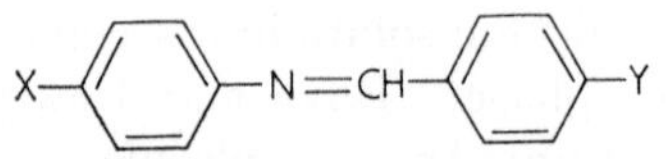

X—⟨benzene⟩—CH=N—⟨benzene⟩—Y

X—⟨benzene⟩—N=N—⟨benzene⟩—Y

X—⟨benzene⟩—N=CH—⟨benzene⟩—Y

Three main points emerged from this work.

(1) The slopes for isomeric pairs of Schiff's bases were similar.

(2) Two polar terminal groups are essential for a low slope, e.g.

$$X = Y = H \qquad \text{Slope} = 29 \cdot 5$$
$$X = Y = OMe \qquad \text{Slope} = 4 \cdot 0 \left.\right\} \text{Central group} —CH=N—$$
$$X = H; Y = OMe \qquad \text{Slope} = 22 \cdot 0$$

(3) The effects of terminal groups on the slopes of the transition lines are approximately additive. In view of this, it was possible to place the various substituents in an order of decreasing efficiency (group efficiency) in giving rise to nematic behaviour in the mixed system. The order was

$$NO_2 > OMe > NMe_2 > Me > Cl > Br > H$$

The authors comment that the order is that of decreasing polarity of the groups, and that the magnitude of the group dipole must be important. The group efficiencies of the methyl and chloro- substituents are closely similar, and this point will be referred to again in Chapter X, where the relative effects of chloro- and methyl substituents on the nematic thermal stabilities of different types of compound will be discussed. Dave and Dewar mention that they are surprised at the efficiency of the nitro- group in promoting mixed liquid crystalline properties, stating that comparatively few mesomorphic nitro- compounds are known. However, this is no longer a fair comment, for the writer alone has published details of the mesomorphic properties of compounds such as the 4'-n-alkoxy-3'-nitrobiphenyl-4-carboxylic acids and their n-propyl esters,[14] the 6-n-alkoxy-5-nitro-2-naphthoic acids,[15] 4-methoxy-4"-nitro-p-terphenyl, 4-cyano-4"-nitro-p-terphenyl, 4-acetamido-3,4"-di-nitro-p-terphenyl, and 4-amino-3,4"-dinitro-p-terphenyl.[16]

It should, however, be emphasized that the above order of group efficiencies obtained by Dave and Dewar would probably not apply to a system in which the mesomorphic component was smectic. As far as the author is aware, mixed smectogenic systems have not been studied in this way. However, as will be discussed fully in Chapters IX and X, it is known that the introduction of substituents into aromatic mesomorphic compounds results in certain changes in the mesomorphic transition temperatures. Thus, if a terminal substituent is introduced into a parent molecule, and results in a decrease in the mesomorphic-isotropic transition temperature, then we may say that the substituent decreases the thermal stability of this particular type of mesophase. By arranging compounds carrying different terminal substituents in order of their decreasing mesomorphic transition temperatures, we should therefore obtain an order for the substituents themselves, an order which should have the same significance as the group efficiency order of Dave and Dewar. For example, let us consider compounds of the type

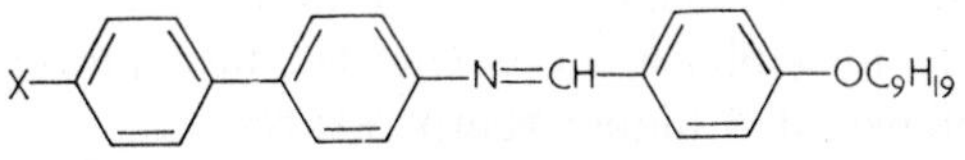

in which the substituent X is varied.[17] These compounds exhibit only smectic mesophases when X = Cl, Br, or I, and a smectic mesophase together with a very short (2·5°) nematic mesophase when X = H. When the smectic-nematic transition temperature for X = H, and the other three smectic-isotropic transition temperatures are compared, we find the following order of decreasing mesomorphic (smectic) thermal stability as designated by the substituents X,

$$I > Br > Cl > H$$

As far as the chloro- and bromo- substituents are concerned, the group efficiency order for the nematic mesophase is now reversed, confirming the idea that this order would not apply to smectic mesophases. The compound with X = Me was then prepared. The anil exhibits both a smectic and a nematic mesophase, but when the smectic-nematic transition temperature is inserted in the above order, we obtain

$$I > Br > Cl > Me > H$$

The Me group, too, is now displaced relative to the group efficiency order for the nematic mesophase, showing that this group is more suited to nematic than to smectic mesophase formation. It is not easy to study a wide range of substituents X in the above type of molecule, because of preparative difficulties. For this reason, work was undertaken[18] on the two series of compounds

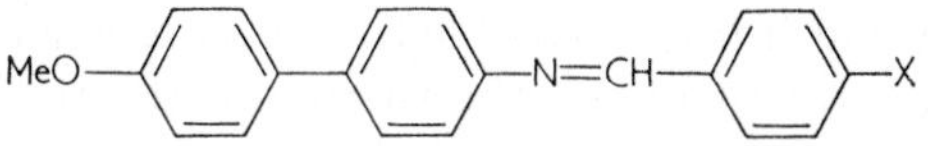

(nematic mesophases)

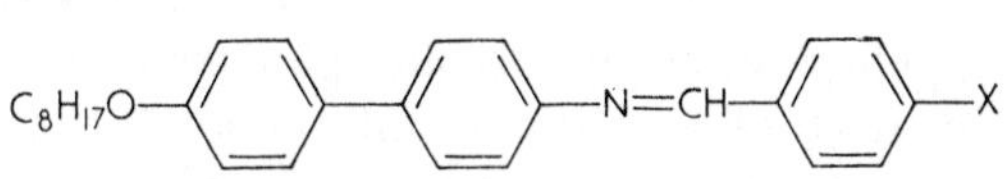

(smectic and possibly also nematic mesophases)

The nature of the terminal substituent X can now be varied easily by condensing the appropriate p-substituted benzaldehyde with one or other of the amines, and by employing a short (methyl) and a long (octyl) alkyl chain in the two series of compounds, evidence for the effects of these substituents, X, on both smectic and nematic mesophases was obtained.

The various transition temperatures for the two sets of compounds are annexed in Tables VII.1 and VII.2 (p. 133) (the transition temperatures were determined by normal capillary methods, and are uncorrected for exposed stem). The methoxy compounds (Table VII.1) exhibited only nematic mesophases, whereas the octyl ethers (Table VII.2) gave either a single smectic mesophase, or a smectic mesophase followed by a nematic mesophase, at a higher temperature.

We may now place the substituents (X) in order of

(a) decreasing smectic thermal stability of the anils (Table VII.2),

$$\text{NHCOCH}_3 > \text{Br} > \text{Cl} > \text{F} > \text{NMe}_2 = \text{n-PnO} > \text{n-PrO} > \text{Me} = \text{iso-PrO} >$$
$$\text{H} > \text{NO}_2 > \text{MeO}$$

(b) decreasing nematic thermal stability of the anils,

(1) $\text{NHCOCH}_3 > \text{MeO} > \text{n-PrO} > \text{n-PnO} > \text{NMe}_2 > \text{Me} > \text{NO}_2 >$
$$\text{iso-PrO (Table VII.2)}$$

(2) $\text{NHCOCH}_3 > \text{MeO} > \text{NO}_2 > \text{n-PrO} > \text{Cl} > \text{Br} > \text{NMe}_2 > \text{Me} >$
$$\text{n-PnO} > \text{F} > \text{iso-PrO} > \text{H (Table VII.1)}$$

It is useful to simplify the above orders by selecting only the seven substituents common to the present study and that made by Dewar.[12] The group efficiency order obtained by Dewar was

$$\text{NO}_2 > \text{MeO} > \text{NMe}_2 > \text{Me} > \text{Cl} > \text{Br} > \text{H}$$

The equivalent order obtained from the nematic thermal stabilities in Table VII.1 is

$$\text{MeO} > \text{NO}_2 > \text{Cl} > \text{Br} > \text{NMe}_2 > \text{Me} > \text{H}$$

and from the more limited range of nematic thermal stabilities in Table VII.2,

$$\text{MeO} > \text{NMe}_2 > \text{Me} > \text{NO}_2$$

It is at once evident that the three orders bear only a general resemblance to one another, and that it is not possible to specify a given order for the effects of terminal substituents on the thermal stabilities of nematic mesophases, and presumably therefore on the mesomorphic potential of a non-mesomorphic compound. Many factors such as conjugative effects, dipole interactions, the overall polarizability of the system, and the occurrence or otherwise of hydrogen bonding in the system will influence the order, such that a given substituent may have quite different effects when it is present in different aromatic systems.

TABLE VII.1

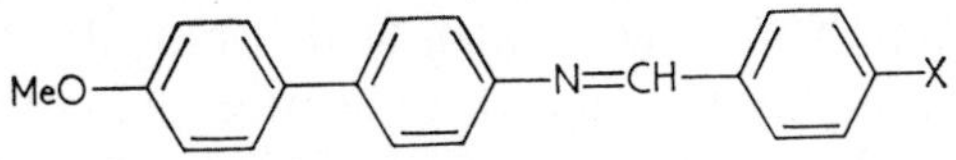

MeO—⬡—⬡—N=CH—⬡—X

Substituent (X)	Solid-nematic transition temp. = m.p. (°)	Nematic-isotropic transition temp. (°)
H	174	176
Me	178	279
MeO	211	318
n-PrO	194	296
n-PnO	176	274
iso-PrO	164	256
F	187	265·5
Cl	205	295
Br	227	294·5
NO_2	204	308
NMe_2	208	293·5
$NHCOCH_3$	271	345

TABLE VII.2

$C_8H_{17}O$—⬡—⬡—N=CH—⬡—X

Substituent (X)	Solid-mesomorphic* transition temp. = m.p. (°)	Smectic-nematic transition temp. (°)	Mesomorphic*-isotropic transition temp. (°)
H	155	—	170·5
Me	155	178	222
MeO	166	167·5	249·5
n-PrO	166	201	242
n-PnO	159	214	234
iso-PrO	161	178	211
F	174	—	230
Cl	193	—	261·5
Br	226	—	267·5
NO_2	137	169	221 (decomp.)
NMe_2	184	214	225
$NHCOCH_3$	228	283	292·5

* When no smectic-nematic transition temperature is recorded for a particular substituent (X), the compound exhibits only a smectic mesophase—the transitions in columns 1 and 3 in the Table then refer to solid-smectic and smectic-isotropic changes respectively.

The simplified order obtained from the smectic thermal stabilities in Table VII.2 is

$$Br > Cl > NMe_2 > Me > H > NO_2 > MeO$$

The example of X = MeO, which leads to highly thermally stable nematic mesophases, but to a smectic mesophase of low thermal stability is sufficient to emphasize that any order of group efficiency for terminal substituents in relation to nematic mesophases will not apply to smectic mesophases, whose thermal stabilities are governed by quite different factors.

de Kock[10] and Du Pont and Lozac'h[19] have used the depressions of the nematic-isotropic transition temperatures of mesomorphic compounds brought about by solutes, in an attempt to determine the solute molecular weights. Dave and Dewar,[12,13] however, point out that the basis of such measurements would be sound only if the solute were nearly insoluble in the mesomorphic solvent, the two-component system consisting of a mixture of the mesomorphic phase and the isotropic mixture of the two components. Since Dave and Dewar have shown that the liquid crystalline states of such mixtures are homogeneous, they reason that reliable molecular weight determinations would be impossible. Their own results do show that the molar depressions for a given solute vary with the nature of the mesomorphic component of the mixture.

Dave continues his interest in mixed liquid crystalline systems and has quite recently[20] described the liquid crystalline properties of mixtures of p-anisal-p-phenetidine and p-nitrobenzal-p-phenetidine. Enantiotropic nematic mesophases are obtained over the range of composition from 21·5 to 67·5 mole% of p-nitrobenzal-p-phenetidine. Dave and Lohar[20] did not study the monotropic nematic properties of mixtures outwith the above composition range, although p-anisal-p-phenetidine is known[21] to exhibit a monotropic nematic mesophase. Byron and Gray[22] showed qualitatively that monotropic nematic mesophases are given in the range 0 to 21·5 mole% of p-nitrobenzal-p-phenetidine, and from 67·5 to about 90 mole% of p-nitrobenzal-p-phenetidine, which does not exhibit a monotropic mesophase. Dave and Lohar[23] have now extended their work to these monotropic systems and have shown that the monotropic nematic mesophases persist up to 89 mole% of p-nitrobenzal-p-phenetidine.

Friedel[24] made many interesting observations on the effects on the textures of various mesophases of adding other mesomorphic compounds to the system. In fact, Friedel quite frequently adopted the technique of employing a mixed mesomorphic system in order to depress the melting point of one of the pure components and so to obtain its mesophase over a more readily accessible temperature range. For example, the addition of a small quantity of ethyl p-azoxycinnamate to ethyl p-azoxybenzoate stabilizes the smectic mesophase of the latter compound and makes it more easy to obtain and examine the stepped smectic drops which are produced. Perhaps the most marked effect of mixing compounds was obtained[24,25] for *p*-azoxyanisole. If minute amounts of an optically active compound (not necessarily mesomorphic) are added to this normally nematic compound, the mesophase is transformed into one which shows optical rotatory power and other characteristic properties of the Grandjean plane texture of the cholesteric mesophase. The optical rotatory power of the mesophase is in fact proportional to the concentration of the optically active compound. These observations led Friedel to argue strongly that the cholesteric mesophase must be nematic in nature, otherwise these properties would not be produced by the modifying influences of small amounts of optically active compounds upon the nematic mesophase. Irrespective of the validity of Friedel's argument, the basically interesting observation remains, and should be linked in one's mind with Friedel's further discovery that nematic properties can be produced in mixtures of two substances which normally give mesophases with the Grandjean plane texture. Friedel examined the effect of mixing the *dextro*-rotatory substance active amyl *p*-(4-cyanobenzylideneamino)cinnamate (I) with a *laevo*-rotatory substance such as cholesteryl benzoate (II). If the ratio of I to II is 3 to 1 or greater, the mesophase obtained from the mixture has the properties of a *dextro*-rotatory cholesteric mesophase, and when the ratio is 2·25 to 1 or less, the cholesteric mesophase becomes *laevo*-rotatory. In the intermediate composition range, Friedel observed the interesting phenomenon of the change-over from a right-handed to a left-handed system. For example, using a mixture of I:II in the ratio of 2·5:1 or 2·75:1, the mesophase gave a *dextro*-rotatory, cholesteric Grandjean plane texture as for I, but as the cholesteric-isotropic transition was approached, the sense of the optical rotatory power changed to *laevo*-rotatory, as obtained for the pure compound II. The change occurred at a temperature designated by Friedel as θ. The temperature was found to increase with increasing concentration of I, becoming higher than the mesomorphic-isotropic transition temperature for a ratio of 3:1 or greater, and to fall with increasing concentration of II, becoming, for a ratio of 2·25:1 or less, lower than the lowest temperature at which the cholesteric mesophase could be maintained in a supercooled condition. On approaching θ, either by heating or cooling the mixed mesophase, the separation of the edges of the Grandjean planes became smaller, until, at θ, the borders were no longer distinguishable and they assumed the appearance of threads, as observed in nematic mesophases. Further, at this temperature θ, the optical rotatory power suddenly disappeared, a very intense Brownian movement became obvious, and the texture of the centred nematic mesophase was obtained. Friedel considered that at this temperature θ, at which all the characteristic

Grandjean plane properties have disappeared, the mixed mesophase is identical with a nematic mesophase. Above the temperature θ, Grandjean planes reseparate and become clearly visible again, the Brownian movement ceases, and at the same time, the optical rotatory power suddenly manifests itself, but with its sense changed from right-handed to left-handed. The optic axial sign of the Grandjean plane texture below and above the temperature θ is negative, but at θ, when the mesophase assumes nematic properties, the optic axial sign is positive, as for a normal nematic mesophase.

The centred texture is seen particularly clearly when a very thin section of material is being observed, and under these conditions, the texture is identical with that obtained from substances such as p-azoxy-anisole, which are purely nematic. With sections or pellicles of thickness much less than the distance between two Grandjean planes, Friedel noticed that the centred texture persisted throughout the thermal stability range of the cholesteric mesophase. Moreover, the texture underwent no change at the temperature θ, and the optical sign remained positive throughout the entire range of the mesophase's existence. Friedel concluded that the centred texture persists even in much thicker preparations, but only in the very thin pellicle in intimate contact with the glass supporting surface, and that the texture is masked at all temperatures other than those close to θ by the Grandjean planes, which reflect a great deal of light and are opaque. In the vicinity of θ, however, the Grandjean planes disappear, and the centred texture of the thin layer next to the glass is then seen clearly as in a nematic mesophase. In the centred texture, the directions of the optic axes are variable, in that they radiate from or circulate round the centres, but they always lie parallel to the surface of the preparation. That is, the positive optic axial direction is normal to the optic axial direction of the optically negative Grandjean plane texture. The value of this observation in assisting towards a better understanding of the molecular arrangement in the cholesteric textures has already been discussed in Chapter II.

Though it hardly falls into the category of mixed liquid crystalline systems, it is convenient to include in this chapter the limited amount of work that has been carried out on the rates of reactions carried out in mesomorphic states which act as the solvents. Svedberg has made all of these studies, but the work, done more than 40 years ago, has not been extended. This is not really surprising, because a non-mesomorphic solute will tend to destroy the mesomorphic properties of the solvent, and may not have to be present in very high concentration to do so. Therefore, the likelihood is remote of finding a suitable mesomorphic compound to act as an anisotropic solvent for two different types of solute molecule between which it is desired to study a chemical reaction.

For this reason, all Svedberg's work was carried out with only one type of solute molecule present in each case, i.e. the reactions studied involved decompositions of the solute molecules.

Although reactions between different compounds are probably impracticable in an anisotropic medium, we may note that such reactions would be extremely useful if they could be carried out. For example, consider an aromatic hydrocarbon such as p-terphenyl,

which undergoes substitution at the 4-, 2-, and 2'-positions. If we imagine that these long narrow molecules are present as a solute in the parallel molecular orientation of a mesomorphic solvent, they would undoubtedly arrange themselves with their own long axes parallel to the long axes of the solvent molecules. If such a condition could be obtained without destroying the mesomorphic properties of the solvent, it is conceivable that a substituting species would find it easier to attack the molecule at the 4- positions rather than at the more protected 2- and 2'-positions. In this way preferential 4-substitution would then be obtained. However, it is likely that such reactions will remain hypothetical, since the attacking species would probably also react with the solvent molecules, which often contain aromatic rings, and would thereby destroy the anisotropy of the system. The idea is, however, interesting.

Svedberg[26] studied the rates of thermal decomposition of picric acid, pyrogallol, and trinitroresorcinol in the nematic melt of p-azoxyphenetole at a temperature of 140°. In all three cases, the rates of the reactions decreased when the nematic melt was orientated by an external magnetic field. This implies that a higher degree of orientation of the molecules or swarms of the nematic melt disfavours decomposition, and we could interpret this by saying that when the solute molecules are to some extent wedged in a well-ordered arrangement of solvent molecules, the thermal vibration is unable to effect such ready decomposition of the solute molecules. Indeed, maleic acid underwent no detectable decomposition at 140° in a magnetically orientated nematic melt of p-azoxyphenetole.

Svedberg[26] also studied the reaction between picric acid and the solvent molecules of p-azoxyphenetole. A plot of reaction rate against temperature showed an apparent increase in rate at the nematic-isotropic transition temperature. Svedberg explained this change in rate, measured by the conductivity change, in terms of increased diffusion, since the dielectric constant and the degree of dissociation remained constant.

The rates of diffusion of m-nitrophenol in a mixed liquid crystalline system of p-azoxyanisole and p-azoxyphenetole were also measured by Svedberg.[27] Magnetic fields were used in all cases, and it was established that the diffusion rate rose when the magnetic field was parallel to the direction of flow, and fell when the field was applied across the direction of flow. This result is to be expected in the light of what has already been said in an earlier chapter on the orientating influences of magnetic fields on the nematic mesophase.

REFERENCES

1. Mlodziejowski, A. (1923). *Z. Physik* **20**, 317; (1928). *Z. phys. Chem.* (*Leipzig*) **135**, 129.
2. Gaubert, P. (1912). *Bull. soc. franç Minér. Crist.* **35**, 64; (1913). *Compt. rend.* **156**, 149.
3. Kravchenko, V. M. and Pastukhova, I. S. (1952). *Zhur. priklad. Khim.* **25**, 313, 328, and 343.
4. Bogojawlensky, A. and Winogradow, N. (1908). *Z. phys. Chem.* (*Leipzig*) **64**, 229.
5. Walter, R. (1925). *Ber.* **58B**, 2303.
6. Tamman, G. (1906). *Ann. Physik* **19**, 421.
7. Lehmann, O. (1906). *Ann. Physik* **21**, 181.
8. Smits, A. (1909). *Z. phys. Chem.* (*Leipzig*) **67**, 464.
9. Vorländer, D. and Ost, K. (1938). *Ber.* **71B** 1688.
10. de Kock, A. C. (1904). *Z. phys. Chem.* (*Leipzig*) **48**, 129.
11. Prins, A. (1909). *Z. phys. Chem.* (*Leipzig*) **67**, 689.
12. Dave, J. S. and Dewar, M. J. S. (1954). *J. Chem. Soc.* 4617.
13. Dave, J. S. and Dewar, M. J. S. (1955). *J. Chem. Soc.* 4305.
14. Gray, G. W., Jones, B. and Marson, F. (1957). *J. Chem. Soc.* 393.
15. Gray, G. W. and Jones, B. (1955). *J. Chem. Soc.* 236.
16. Culling, P., Gray, G. W. and Lewis, D. (1960). *J. Chem. Soc.* 2699.
17. Byron, D. J. and Gray, G. W. Unpublished work.
18. Aaron, C., Byron, D. J. and Gray, G. W. Unpublished work.
19. Du Pont, G. and Lozac'h, O. (1945). *Compt. rend.* **221**, 751.
20. Dave, J. S. and Lohar, J. M. (1959). *Chem. and Ind.* 597.
21. Vorländer, D. (1908). " Kristallinish-flüssige Substanzen ", Ferdinand Enke, Stuttgart. pp. 53, 61.
22. Byron, D. J. and Gray, G. W. (1959). *Chem. and Ind.* 1021.
23. Dave, J. S. and Lohar, J. M. (1960). *Chem. and Ind.* 494.
24. Friedel, G. (1922). *Ann. Physique* **18**, 273.
25. Friedel, G. (1923). *Compt. rend.* **176**, 475.
26. Svedberg, T. (1916). *Kolloid Z.* **18**, 54 and 101; (1917). **21**, 19.
27. Svedberg, T. (1918). *Kolloid Z.* **22**, 68.

CHAPTER VIII

THE MESOMORPHIC BEHAVIOUR OF COMPOUNDS AND THEIR CHEMICAL CONSTITUTION

THE relationship between mesomorphic behaviour and chemical constitution has been studied quite fully in an attempt to throw light upon the following points:

(a) the fact that some compounds are mesomorphic and some are not,

(b) the manner in which the chemical constitution of a compound determines whether the mesophase exhibited is smectic, nematic, or cholesteric, and

(c) the interpretation of the changes in the mesomorphic transition temperatures which occur when the chemical constitution of a compound is altered.

Attempts to obtain such correlations were begun by Vorländer and Lehmann soon after the discovery of the first mesomorphic compound in 1888. The fact that attempts continue in this direction today, is an indication that the correlations are neither simple nor obvious. However, considerable progress has been made, and points (a) and (b) above are now much more thoroughly understood. In fact, most present-day studies centre around (c), and seek to relate quite small changes in smectic-nematic, smectic-isotropic, or nematic-isotropic transition temperatures to controlled changes in molecular shape, polarity, and polarizability. A great deal remains to be learned about this particular aspect of the problem of mesomorphism and chemical constitution, but the fact that it is a problem which can be tackled with some hope of reaching reasonable conclusions is in itself of interest. Thus, except in the most general terms, the melting point of an organic compound is unpredictable. One can make generalizations of the kind that compounds comprised of high molecular weight molecules or of highly dipolar molecules will be high melting, and that a low molecular weight and the absence of permanent dipoles will lead to low melting points. On the other hand, quite marked fluctuations in melting point are frequently observed when only relatively minor alterations are made to the molecular structure or geometry. Consider for example, the melting points for the homologous series of p-n-alkoxybenzoic acids.[1]

n-Alkyl	m.p. (°)	n-Alkyl	m.p. (°)	n-Alkyl	m.p. (°)
CH_3	184	C_6H_{13}	105	$C_{10}H_{21}$	97
C_2H_5	196	C_7H_{15}	92	$C_{12}H_{25}$	95
C_3H_7	145	C_8H_{17}	101	$C_{16}H_{33}$	85
C_4H_9	147	C_9H_{19}	94	$C_{18}H_{37}$	102
C_5H_{11}	124				

It is clear that the effect upon the melting point of adding methylene groups to the alkyl chain is largely unpredictable, with only a general trend towards lower melting points with longer alkyl chains. Yet, ascending an homologous series involves a regular and orderly change in the molecular constitution.

Taking a still simpler example, consider the effect upon the melting point of benzene of adding a methyl group. Here we find that the melting point of benzene has decreased from about $5 \cdot 5°$ to about $-95°$, and yet the same structural alteration made to nitrobenzene gives a significant increase in the melting point from $5 \cdot 7°$ to $51 \cdot 3°$ for p-nitrotoluene and to $15 \cdot 5°$ for m-nitrotoluene—only o-nitrotoluene melts lower than nitrobenzene.

Admittedly, quite regular trends in melting point are observed in certain homologous series, e.g. for the n-paraffins, but in the majority of cases it is difficult to predict even whether a given structural modification will result in a decrease or an increase in melting point, quite apart from the extent of the change which will be observed.

Now, it is hardly surprising that this is the case. The melting point of a compound marks the temperature at which a three-dimensional, ordered, geometrical arrangement of the molecules suddenly collapses and gives rise to the disordered isotropic liquid. This is a profound change indeed in the state of aggregation of the system. Now, the temperature at which this occurs will depend upon the intermolecular attractive forces—dipole-dipole, induced dipole, and/or van der Waal's —between the sides, the planes, and the ends of the molecules, and the extent to which these forces operate to maintain the regular molecular arrangement against the disturbing influences of thermal vibration, as the temperature rises. However, even if the polarizability of a molecule is high, and its permanent dipole moment is strong, the strength of the intermolecular attractive forces arising from these quantities will depend finally upon the way in which the molecules are packed together in the crystal lattice. Whilst one would expect the potential energy of the system to be as low as possible, i.e. that the molecules would arrange themselves in the solid lattice so that the maximum attractive forces would operate between them, it is the very fact that the best packing of the molecules cannot be foreseen with any accuracy which leads to the difficulties in predicting the melting points of compounds except in the most general terms.

When we ascend the homologous series of p-n-alkoxybenzoic acids, the gradual lengthening of the alkyl chain might appear to be a small and regular modification to the molecular structure, but if this modification leads to only slight but random changes in the relative arrangments of the molecules in the crystal lattices of the various homologues, the melting points will not change in a regular way along the series. Indeed, recent X-ray work by Bryan[2] shows that the p-n-alkoxybenzoic acids " appear to adopt a variety of crystal structures, each individual structure being determined by the relative weights of the aromatic and aliphatic parts of the molecule ", and that the unit cell of p-n-hexyloxybenzoic acid has a particularly peculiar nature.

The melting point of a compound is therefore affected by factors arising from detailed and unpredictable aspects of the packing of the molecules in the crystal lattice, and upon the crystal lattice type adopted.

Bearing these points in mind, it is all the more interesting to record that, for all the homologous series of mesomorphic compounds which the author has studied, the nematic-isotropic, smectic-nematic, and smectic-isotropic transition temperatures change in such a way that smooth curves may be drawn through points representing temperatures at which like transitions occur, when these are plotted against the number of carbon atoms in the alkyl chain. These smooth curve relationships will be discussed fully in the next chapter, and it is only necessary to say that a sufficient number (20) of homologous series (each of thirteen compounds) and also parts of homologous series have been found to behave in this way for it to appear that this is a general behaviour to be expected for the transition temperatures of all homologous series of mesomorphic compounds. There are of course several instances in the literature where the reported transition temperatures for members of homologous series of mesomorphic compounds do not give smooth curve relationships when plotted against the alkyl chain length. The general pattern or trend of the transition temperatures is however obvious in all these cases, and it is probable that if the compounds were obtained pure, and their mesomorphic transition temperatures determined accurately, the smooth curve relationships would be found.

Meanwhile, the main point is that, in a considerable number of cases, it is found that these regular changes in the mesomorphic transition temperatures occur as an homologous series of compounds is ascended, even when the melting points for the series are randomly distributed, e.g. as in the p-n-alkoxybenzoic acids.[1]

The observation of such regular trends in the mesomorphic transition temperatures in homologous series does of course encourage the search for other and wider correlations between changes in molecular structure and changes in the mesomorphic transition temperatures of the compounds.

Let us then consider, in a general and simple way, why such regular trends should exist for the smectic and nematic transition temperatures of a series of compounds, when no such regularities occur for the melting points. We should first remember that, with mesomorphic compounds, we are dealing with a melting process which occurs *in stages*. Unlike the non-mesomorphic compound which must pass from the three-dimensional order of the solid state to the disorder of the isotropic liquid at a given temperature, the mesomorphic compound passes through one or more ordered intermediate states before the increasing thermal agitations give rise to the isotropic liquid. Each transition for a mesomorphic compound therefore involves a much less profound decrease in

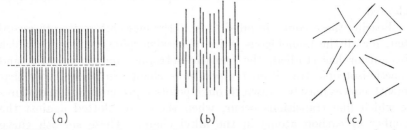

(a)   (b)   (c)

FIG. VIII.1 (*a*), (*b*), and (*c*). The changes in molecular arrangement involved on passing from (*a*) the smectic mesophase to (*b*) the nematic mesophase to (*c*) the isotropic liquid.

the state of order than that which occurs at the melting point of an ordinary compound. It is therefore more likely that the transition temperatures which mark these simpler changes in the state of aggregation may bear more direct relationships to molecular constitution than will *ordinary* melting points, at which the lateral, planar, and terminal intermolecular attractions must all weaken sufficiently for the molecules to move freely from their ordered pattern and give the disordered isotropic liquid. Let us now consider the changes which occur at the smectic-nematic and nematic-isotropic transitions.

Figure VIII.1 (*a*) represents two layers of a smectic molecular arrangement, and Fig. VIII.1 (*b*) a typical nematic arrangement which may arise from this. Figure VIII.1 (*c*) is intended to represent the disordered isotropic liquid, and the transition from VIII.1 (*a*) to VIII.1 (*b*) occurs at the smectic-nematic transition temperature. At this transition, the molecular arrangement must change by a movement of the molecules, in the direction of their long axes, out of the layers of the smectic mesophase. This movement will give the nematic arrangement, in which the molecules remain parallel to one another, but have the positions of their ends in a state of disorder. The smectic-nematic transition occurs therefore when the molecules become free to slide out of the layers. The molecular interactions which resist this movement will be the average attractions operating between the sides and planes of the elongated molecules. The terminal attractions between the ends of the molecules need not be considered for the moment from the point of view of this transition, and no rotation of the molecules from the parallel arrangement occurs.   A regular change in constitution made to a parent molecule should therefore lead to a regular increase or decrease in the average lateral and planar intermolecular attractions, which are the sole factors governing the smectic-nematic transition temperature. Considered in this light, the regular changes in smectic-nematic transition temperatures which accompany regular changes in chemical constitution are more readily understood.

The change from the nematic melt to the isotropic liquid (VIII.1 (b) to VIII.1 (c)) is certainly more complex, but less so than the change which occurs at an *ordinary* melting point. The residual intermolecular attractions which operate between the planes, sides, and ends of the molecules must loosen further, so that the molecules break away rapidly from the parallel arrangement in the swarm, which then quickly decreases in size, and gives the isotropic liquid.   The intermolecular attractive forces involved at this transition are residual attractions— the main lateral, planar, and terminal attractions having been overcome at the melting point and the smectic-nematic transition of the compound. Evidence will be brought forward later to show that the residual terminal attractions, i.e. the attractions between the ends of the molecules arranged in a head-to-tail fashion, are probably very important in determining the temperature at which the final breakdown in molecular order of the nematic mesophase occurs. Now, whatever variations occur in the side-to-side packing of the molecules in the nematic melt, the molecules remain parallel with the ends of neighbouring molecules in close proximity.   The strength of the residual terminal attractions should therefore vary consistently with variation in chemical constitution, and on this basis, a relationship between chemical constitution and nematic-isotropic transition temperature may be expected.

On grounds such as these, the difference between an *ordinary* melting point and a smectic-nematic or nematic-isotropic transition is obvious. One might legitimately say, however, that the changes occurring at the melting points of smectogenic (solid to smectic mesophase) and nematogenic (solid to nematic mesophase) compounds are also simpler than those occurring at the melting point of a non-mesomorphic compound. Why then, in the homologous series of *p*-n-alkoxybenzoic acids and in other series of mesomorphic compounds, are the melting points of the smectogenic and nematogenic compounds not regularly distributed when plotted against the alkyl chain lengths? However, the changes occurring at the melting points of mesomorphic compounds are probably more complex than they appear at first sight. Consider the two cases represented in Fig. VIII.2 and Fig. VIII.3.

Smectogenic Crystal

The reasonable assumption has been made that a stratified meso-phase is most likely to arise from a stratified solid, i.e. from a layer crystal lattice, and the work by Bernal and Crowfoot[3] makes this fairly certain. It appears that when the smectogenic crystal melts, only the terminal cohesions between the molecules are weakened, so that the strata become free to slide over one another in the manner typical of the smectic mesophase. However, it is clear that the exact location of the ends of the molecules across the layer interfaces may vary from one

Smectogenic compound   Smectic mesophase
(layer crystal lattice)

Fig. VIII.2. The change in molecular arrangement on passing from a smectogenic solid to a smectic mesophase.

crystal lattice in the homologous series to the next, and the melting points may fluctuate if these variations are big enough to affect the interlayer attractions. A further factor is that it is unlikely that the molecules in a given layer in the smectic mesophase retain the precise, ordered arrangement which they have in the crystal layer. Thus, if the packing of the molecules (rod-like) is hexagonal in the solid, one would expect a statistical variation about an average hexagonal packing in the layers of the mesophase. In other words, the attractions between the sides of the molecules are probably affected to some extent, and although these attractions remain strong enough to retain the layer arrangement, the weakening of the terminal attractions and the partial weakening of the side-to-side cohesions may both play their part in determining the exact location of the melting point. Such factors being considered, the transition from the solid to the smectic mesophase is less simple than would appear at first sight, and obviously this must be the case, because the melting points do not show regular trends as the chemical constitu-tions of the compounds are changed.

NEMATOGENIC CRYSTAL

The solid-nematic transition is obviously more complex in nature than the solid-smectic change. In the crystal, the molecules lie parallel to one another, and each molecule is locked in a regular geometrical arrangement, in which the ends of say every third molecule lie in line. In the nematic melt, only the parallel arrangement persists, the molecules are free to move, and the positions of the ends of the molecules are disorganized. The lateral, planar, and terminal cohesions must weaken profoundly at the solid-nematic transition. Now, whilst it is difficult to imagine substantial variations in the nature of layer crystal lattices, a nematogenic arrangement may change greatly from the crys-

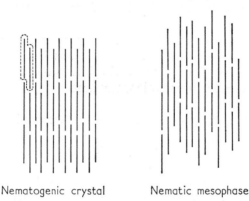

Nematogenic crystal   Nematic mesophase

FIG. VIII.3. The change in molecular arrangement on passing from a nematogenic solid to a nematic mesophase.

tal of one homologue to that of the next, and not necessarily in any regular fashion. Considering two neighbouring molecules, e.g. the ringed pair in Fig. VIII.3, the location of the end of one molecule with respect to the side of its near neighbour may be quite different in the crystal of one homologue compared with that in the next member of the series, yet all the crystals may remain nematogenic and capable of giving a nematic melt. The exact arrangements of the molecules in the crystals will determine the strengths of the lateral and planar attractions which must weaken at the melting point, and therefore the melting points of nematogenic compounds, as for those of non-mesomorphic compounds, will depend on the exact nature of the crystal packing.

Solid-nematic transition temperatures do in general fluctuate more along homologous series than solid-smectic transition temperatures. This would be expected from what has been said above, and in this context, we should again mention the work of Bryan.[2] Whilst this shows that a variety of crystal structures are adopted by the series of

p-n-alkoxybenzoic acids, the highest members (heptyloxy to decyloxy) achieve more closely packed structures which are closely related to one another, with cell constants similar to those of the long-chain normal fatty acids. It is noted by Bryan that the heptyloxy acid is the first in the series to exhibit a smectic mesophase in addition to the nematic mesophase which is shown by each of the earlier homologues from n-propyloxy onwards.

Mesomorphic transition temperatures for the changes smectic-nematic, smectic-cholesteric, and mesomorphic-isotropic therefore appear to be related much more closely to the chemical constitutions of the compounds than are melting points. For this reason, these mesomorphic transitions are interesting, and indeed, a study of them may help towards a better understanding of melting temperatures of the ordinary kind.

From what has been said, it will become clear that mesomorphic transition temperatures are a means of comparing the relative mesomorphic tendencies of compounds. Consider two compounds A and B, each of which exhibits a nematic mesophase.

Compound A   Solid-nematic (249°)   Nematic-isotropic (250°)

Compound B   Solid-nematic (148°)   Nematic-isotropic (249°)

How should we compare the relative mesomorphic properties of the two compounds? Compound A has a nematic mesophase which persists for only 1°, whilst for compound B, the phase length is 101°. However, more thermal energy has to be supplied to disorganize the parallel molecular arrangement of the nematic melt of compound A, since it passes to the isotropic liquid 1° higher, at 250°, than is required to destroy the nematic melt of compound B. The mesophase of compound A is therefore the more thermally stable, although it is exhibited over a much smaller temperature range than that of compound B. The thermal stability of the mesophase is the more important factor in relating mesomorphic behaviour to chemical constitution, since the chemical groupings give rise to intermolecular attractions which in turn determine the mesomorphic thermal stability. The rather loose phraseology that compound A is more mesomorphic than compound B is frequently used. We should remember too that the length of the mesophase is determined partly by the temperature of melting, i.e. of the solid-nematic change, and this, as has been discussed in the last few pages, is a very variable quantity.

Nematic-isotropic transition temperatures are therefore a guide to the relative nematic tendencies of compounds. Similarly, smectic-nematic, smectic-cholesteric, and smectic-isotropic transition temperatures allow a comparison of relative smectic thermal stabilities, and cholesteric-isotropic transition temperatures of relative cholesteric thermal stabilities.

Returning to the question of phase length, if we have a compound which exhibits both a smectic and a nematic mesophase, then the temperature range over which the nematic mesophase persists *is* of interest. The melting point of the compound does not affect this temperature range, which is therefore a measure of the relative thermal stabilities of the smectic and nematic mesophases of the particular compound. For a compound which exhibits both a smectic and a cholesteric mesophase, the temperature range for the cholesteric meso-phase is similarly a measure of the relative thermal stabilities of the cholesteric and smectic mesophases.

STRUCTURAL REQUIREMENTS FOR MESOMORPHIC BEHAVIOUR

Compounds which exhibit thermotropic mesomorphic properties vary widely in chemical constitution, but all possess the common feature of molecular geometric anisotropy. That is, generally speaking, the molecules of mesomorphic compounds are elongated and rod- or lath-like in shape, and that this should be a necessary requirement may be understood by using a very simple analogy. We know that the molecules in the smectic and nematic mesophases are arranged parallel to one another, if not throughout the entire bulk of the mesophase, at any rate in substantially large molecular aggregates—the swarms. When the mesophase becomes isotropic, thermal vibrations must destroy the parallel arrangement of the molecules. Now it is impossible to speak of a parallel arrangement of spherical molecules, so that a somewhat elongated molecule is an obvious necessity for the formation of an anisotropic melt. Let us imagine that the molecules are matchsticks, and that we arrange them parallel to one another on a flat surface which is made to vibrate. The vibration simulates the thermal vibration which will affect the orientated molecules when we heat the mesophase. It is obvious that a greater intensity of vibration will be required to dislodge the matchsticks from their parallel arrangement than would be required to destroy an arrangement of small, egg-shaped particles originally lying with their major axes parallel. Because of their more elongated shape, the matchsticks are better able to resist the vibration than are the more nearly spherical particles. It is now possible to say that, whilst spherical molecules cannot possibly give rise to mesophases, there is a distinct possibility that the melts of compounds which are comprised of long, narrow molecules will exhibit anisotropic properties.

However, as we shall see later, we cannot make the generalization that the longer the molecules are, the more mesomorphic the compound will be, i.e. the more thermally stable the mesophases will be, or that because the molecules are elongated the compound will necessarily be mesomorphic. Consider for example, the open chain or normal paraffins. The molecules of n-decane and n-dodecane, for instance, are very long and narrow, and fulfil the requirement of geometric anisotropy, yet these compounds do not exhibit mesomorphic properties. Even more striking examples are given by the long-chain homologues of acetic acid, which are comprised of much more elongated molecules than the hydrocarbons from which they are derived, because of the dimerization of the carboxyl groups. These dimers are linear, but the normal aliphatic fatty acids are not mesomorphic, irrespective of the length of the alkyl chain present in the molecule.

Compounds such as the normal paraffins and the homologues of acetic acid, apparently geometrically suitable for mesophase formation, exhibit no liquid crystalline properties for the simple reason that the attractive forces operating between the molecules are insufficiently strong to maintain a parallel arrangement of the molecules after the crystal lattice has melted. In predicting whether or not a compound will be mesomorphic, the nature and probable strength of the inter-molecular attractions must enter into our considerations, together with the purely geometric aspects of the molecule.

Intermolecular attractions may be divided into three classes:

(1) dipole-dipole attractions—the direct interactions between perma-nent dipoles in the molecules;

(2) Induced dipole attractions arising from the mutual polarization of the molecules by their permanent dipole moments;

(3) Dispersion forces—the attractions between instantaneous dipoles produced by spontaneous oscillations of the electron clouds of the molecules.

Between the non-polar molecules of the n-paraffins, attractions of types (1) and (2) do not operate, and the polarizability of an alkyl chain is not sufficiently high for the dispersion forces to be strong. The overall intermolecular attractions are therefore relatively low, and as we would expect, the paraffins are low-melting compounds which exhibit no meso-phases. The same considerations apply to the homologues of acetic acid. Although the monomeric molecule of a carboxylic acid would possess a dipole moment operating across the long axis of the molecule as shown in I, in the dimeric system II, the effective

I   II

unit in the crystal lattice, the resultant dipole should be zero. Dipole-dipole and induced dipole attractions will again be of little significance.

To constitute a potentially mesomorphic system, the long narrow molecules must therefore contain groups of atoms with which are associated permanent dipole moments, and the molecule itself must be highly polarizable.

Considering the last of these points first, what molecular components will contribute most to the polarizability of a molecule? Generally speaking, the polarizability of an atom increases with increasing atomic radius, and the polarizability of a bond between two atoms A and B increases with increasing bond order, i.e. from A — B to A $=$ B to A $\equiv$ B. One means of ensuring a high polarizability for the rod-like molecule would therefore be to incorporate in it polarizable aromatic rings and unsaturated linkages. Indeed we find that the majority of organic mesomorphic compounds are aromatic in character and frequently contain additional double or even triple bonds. In the aromatic compounds it is of course necessary to maintain the linearity of the system. Taking the benzene ring as an example, *ortho-* or *meta-* disubstituted benzenes do not possess linear molecules, whilst the molecules of the *para-* isomers are rod-like, provided that the substituents are of a suitable shape. For these reasons most benzene derivatives which exhibit mesomorphism are *para*-substituted, and on the same basis, we find that 4,4'-disubstituted biphenyls and 4,4''-disubstituted *p*-terphenyls are frequently mesomorphic. The following examples illustrate these points.

System	*Comments*
p-n-alkoxybenzoic acids[1]	Linear dimers, two aromatic rings, dipolar ether groups, polarizable C$=$O bond.
trans-p-n-alkoxycinnamic acids[4]	Linear dimers, two aromatic rings, dipolar ether groups, polarizable C$=$O and C$=$C bonds.
N,N'-dibenzylidene-*p*-phenylenediamine	Essentially linear molecule, three aromatic rings, two polarizable CH$=$N bonds.

The *cis-p*-n-alkoxycinnamic acids (III) do not however form linear dimers, and these compounds are not mesomorphic. If we compare (Table VIII.1) a *trans-p*-n-alkoxycinnamic acid (IV) with a *p*-n-alkoxybenzoic acid of the *same* molecular length, the cinnamic acid exhibits the more thermally stable smectic and/or nematic mesophase. This

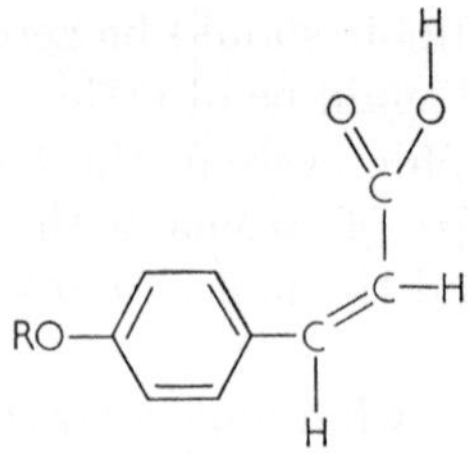

III 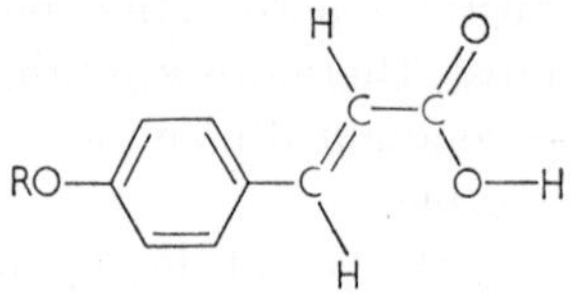   IV

illustrates that the greater mesomorphic thermal stability of the cinnamic acid must be explained, not in terms of the greater molecular length resulting from the —CH=CH— units, but rather by the greater polarizability conferred on the dimeric molecule by the double bonds. In fact, for the series of alkyl groups methyl-decyl, dodecyl, hexadecyl, and octadecyl, the most thermally stable smectic (132·5°) and nematic (160°) mesophases for the benzoic acids are *less* thermally stable than the least thermally stable smectic (144°) and nematic (165°) mesophases for the cinnamic acids.

TABLE VIII.1

Compound	Smectic-nematic (°)	Nematic-isotropic (°)
p-n-octyloxybenzoic acid	108	147
trans-p-n-octyloxycinnamic acid	146	174·5
p-n-dodecyloxybenzoic acid	129	137
p-n-propyloxybenzoic acid	—	154
p-n-decyloxybenzoic acid	122	142
4'-n-propyloxybiphenyl-4-carboxylic acid	—	287
4'-n-decyloxybiphenyl-4-carboxylic acid	256·5	257

Table VIII.1 also includes data which permit a comparison of the mesomorphic thermal stabilities of the *p*-n-alkoxybenzoic acids[1] (V) with those of the aromatic " homologues ", the 4'-n-alkoxybiphenyl-4-carboxylic acids[5] (VI).

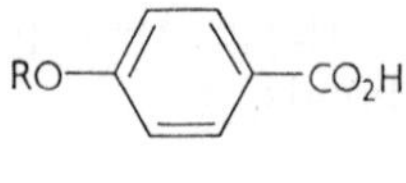

V 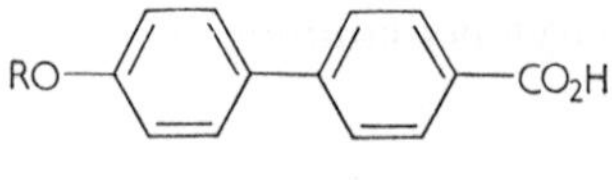   VI

The mesomorphic thermal stabilities of the biphenyl acids are very much greater than those of the benzoic acids, because there are four aromatic rings in each biphenyl acid molecule (dimeric), and only two in each benzoic acid molecule. The greater polarizability arising from the two extra aromatic rings explains the much-enhanced smectic and nematic thermal stabilities, which are not simply a function of the greater lengths of the biphenyl acid molecules. The latter point is made clear by comparing (Table VIII.1) the nematic-isotropic transition temperature of the decyloxybenzoic acid with that of the propyloxy-biphenyl acid, which has a higher nematic thermal stability.

Another simple example which illustrates the importance of molecular polarizability in relation to potential mesomorphic behaviour may now be considered. As noted above, the n-aliphatic carboxylic acids are not mesomorphic, but the analogous olefenic compound, 2,4-nonadi-enoic acid[6] (VII), is in fact liquid crystalline. In this unsaturated system, the polarizabilities of the double bonds raise the intermolecular attractions to a level suitable for mesophase formation.

$$C^9H_3—CH_2—CH_2—CH_2—CH=C^4H—CH=C^2H—C^1O_2H$$

VII

It has been mentioned above that the introduction of large atoms or groups of atoms into a molecule will increase the polarizability of the system. If such a modification is made to a molecule, the mesomorphic potential, or the mesomorphic thermal stability if the compound were originally mesomorphic, is usually *reduced* however. The reason is that a bulky atom or group, which is introduced in a position other than at the end of the molecule, will appreciably broaden the rod-like molecule. The molecules, which are orientated parallel to one another, are therefore forced further apart. Now the interaction energy associated with all three types of intermolecular attraction is inversely proportional to a power of r, the distance between the attracting centres, i.e.

Interaction energy $\propto \dfrac{1}{r^y}$ (where $y = 6$ for the gas phase)

The interaction energy will therefore fall off rapidly with increase in r, and this effect will probably more than counterbalance the increase in energy of attraction arising from the enhanced polarizability conferred on the molecule by the substituent atom or group.

This again emphasizes the fact that, although the molecule must contain groups which will give rise to suitably high intermolecular attractions, the basic requirement that the molecule should be essentially linear must not be sacrificed to any great extent. An increase in molecular breadth reduces the length:breadth ratio, and the rod-like molecule has moved at least some way towards becoming a spherical system which is structurally unsuitable for liquid crystalline behaviour.

The introduction of dipolar groups into the parent molecule will of course increase the intermolecular attractions, but again, only if the separation of the molecular axes is not increased too greatly. Thus, as will be discussed later, the introduction of a dipolar group into the side of a molecule usually decreases the thermal stabilities of the mesophases of the parent compound, because of the broadening effect of the substituent upon the molecule. The data in Table VIII.2 show that this occurs even with the comparatively small fluoro-substituent, and that a bromo-substituent may *eliminate* the mesomorphic behaviour.

TABLE VIII.2

	Smectic –nematic (°)	Nematic –isotropic (°)
$C_{10}H_{21}O$—⟨ring⟩—CO_2H ¹	122	142
$C_{10}H_{21}O$—⟨ring, F⟩—CO_2H ⁷	112	116·5
$C_{10}H_{21}O$—⟨ring, Cl⟩—CO_2H ⁷	86	90·5
$C_{10}H_{21}O$—⟨ring, Br⟩—CO_2H ⁷	—	—

We therefore return to the point that the presence in a molecule of readily polarizable aromatic rings, atoms, or groups, or of permanently dipolar groups will render the system potentially mesomorphic only if these parts of the molecule that are capable of enhancing the intermolecular attractions do not destroy the essential linearity of the molecule. Expressed in another way, the thermal stabilities of the mesophases of a liquid crystalline compound are likely to be high if dipolar or polarizable groups occur terminally (Y) or centrally (X) in the rod-like molecule, but to be low if these occur along the side of the molecule and lead to any significant increase in the molecular breadth. This is a general statement of course, and certain exceptions are known which will be referred to later.

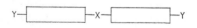

The following examples are listed to illustrate some of the above points.

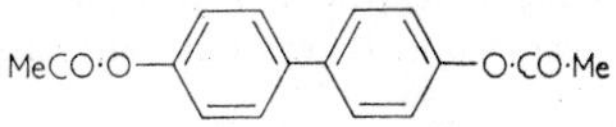

MeCO·O— ⬡—⬡ —O·CO·Me   Not mesomorphic

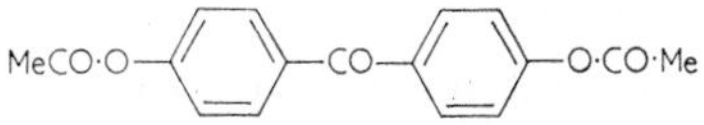

MeCO·O— ⬡—CO—⬡ —O·CO·Me   Not mesomorphic—dipolar C=O group, but not a linear molecule

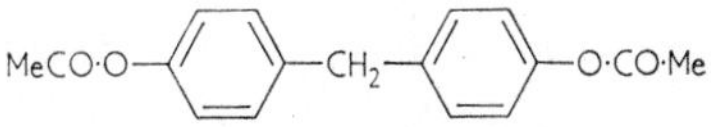

MeCO·O— ⬡—CH₂—⬡ —O·CO·Me   Not mesomorphic—not a linear molecule

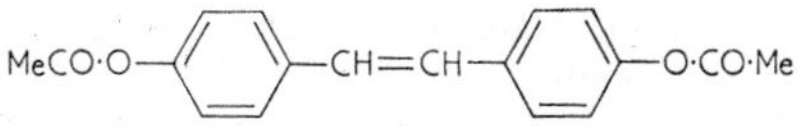

MeCO·O— ⬡—CH=CH—⬡ —O·CO·Me   Mesomorphic—the essentially linear molecules contain the polarizable C=C bond

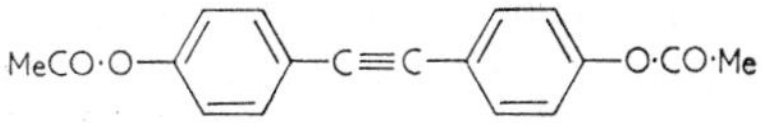

MeCO·O— ⬡—C≡C—⬡ —O·CO·Me   Mesomorphic thermal stability greater than for the analogous olefin. The molecule is more linear and more polarizable

Dimer   (naphthalene)—CO₂H   Not mesomorphic

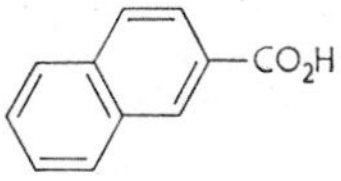

Dimer   RO—(naphthalene)—CO₂H   Mesomorphic—introduction of the dipolar alkoxy group (—OR)

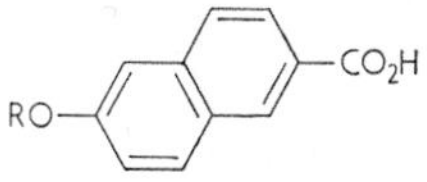

Dimer   (naphthalene, RO)—CO₂H   Not mesomorphic—the dimeric system is not linear

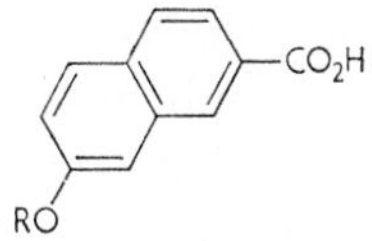

Dimer   ⬡—CO₂H   Not mesomorphic

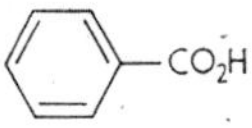

Dimer   RO—⬡—CO₂H   Mesomorphic if R=n-propyl or a longer n-alkyl chain—introduction of the dipolar group, —OR

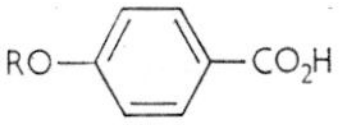

Dimer   R—⬡—CO₂H   Mesomorphic—the mesophases are less thermally stable than for the analogous ether acids which contain the more dipolar —OR group

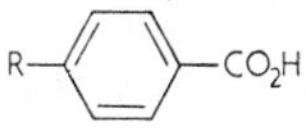

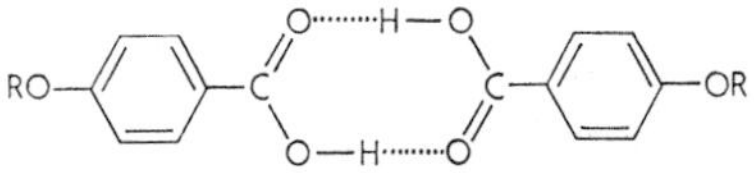

RO—⬡—C(O⋯H—O)(O—H⋯O)C—⬡—OR   Mesomorphic

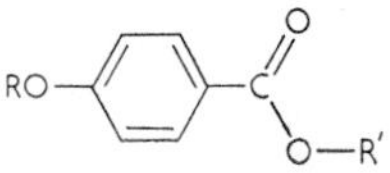

RO—⬡—C(=O)(O—R')   Not mesomorphic—the ester group is dipolar, but does not compensate for the shortness of the ester molecule

mesomorphic — characterized by a sturdy body structure.

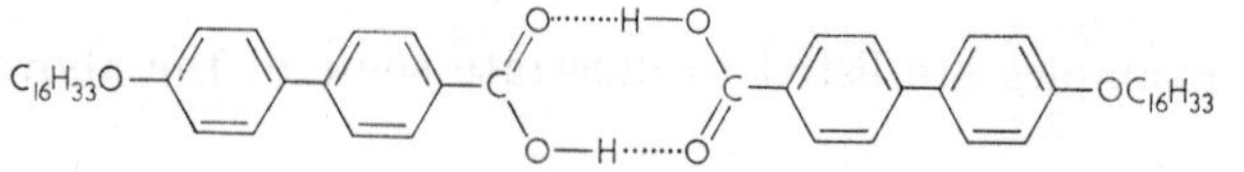

$C_{16}H_{33}O$ —[structure]— Smectic-isotropic transition at 241·5°

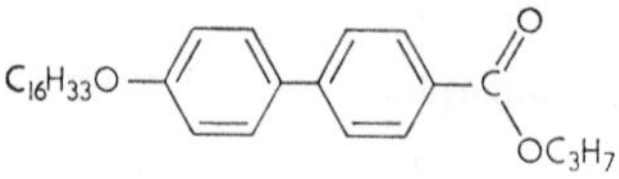

$C_{16}H_{33}O$ —[structure]— Smectic-isotropic transition at 90·5°—decrease in thermal stability from parent acid = 151°

Dimers

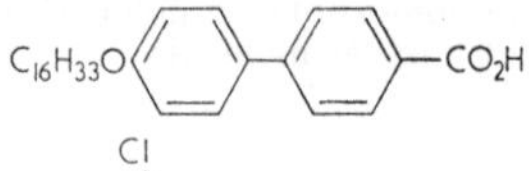

$C_{16}H_{33}O$ —[structure]—CO_2H Smectic-isotropic transition at 241·5°

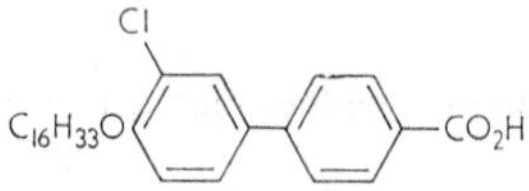

$C_{16}H_{33}O$ —[structure with Cl]—CO_2H Smectic-isotropic transition at 211°—a decrease in smectic thermal stability occurs despite the introduction of the dipolar C—Cl bond, because of the broadening effect on the molecule

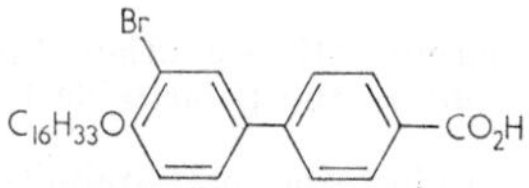

$C_{16}H_{33}O$ —[structure with Br]—CO_2H Smectic-isotropic transition at 202°—a further decrease in the smectic thermal stability occurs with the larger bromo-substituent, despite the greater polarizability of the molecule

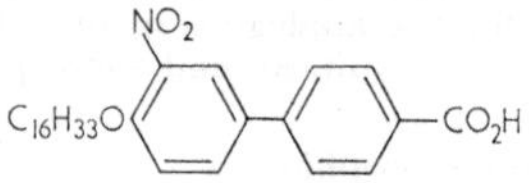

$C_{16}H_{33}O$ —[structure with NO_2]—CO_2H Smectic-isotropic transition at 198·5°—the molecular breadth increase is greater than with a bromo- or chloro- substituent, and this more than counteracts the strong dipole moment and the high polarizability of the nitro- group

Dimers

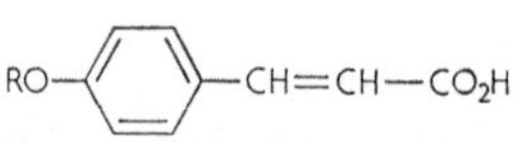

RO—[structure]—$CH=CH—CO_2H$ All homologues from R=Me to R=$C_{18}H_{37}$ are mesomorphic

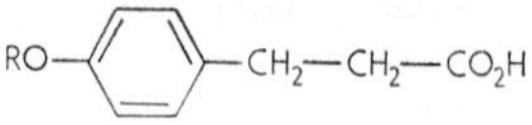

RO—[structure]—$CH_2—CH_2—CO_2H$ Not mesomorphic

In this last case, the elimination of the polarizable double bond by hydrogenation of the cinnamic acid will no doubt reduce the tendency of the system to be mesomorphic. However, this is hardly likely to be the reason for the complete elimination of the mesomorphic properties, for we know that many of the p-n-alkoxybenzoic acids,[1] which contain no polarizable olefinic link, are mesomorphic compounds. The different properties shown by the cinnamic acids[4] and the phenylpropionic acids are explained most effectively by the relative rigidities of the dimerized molecules. For the *trans-p*-n-alkoxycinnamic acids we have an essentially linear molecule (VIII). The rings, the olefinic linkages, and the dimerized carboxyl groups will tend to lie in one plane, so that conjugation may occur as far as possible, and the energy of the system be a minimum.

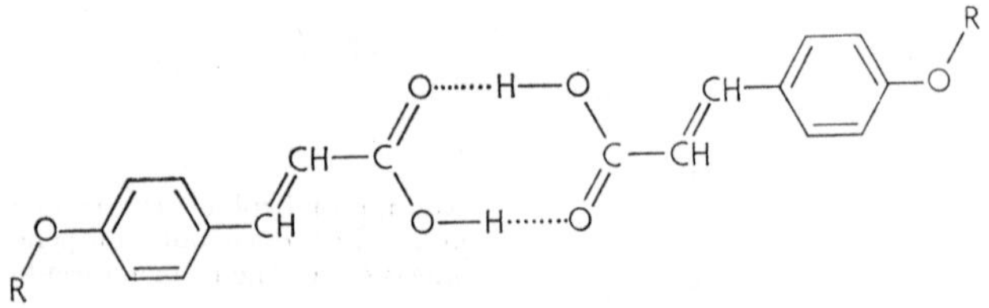

VIII

For the phenyl propionic acids we may draw structure IX.

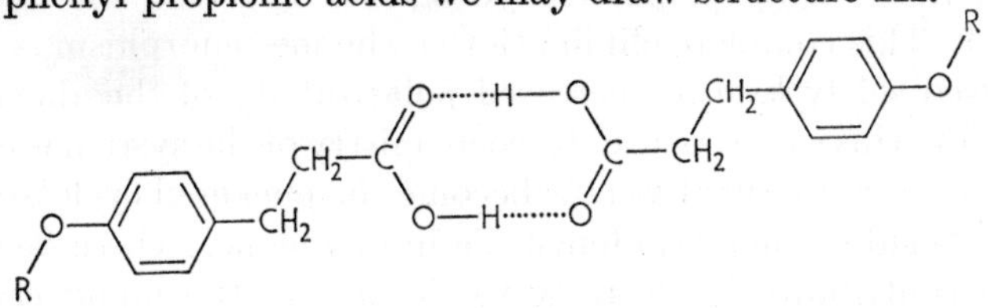

IX

Again, structure IX represents an essentially linear molecule, but the rod-like nature depends upon whether the —CH_2—CH_2— units lie in the plane of the rings and the dimerized carboxyl groups. The double methylene bridge will, however, be flexible like any other alkyl chain, and in this case it is possible that thermal vibrations cause the dimeric molecule to adopt a kinked, non-linear arrangement as a result of their disturbing influence on the —CH_2—CH_2— bridge.

An analogous case is found with the non-mesomorphic compound X,

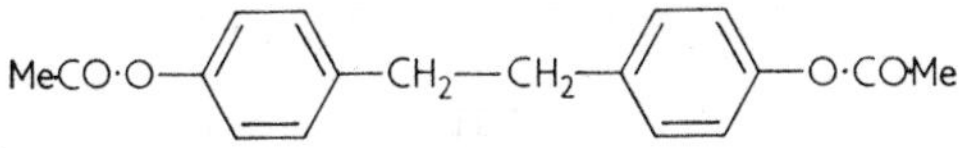

X

whereas the corresponding stilbene derivative is mesomorphic.

Similar arguments in relation to the flexibility of molecules may be applied to the general group of compounds p-$RO.C_6H_4.(CH_2)_n.CO_2H$, where n is an even number. When n is an odd number, the absence of mesomorphic properties, in for example p-alkoxyphenylacetic acids (XI), may be attributed to the non-linear nature of the dimer, as well as to the flexibility about the methylene bridge.

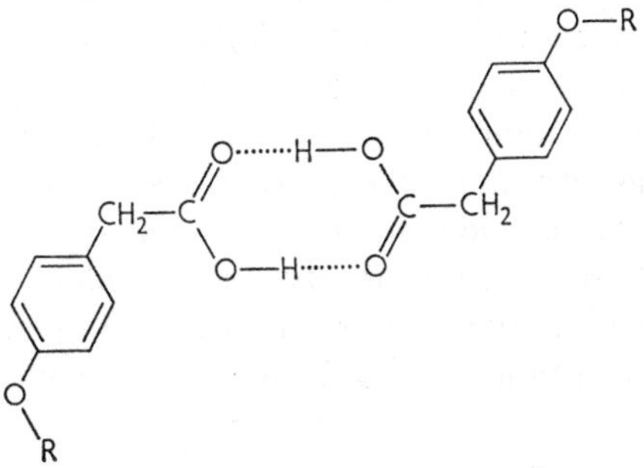

XI

The low melting points of the acids (XI) compared with the cinnamic acids suggest that the cohesive forces are indeed readily overcome.

The mesomorphic properties of the p-n-alkoxybenzoic acids are destroyed if the ring system is hydrogenated, giving the cyclohexyl compound. This complete elimination of the mesomorphism is unlikely to be caused solely by the decreased polarizabilty of the alicyclic ring system, for in this case too, the stereochemistry of the system is changed. The planar aromatic ring has now become the puckered cyclohexyl ring, and the 1,4- substituents no longer lie in one plane. These factors will obviously contribute significantly to the loss of the liquid crystalline properties.

It should be emphasized of course that we cannot generalize too widely on comments such as these made above. For example, although the 2-*p*-n-alkoxyphenylpropionic acids are not mesomorphic, it is not impossible that the compound (XII), derived from *p*-terphenyl, may be liquid crystalline. This compound has not yet been prepared, but the much higher intermolecular attractions between the terphenyl rings may

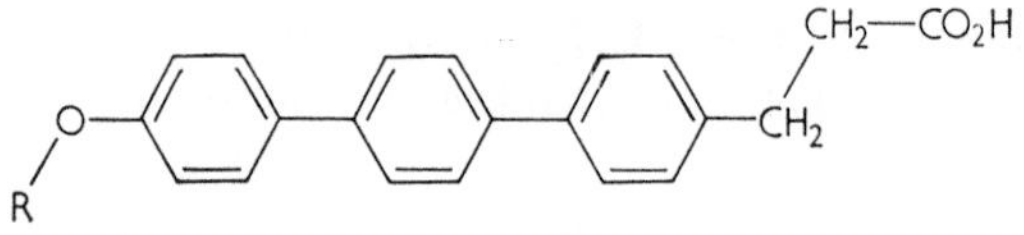

XII

be able to maintain the essentially parallel arrangement of the dimeric molecules and to resist any rotational tendencies about the $-CH_2-CH_2-$ bonds.

Similarly, although the cyclohexane analogues of the alkoxybenzoic acids are not mesomorphic, it must not be assumed that no cyclohexane derivative can be mesomorphic. Indeed, we must remember that the mesomorphic esters derived from cholesterol and cholestanol contain such alicyclic ring systems.

Hence, although the planar and readily polarizable aromatic ring system is well suited to give a potentially mesomorphic system, mesomorphic compounds can and do contain other ring systems. The molecules of such compounds may have to be larger, e.g. the cholesteryl esters, so that the intermolecular attractions are high enough to maintain an ordered arrangement in the melt, but other ring systems may give rise to quite simple, essentially linear molecules, between which strong intermolecular attractions can operate, e.g. 2,5-di(*p*-ethoxy-benzylidene)cyclopentanone (XIII). In this molecule, the two aromatic

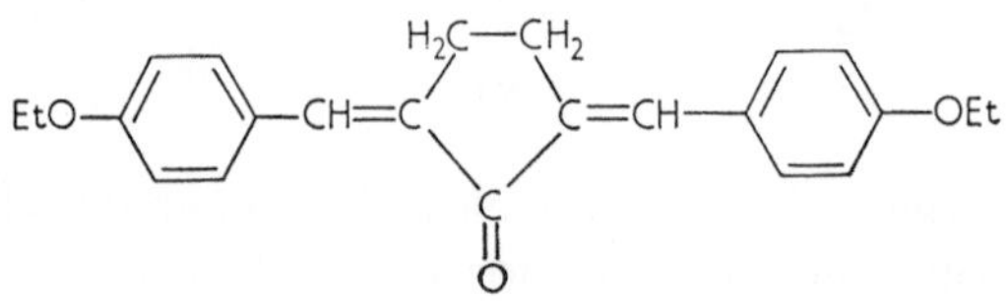

XIII

rings in the benzylidene groups and the dipolar ether groups will, of course, contribute strongly to the intermolecular attractions.

The planar pyridazine ring is very similar to the aromatic benzene ring, and this heterocyclic ring system is found in the molecules of mesomorphic compounds such as XIV, which again contain two ordinary aromatic rings.

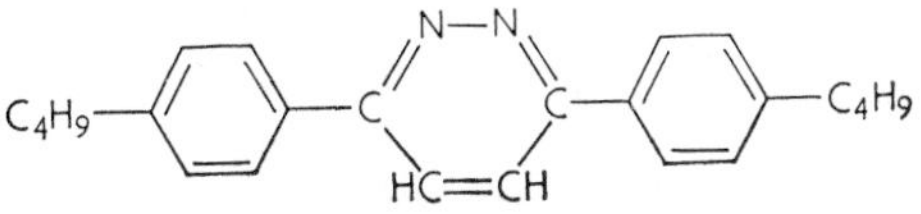

C_4H_9—⟨ring⟩—C〈N—N〉C—⟨ring⟩—C_4H_9 C_4H_9=n-butyl
HC=CH

XIV

With this background material in mind, we may now examine in more detail the question of the significance of the length of the molecule, because the tendency of a compound to be mesomorphic does not necessarily increase with the molecular length. Whilst the molecule must be geometrically anisotropic in order to favour the adoption of the required, parallel arrangement of the molecules, whether a given structural modification which lengthens the molecule of a mesomorphic compound will increase or decrease the mesomorphic thermal stability depends upon two factors:

(1) the nature of the mesophase, and
(2) the effect of the structural alteration upon the average intermolecular attractive forces.

For example, if we add a unit such as an aromatic ring to the molecule of a mesomorphic compound, the thermal stabilities of both the smectic and nematic mesophases will increase, provided that the molecule is not broadened. Thus, the smectic and nematic thermal stabilities of a biphenyl compound are higher than those of the corresponding benzene compound. Similarly, certain mesomorphic p-ter-phenyl or biphenyl compounds may have non-mesomorphic biphenyl and phenyl, or phenyl analogues, respectively, e.g.

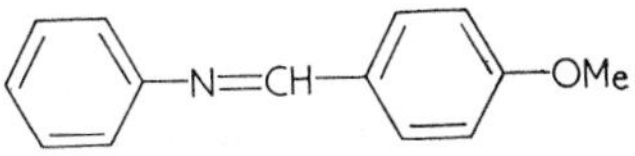

⟨ring⟩—N=CH—⟨ring⟩—OMe O_2N—⟨ring⟩—OMe

Not mesomorphic 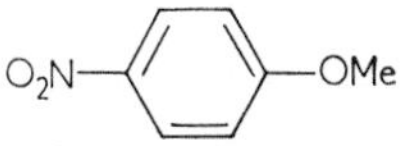   Not mesomorphic

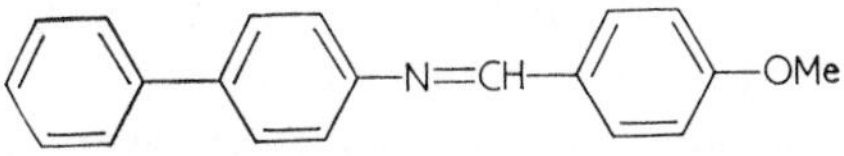

⟨ring⟩—⟨ring⟩—N=CH—⟨ring⟩—OMe O_2N—⟨ring⟩—⟨ring⟩—OMe

Mesomorphic 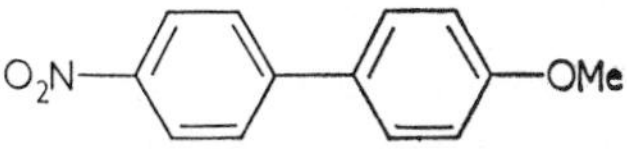   Not mesomorphic

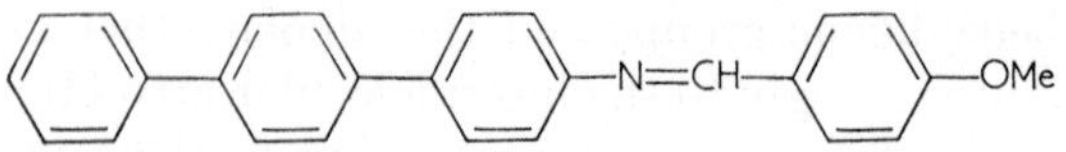

Mesomorphic

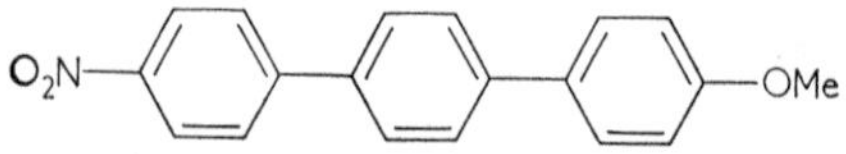

Mesomorphic

In the above cases, the length of the molecule is increased by a unit which contributes strongly to the intermolecular attractions. The result is that the enhanced cohesive forces and geometric anisotropy combine to increase the probability of liquid crystalline behaviour and to raise the thermal stabilities of the mesophases.

However, if we increase the length of a molecule by increasing the length of an alkyl chain, the position is less straightforward. Four methylene groups will increase the length to approximately the same extent as one aromatic ring, but the methylene chain will contribute much less to the intermolecular cohesions. In these circumstances, we find that on ascending an homologous series of mesomorphic compounds:

(1) The nematic-isotropic transition temperatures usually fall. Exceptions to this general behaviour are known, but systems which behave in this way are probably anomalous, and will be discussed in Chapter IX.

(2) Smectic-nematic transition temperatures rise quickly at first and then more gradually with increasing alkyl chain length.

(3) Smectic-isotropic transition temperatures may rise to a maximum early in an homologous series, and then fall steadily, although cases are known in which a steady increase occurs up to chain lengths as great as hexadecyl, before the decrease begins, e.g. in the esters XV.

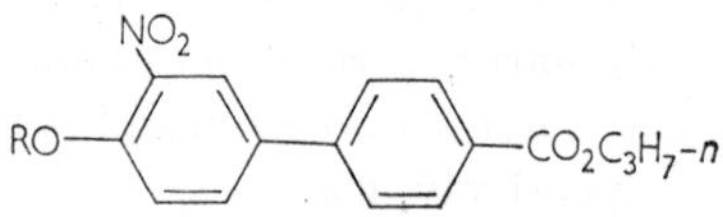

XV

Unless it is quite clear in what way a given substituent which has been used to increase the molecular length will affect the over-all intermolecular attractions, it is unwise to make predictions about the effect on the mesomorphic thermal stability of a compound. Any generalization to the effect that increase in molecular length increases the mesomorphic thermal stability would most certainly be erroneous. In all mesomorphic systems, we are dealing with a balance between the intermolecular attractions which operate between the sides and planes

of the molecules and between the ends of the molecules, and the manner
in which the relative strengths of these cohesions are influenced by the
change in length, the change in breadth, etc. is intimately related to
whether the smectic and/or nematic thermal stabilities of the compound
will be increased or decreased. The balance between the intermolecular
attractions is particularly critical in determining the effects summarized
above and observed on ascending an homologous series of mesomorphic
compounds. The detailed aspects of smooth curve relationships for the
mesomorphic transition temperatures in homologous series will be discussed in the next chapter, and at this stage it is sufficient to point out
that it is dangerous to make over-generalizations concerning the relationship between mesomorphism and chemical constitution.

The melting point of the solid presents an added difficulty in making
predictions about the potential mesomorphic properties of a compound.
For example, we may have a compound comprised of molecules which
are long, narrow, and linear, and in which there are dipolar groups which
should give strong intermolecular attractions. If, however, these intermolecular attractions are too strong, selective weakening of the cohesive
forces may not occur until high temperatures are reached, and when the
melting process does begin, the thermal vibrations may be too great to
allow an ordered arrangement of the molecules to persist. The unpredictable nature of the melting point of an unknown compound therefore
presents a very real difficulty. For instance, consider the following
examples:

(1) Since p-n-propyloxybenzoic acid exhibits an enantiotropic
nematic mesophase, we would expect that the ethyl either too would
exhibit a nematic mesophase, but of higher thermal stability. The
compound is in fact not mesomorphic, the melting point being greater
than the predicted nematic-isotropic transition temperature. The
isotropic liquid does not supercool sufficiently for a monotropic nematic
mesophase to be obtained.

(2) 2-p-n-Decyloxybenzylideneaminofluorene[8] (XVI) and 2-p-n-
decyloxybenzylideneaminofluorenone[8] (XVII) are mesomorphic, exhibiting both smectic and nematic mesophases. Propyl 7-n-decyloxy-
fluorene-2-carboxylate[8] (XVIII) exhibits only a smectic mesophase.
What mesomorphic behaviour, if any, would we expect for propyl
7-n-decyloxyfluorenone-2-carboxylate[8] (XIX)?

We might be tempted to answer that XIX will be mesomorphic and
will exhibit a smectic mesophase. In fact, we must pay regard to the
actual transition temperatures of the compounds concerned, and if we
do, we come to a somewhat modified conclusion.

By comparing the smectic-nematic transition temperatures for XVI
and XVII, we see that the smectic thermal stability has decreased by
81·5° (the effect of the C=O group, which increases the molecular

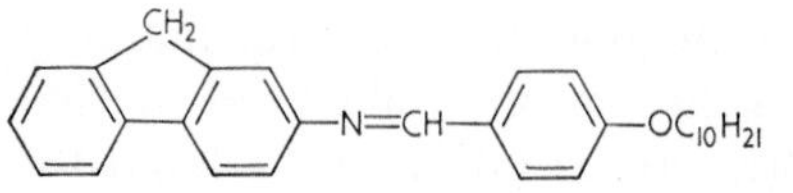

$—N{=}CH—$ ... $—OC_{10}H_{21}$ Solid $\xrightarrow{115°}$ smectic $\xrightarrow{170\cdot5°}$ nematic $\xrightarrow{181°}$ isotropic

XVI

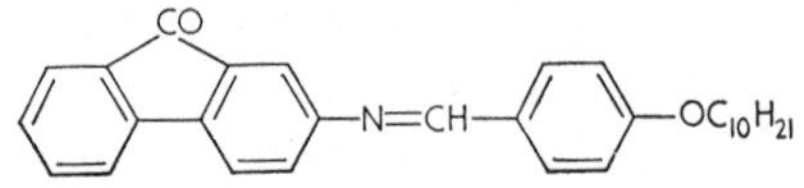

$—N{=}CH—$ ... $—OC_{10}H_{21}$ Solid $\xrightarrow{88\cdot5°}$ smectic $\xrightarrow{89°}$ nematic $\xrightarrow{139\cdot5°}$ isotropic

XVII

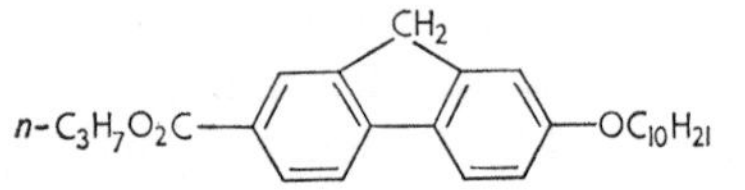

$n\text{-}C_3H_7O_2C—$ ... $—OC_{10}H_{21}$ Solid $\xrightarrow{68°}$ smectic $\xrightarrow{108°}$ isotropic

XVIII

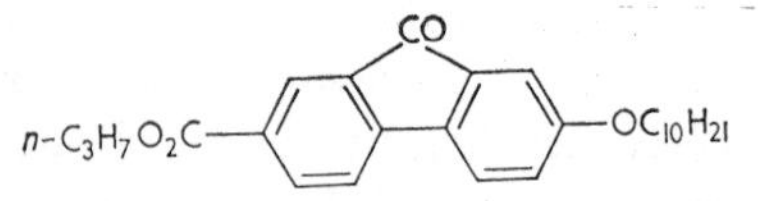

$n\text{-}C_3H_7O_2C—$ ... $—OC_{10}H_{21}$

XIX

breadth). Whilst we cannot say that this same decrease will be found between all pairs of mesomorphic fluorene and fluorenone compounds, we can say that the thermal stability of the smectic mesophase of the fluorenone ester (XIX) will be considerably less than that of the fluorene ester (XVIII). Indeed, if the same decrease of 81·5° applies on passing from XVIII to XIX, the smectic-isotropic transition temperature of XIX will be 26·5°. The melting point of the fluorenone ester would therefore have to be below 26·5° for the compound to exhibit an enantiotropic smectic mesophase. Looked at in this way, we would be more cautious about predicting smectic behaviour for XIX, and in fact, XIX melts at 96·5°, 70° higher than the expected transition temperature. No mesophase is therefore observed on heating the compound, and the isotropic melt cannot be supercooled sufficiently for a mono-tropic mesophase to appear, i.e. the melt crystallizes well above the predicted isotropic-smectic transition temperature of 26·5°. Here then we have normal melting behaviour for a compound for which mesomorphic properties might have been expected on structural grounds. This example emphasizes that melting points do not show regular trends such as those given by mesomorphic transition temperatures, and that for mesomorphic properties to appear in a compound, the strength of the intermolecular forces must be suitable—not too weak, or the ordered arrangement of the molecules will not persist after melting, and not too strong, or the crystal lattice will persist up to temperatures which are too high for the maintenance of the mesomorphic molecular orientations.

Another example may conveniently be included at this stage, since it illustrates a further important factor in relation to melting points. The compound XX, 4-acetamido-3,4″-dinitro-p-terphenyl[9] has a nematic-isotropic transition at 228°.

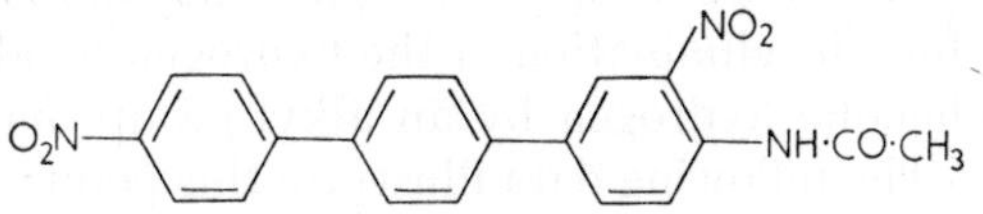

XX

Would we expect 4-acetamido-4″-nitro-p-terphenyl to be mesomorphic? In this compound we have no 3-nitro- group to broaden the molecule, and the structure should, at first sight, be more suitable for meso-morphic behaviour than that of XX.   In fact, 4-acetamido-4″-nitro-p-terphenyl melts much higher (332–333°) than the dinitro- compound, and in order that an enantiotropic mesophase be exhibited, this would have to be some 100° more thermally stable than that of XX.   The elimination of the 3-nitro- group would not increase the nematic thermal stability to this extent, and 4-acetamido-4″-nitro-p-terphenyl is not meso-morphic.   The high melting point of the compound is again responsible for the absence of mesomorphic properties, but we might have foreseen that this would be the case.   In the dinitro- compound XXI, intra-molecular hydrogen bonding will occur between the 3-nitro- group and the 4-acetamido- group, whilst in 4-acetamido-4″-nitro-p-terphenyl (XXII), the hydrogen on the nitrogen atom of the acetamido- group

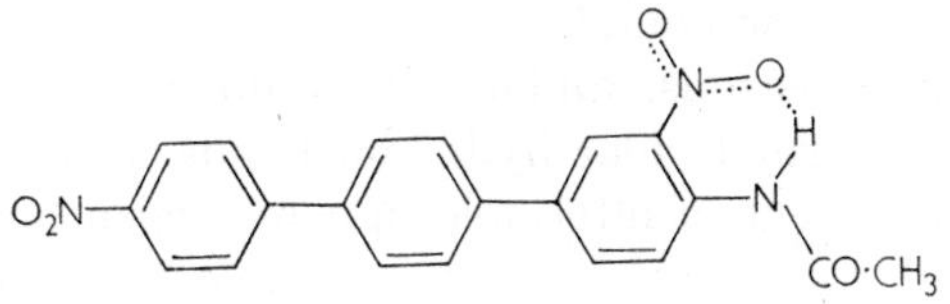

XXI

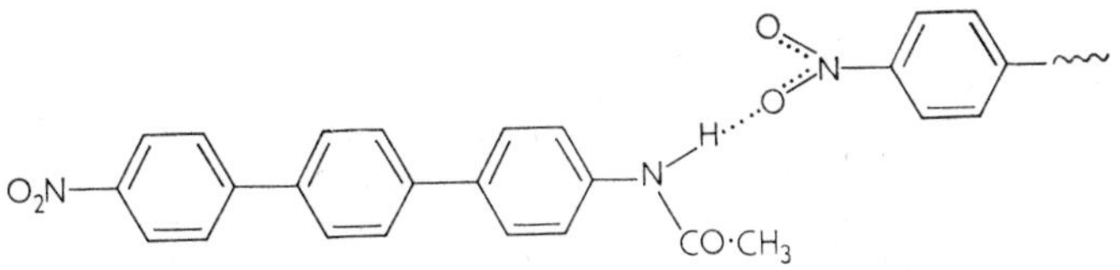

XXII

will tend to hydrogen bond intermolecularly with the 4″-nitro- group of another molecule.   Intermolecular association of this kind invariably increases the melting point of a compound (c.f. the melting points of o- and p-nitroacetanilides), in this case, the increase being more than 100°.

For these reasons, it is not usual to expect mesomorphic behaviour in any system which will give rise to intermolecular hydrogen bonding effects. The association not only increases the melting point markedly, but may *also* encourage the adoption of a non-linear arrangement of the molecules. For instance, we find that phenolic compounds are never mesomorphic, but the elimination of the hydrogen bonding by replacement of the phenolic hydrogen by an alkyl group may give a mesomorphic ether. The following data illustrate this point:

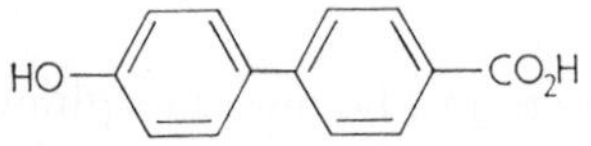

HO—⟨⟩—⟨⟩—CO_2H (dimer)   Solid $\xrightarrow{294\cdot5°}$ isotropic[5]

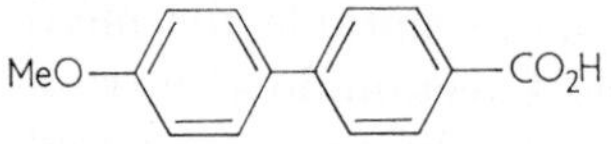

MeO—⟨⟩—⟨⟩—CO_2H (dimer)   Solid $\xrightarrow{258°}$ nematic $\xrightarrow{300°}$ isotropic[5]

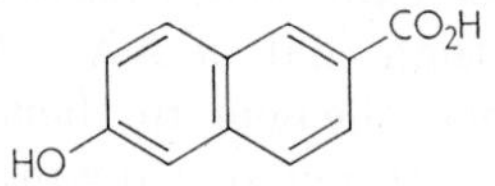

(naphthalene)—CO_2H, HO—   (dimer)   Solid $\xrightarrow{250°}$ isotropic[10]

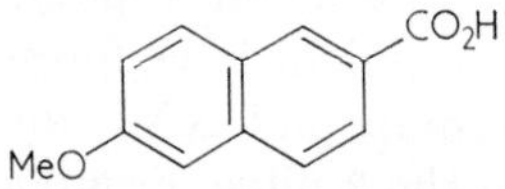

(naphthalene)—CO_2H, MeO—   (dimer)   Solid $\xrightarrow{206°}$ nematic $\xrightarrow{219°}$ isotropic[10]

The first pair of compounds shows that the effect of the hydrogen bonding is not solely because of the high melting point which it confers upon the hydroxy- compound.

For the same reasons, amines are unlikely to be mesomorphic, because of the intermolecular hydrogen bonds which may be formed. However, if the extent of intermolecular hydrogen bonding is reduced by intramolecular association, as in 4-amino-3,4″-dinitro-*p*-terphenyl (XXIII),[9] mesomorphic properties may be observed.

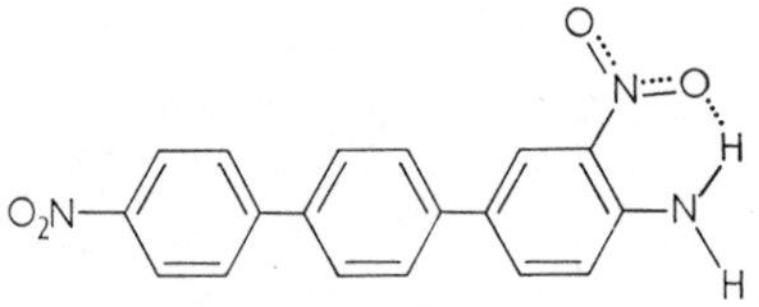

XXIII

Mesomorphic

Only one hydrogen atom of the amino- group is free to hydrogen bond.

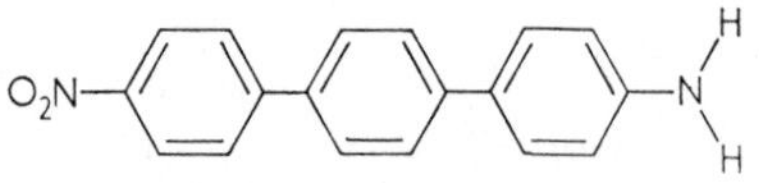

XXIV

Not mesomorphic

Both hydrogen atoms of the amino- group may participate in intermolecular associations.

4-Amino-4″-nitro-*p*-terphenyl is not therefore mesomorphic, and has a high melting point of 300–301°.

One particularly well-recognized example of intermolecular hydrogen bonding has the reverse effect, increasing the tendency to mesophase formation by greatly lengthening the molecule. This refers to the dimerization of carboxylic acids by the intermolecular hydrogen bonding of the carboxyl groups.

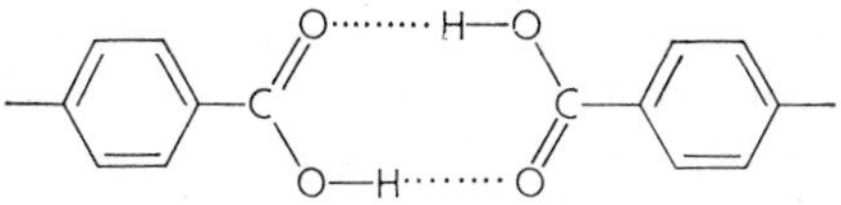

The association preserves the linearity of the molecule and increases the molecular length, maintaining the intermolecular attractions at a suitably high level. The fact that this association is necessary in order that the p-n-alkoxybenzoic acids may exhibit mesophases, is illustrated by the fact that the acids give non-mesomorphic alkyl esters. Only when we are dealing with the analogous biphenyl compounds[5] are the lengths and the polarizabilities of the monomeric esters great enough for them to be mesomorphic, although the thermal stabilities of their mesophases are much lower than those of the corresponding dimeric biphenyl acids.

From this review of the structural features of a range of mesomorphic and non-mesomorphic compounds, it is quite obviously unsafe to make broad generalizations about the molecular characteristics which are likely to lead to mesomorphic behaviour. Whilst the molecules of a mesomorphic compound should preferably have a high length:breadth ratio, it is necessary that the long molecule should be made up of a sufficient number of groups of atoms which are either permanently dipolar or readily polarizable, so that the intermolecular attractions are sufficiently great to maintain the anisotropic arrangement of the molecules. The actual length of the molecule is not therefore the sole critical factor, as might appear at first sight. On the other hand, if our molecule contains groups which lead to very strong intermolecular attractions or to intermolecular hydrogen bonding of a polymeric nature, such that the melting point of the compound is very high, then, irrespective of the molecular shape, mesomorphism will not occur. That the shape of the molecule does play an important part in determining mesomorphic behaviour is, however, clearly illustrated by the fact that increases in the molecular breadth of a mesomorphic compound lead to decreased mesomorphic properties. Again, however, a breadth increasing effect— whether it arises from the introduction of a substituent into a ring, or the branching of an alkyl chain, etc.—which may eliminate the mesomorphic properties of one particular system may only decrease the mesomorphic transition temperatures of another system in which stronger intermolecular attractions operate, and are able to counteract the increased separation between the molecules. The potential meso-morphic behaviour of a compound comprised of rod-like molecules is in fact determined by the relative strengths of the terminal and lateral intermolecular attractions. If the difference between these cohesions is such that melting occurs in stages, then mesomorphic properties will be observed. The balance between these terminal and lateral inter-molecular attractions is of course very sensitive to change in chemical constitution, and this explains why it is not possible to give simple definitions of the most suitable molecular structures for mesophase formation.

STRUCTURAL FEATURES DETERMINING THE SMECTIC OR NEMATIC BEHAVIOUR OF A COMPOUND

We should now turn to the question of whether one can define any particular molecular features which are likely to determine whether the mesophase exhibited by a compound will be smectic or nematic, or smectic and nematic, in this order, with rising temperature. Let us first consider smectogenic systems.

SMECTOGENIC SYSTEMS

Considering a simplified picture (Fig. VIII.4), in the smectic meso-phase we have layers of parallel molecules, the layers being free to move over one another. A layer arrangement of this kind will most probably arise from a layer crystal lattice (Fig. VIII.4).

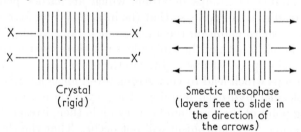

Crystal
(rigid)

Smectic mesophase
(layers free to slide in
the direction of
the arrows)

FIG. VIII.4. The change in molecular arrangement on passing from a smectogenic solid to a smectic mesophase.

The change occurring at the solid-smectic transition is therefore primarily a weakening of the molecular attractions operating between the ends of the molecules, across the planes X——X'. The cohesive forces between the sides of the molecules must be great enough to prevent the molecules from moving out of the layers to give the nematic or isotropic states. The obvious requirement for smectic behaviour is that we should have much stronger cohesions operating between the sides of the molecules than between the ends of the molecules. That is, the intermolecular lateral attractions must be considerably greater than the terminal attractions. This is likely to be the case in any system comprised of long narrow molecules, since the area of contact between the sides is so much greater than that between the ends of the molecules. Therefore, the probability that a smectic mesophase be exhibited by a compound must depend on the degree of difference between the terminal and lateral attractions, rather than upon the simple fact that a difference exists. Two points may now be made:

(1) If we have a molecule (represented by a rectangle) which carries alkoxy- groups at either end,

$$CH_3(CH_2)_n—O —\boxed{}— O—(CH_2)_nCH_3$$

and these molecules are arranged in a layer crystal lattice, then the addition of successive methylene groups should have two effects,

(a) to increase the intermolecular attractions between the sides of the molecules, because of the polarizability of each added methylene group, and

(b) to decrease the intermolecular terminal attractions (see later for a fuller discussion), because of the increasing separation of the parts (represented by the rectangle) of the molecules containing the dipolar and polarizable units.

Increase in the alkyl chain length should therefore increase the ratio of the lateral to the terminal attractions between the molecules, so making the probability greater that the layer arrangement will persist after melting, when the terminal attractions are weakened. Smectic properties are therefore most likely to be observed in the long chain members of an homologous series of mesomorphic compounds. This is indeed a well-recognized fact for many homologous series which have been studied, and will be illustrated in more detail when smooth curve relationships in such series are discussed (Chapter IX). A common pattern of behaviour is that the lower homologues are nematic, the middle members exhibit a smectic mesophase followed by a nematic mesophase, and the long-chain members, e.g. C_{12}, C_{16}, and C_{18}, are purely smectic.

Lateral intermolecular attractions are therefore important in determining smectic properties, but only in relation to the weakness of the accompanying terminal attractions. Thus, if both the lateral and terminal attractive forces were strong, the melting point of the compound might be too high for mesophase formation to result.

(2) The lateral attractive forces between elongated molecules would be enhanced by the presence of strong dipole moments operating across

the major axes of the molecules, because, with a suitable layer arrangement, dipole-dipole reinforcement would occur (see Fig. VIII.5). In an elongated molecule with a terminally situated ester group, the dipole

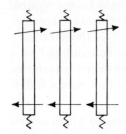

FIG. VIII.5. The reinforcement of dipole moments which operate across the long axes of molecules arranged in a layer.

moment of the carboalkoxy group will operate across the major axis of the molecule, e.g. in ethyl benzoate (XXV).

XXV

XXVI

Ethyl benzoate is not of course mesomorphic, but if we modify the structure to that of XXVI, ethyl 4'-n-pentyloxybiphenyl-4-carboxylate,[5] we now have a mesomorphic ester which exhibits a smectic mesophase. Indeed, purely smectic properties are exhibited by all

XXVII

XXVIII

biphenyl esters of the type XXVII,[5] provided that the melting points are not too high, and esters such as ethyl p-azoxybenzoate (XXVIII) and ethyl p-azoxycinnamate are likewise purely smectic. We must conclude that the strong dipole moment of the carboalkoxy group operating across the long axis of the molecule first of all encourages the molecules

XXIX

to adopt a layer lattice when crystallization occurs, and maintains the molecules in the layer arrangement of the smectic mesophase when melting takes place. The dipole of the ester group does not appear to be sufficient in itself to give mesomorphic properties, since ethyl biphenyl-4-carboxylate is not mesomorphic, i.e. in XXVII, the dipole moment of the alkoxy group, operating across the long molecular axis, is required to supplement the intermolecular lateral attractions. The n-propyl 4'-n-alkoxy-3'-nitrobiphenyl-4-carboxylates[5] (XXIX) have structures even more favourable for smectic behaviour, for here we have three dipole moments operating across the long axes to supplement the lateral cohesive forces.

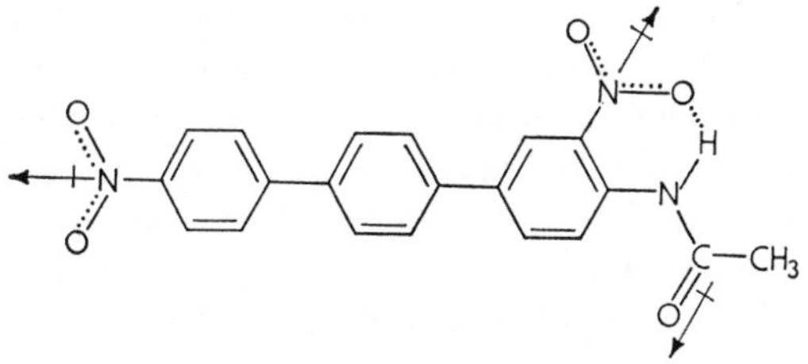

XXX

In a compound such as 4-acetamido-3,4″-dinitro-p-terphenyl[9] (XXX), the mesophase observed is nematic, not smectic, despite the strong dipole moment of the 3-nitro- group. There are two reasons for the absence of smectic properties:

(a) The dipole of the 3-nitro- group is partly cancelled by the dipole of the 4-acetamido- group, which is most likely to lie with its C=O group *trans-* to the nitro- group, and

(b) there is no dipole acting *across* the other end of the long axis of the molecule.

The purely smectic properties of the essentially covalent thallous salts of open-chain fatty acids studied by K. Herrmann[11] may now be mentioned. The free fatty acids are not mesomorphic, because sufficiently strong intermolecular attractions do not operate between the molecules of the dimeric acids. On forming the salt, we eliminate the dimerization, but introduce a dipolar group, similar to an ester group, and having a dipole which will operate across the long axis of the molecule.

Herrmann's X-ray studies on the long spacings in the smectic mesophase lead to the conclusion that, for the thallous salts of stearic and oleic acids, the molecules are arranged in double layers, with the long axes inclined to the layer interfaces. Herrmann[11] does not appear to be sure which ends of the molecules are associated in each layer, but it would seem most likely that the —COOTl ends of the molecules lie together as a result of dipole-dipole attraction. This association must lead to a cancellation of the effective dipole of each —COOTl group acting across the long axis of the molecule. However, relative to the free acids which are not mesomorphic, the lateral attractions must be enhanced sufficiently for smectic mesophase formation to occur. The great length of the alkyl chains will, of course, also contribute to the smectic characteristics.

The fact that molecules must give rise to strong lateral attractive forces in order to lead to smectic behaviour is also shown by the following data. It will be remembered that substitution of a molecule normally decreases the thermal stabilities of both the smectic and nematic mesophases, as a result of the broadening effect and the forcing apart of the molecules. In the 6-n-alkoxy-2-naphthoic acids[10] (XXXI), 5- substitution leads to quite a small increase in the molecular breadth, because of the projection of the 4-hydrogen atom. This means that substituents such as chloro- and bromo- do not decrease the thermal stabilities of the mesophases, but *increase* them, because the dipolar and polarizability effects of the substituents operate, whilst the counteracting breadth-increasing effects do not.

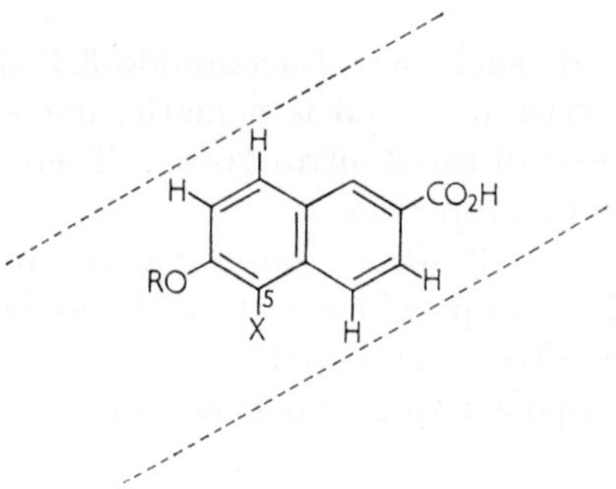

XXXI

TABLE VIII.3. *5-Substituted 6-n-Decyloxy-2-naphthoic Acids*

5-Substituent (X)	H	Cl	Br	I
Smectic-nematic transition temp. (°)	147	186·5	182·5	164·5
$\varDelta t$ (H-X) smectic (°)		+39·5	+35·5	+17·5
Nematic-isotropic transition temp. (°)	181	192·5	189·5	178·5
$\varDelta t$ (H-X) nematic (°)		+11·5	+8·5	—2·5

It is immediately obvious (Table VIII.3) that the smectic thermal stabilities are enhanced for all three 5-halogeno- compounds even with iodo- as substituent, and that the increases in smectic thermal stability are much more marked than the increases in nematic thermal stability, which are observed only with chloro- and bromo- substituents. In other words, the thermal stability of a smectic mesophase is much more influenced by a dipole moment which acts across the long molecular axis and enhances the lateral attractive forces.

The corresponding 5-nitro-6-n-alkoxy-2-naphthoic acids (XXXII) provide further evidence along these lines, for in this homologous series, whose members contain the much stronger ring-NO_2 dipole moment, nematic properties are not observed, and we have purely

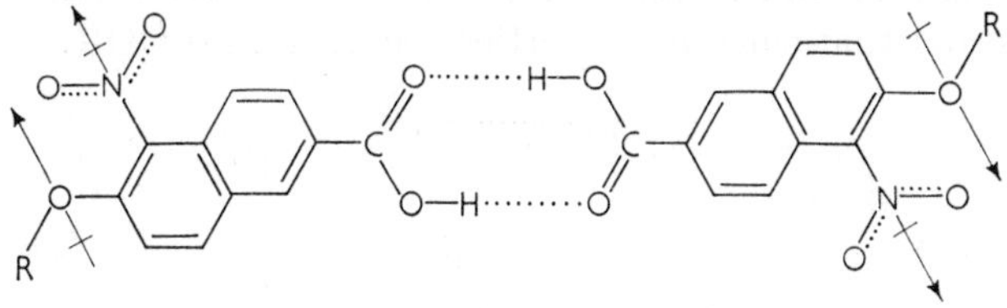

XXXII

smectic behaviour—the average smectic thermal stability for the series studied being again greater than that for the same series of unsubstituted alkoxynaphthoic acids.

In the 4′-n-alkoxy-3′-nitrobiphenyl-4-carboxylic acids[5] (XXXIII), the nitro- group exerts its full breadth-increasing effect, and the smectic mesophases are of lower thermal stability than those of the unsubstituted alkoxy acids. However, the nematic mesophases are more seriously decreased in thermal stability, and indeed cease to appear at alkyl chain lengths greater than hexyl. This adoption of purely smectic

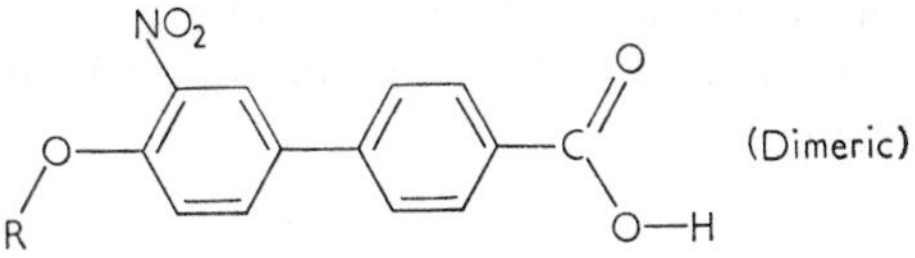

XXXIII

properties so early in the homologous series is a further example of the effect of the nitro- group, which by its dipole moment maintains the ratio of the lateral to the terminal intermolecular attractions at a high level, despite the broadening effect which it has on the molecule.

Whilst it is once more difficult to define exactly the types of molecular structure which will result in smectic properties, it may be said that any system comprised of elongated molecules, for which the ratio of the lateral to the terminal attractions is high, is likely to be smectic. Such a ratio of the intermolecular attractions may arise through having sufficiently long alkoxy groups (C_{12}, C_{16}, C_{18}) attached to suitable aromatic ring systems carrying dipolar groups, or in less elongated molecules, such as the biphenyl esters, provided that these molecules possess at least one strong dipole moment acting across each end of their long axes. If, however, a dipolar group increases the molecular breadth, the smectogenic tendencies will be reduced, unless the dipole is strong enough to counterbalance the decrease in thermal stability arising from the increased molecular separation.

When we remember that p-n-propoxybenzoic acid[1] (XXXIV) is a nematogenic compound, despite the presence of the two alkoxy groups with their dipoles operating across the long molecular axis, we might postulate that one of the dipoles must be stronger than that of an ether group in order that smectic properties occur, e.g. —COOR.

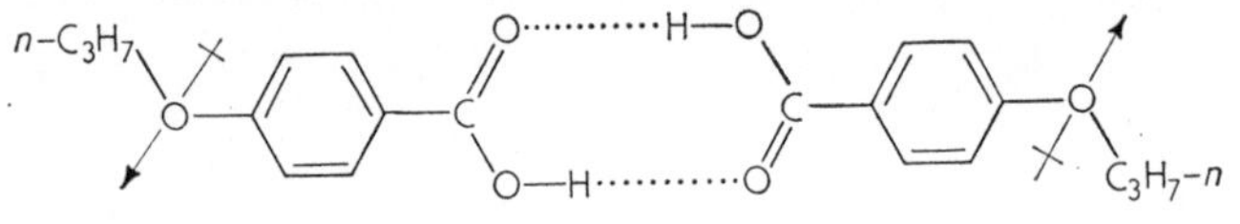

XXXIV

However, the strengths of the dipole moments required for smectic behaviour will depend upon the length of the molecule in question. The above acid dimer represents a considerably longer molecule that that of an alkoxybiphenyl ester, and there is not such a high concentration of dipole moment in the dimer molecule. Moreover, *terminal* attractions between the dipolar groups of the shorter alkyl chain alkoxy acids will reduce the ratio of the lateral to the terminal attractions and favour the occurrence of nematic properties (see pages 174 and 185).

A further type of purely smectic compound may now be mentioned— the 4-p-n-alkoxybenzylideneamino-3'-bromobiphenyls [12,13] (XXXV), which have been examined with the alkoxy groups heptyloxy, octyloxy, nonyloxy, and decyloxy.

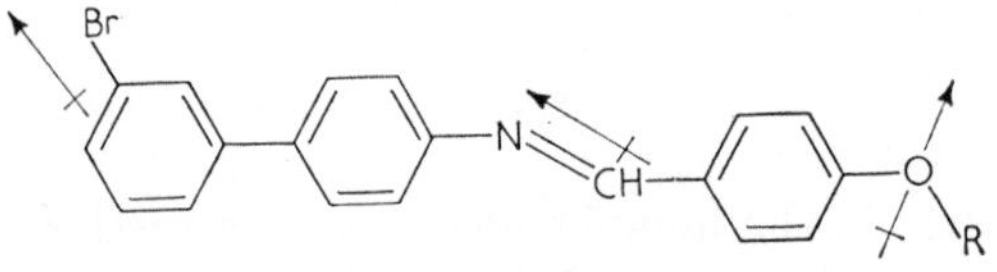

XXXV

For the unbrominated system, we find the usual pattern of behaviour for the homologous series, i.e. nematic mesophases from methyl to butyl, smectic and nematic mesophases from pentyl to decyl, and smectic mesophases alone from dodecyl to octadecyl. The 3'-bromo- substituent has the effect of introducing a third dipole moment, and the smectic forming tendency is now such that the shortest chain ether so far examined, R = heptyl, exhibits purely smectic behaviour. However, this does not mean that the *thermal stabilities* of the smectic mesophases are enhanced by the 3'-bromo- substituent. Quite the reverse is the case, and considering the average transition temperatures for the heptyl-decyl ethers, the smectic thermal stability decreases by 27·9° from the unsubstituted system. The breadth-increasing effect of the 3'-bromo-substituent therefore decreases the lateral attractions more than the dipole moment and polarizability of the C—Br bond tend to increase them.

The corresponding 3'-chloro- compounds[12,13] are also purely smectic in behaviour, but the mesophases are again less thermally stable than those of the analogous unsubstituted compounds—average decrease in smectic thermal stability (heptyl-decyl) = 17°. The 3'-methyl deriva-tives[12,13] possessing the much weaker Me-ring dipole, exhibit nematic mesophases in addition to smectic mesophases in the case of the heptyl and octyl ethers, and the average decrease in smectic thermal stability (heptyl-decyl) from the unsubstituted compounds is now 37·5°, i.e. the broadening effect of the methyl group is less effectively counteracted because of the smaller Me-ring dipole.

It is not easy to resolve this problem concerning the exact signifi-cance of the number, the distribution, and the strengths of the dipole moments in relation to the smectogenic tendencies of a compound. If we take the 3'-chloro- compounds as our model (XXXVI), and move the chloro- substituent gradually nearer to the —N=CH— link, i.e. into

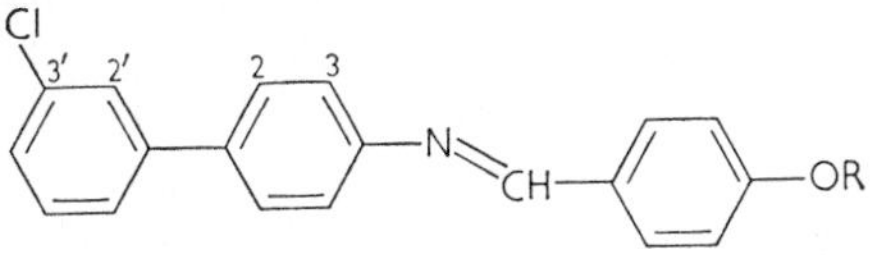

XXXVI

the 2'-, 2-, and 3- positions, in an attempt to study the effect upon the smectic tendencies, we introduce certain complications. Thus, in the 2'- and 2-chloro- compounds, the benzene rings of the biphenyl nucleus are probably rotated out of the planar arrangement by the steric effect of the substituent. This will force the molecules apart and reduce the lateral attractions, so that the fact that the heptyl to decyl ethers of the two compounds exhibit both smectic and nematic mesophases of very low thermal stability[12,13] cannot be related directly to the movement of the ring-Cl dipole nearer to the —N=CH— link. In the 3-chloro- com-pounds[12,13], purely nematic properties are in fact observed, but again, the *ortho*- disposition of the chloro- substituent and the —N=CH— group may lead to complicating features such as dipole cancellation or even a steric effect.

Unanswered problems do therefore exist in connection with the number of dipoles which must be present in a molecule and how strong these must be in order that smectic properties be conferred upon a compound. The critical factor is again the relative strengths of the lateral and terminal attractions, and at present, it is impossible to be more precise than to say that two or three dipoles acting across the long axis of a molecule are likely to give rise to smectic mesophases of high thermal stability, provided that the dipolar groups do not unduly enhance the terminal attractions or broaden the molecule too greatly (see under *p*-azoxyanisole, page 185).

Whether or not a nematic mesophase succeeds a smectic mesophase is, of course, again determined by the ratio of the lateral to the terminal attractive forces. If the lateral cohesions are very strong, the temperature to which the smectic mesophase persists is high, and the thermal vibrations needed to destroy the layer arrangement are sufficiently intense to disrupt the molecular order *completely*. The isotropic liquid is then obtained. If, on the other hand, the lateral attractions are relatively easily overcome, the breakdown of the smectic order occurs at a lower temperature, at which it is more likely that a nematic arrangement of the molecules will persist.

Finally we should consider the effects of the dipole moments of terminally situated groups on the smectic tendencies of compounds. Such a study emphasizes the difficulties involved in attempting to predict the type of mesophase likely to be produced by a compound of given structure. 4-*p*-n-Nonyloxybenzylideneaminobiphenyl[8] (XXXVII) exhibits both smectic and nematic mesophases, but 4-*p*-n-nonyloxy-benzylideneamino-4'-chlorobiphenyl[14] (XXXVIII) is purely smectic. Moreover, the smectic mesophase of the 4'-chloro- compound is more thermally stable than that of the unsubstituted compound (XXXVII),

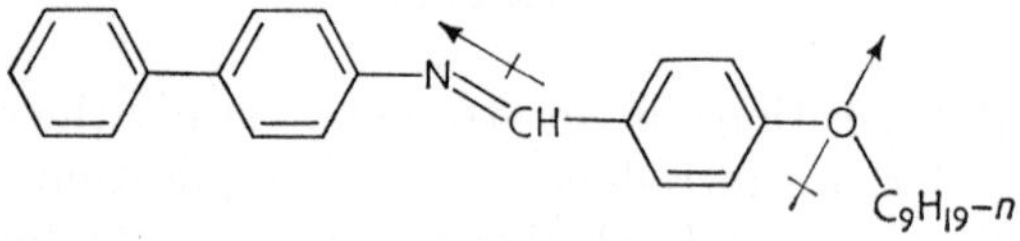

XXXVII

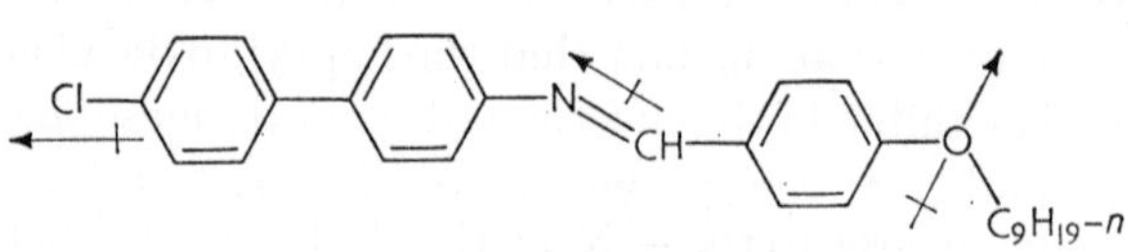

XXXVIII

and this can be explained only in terms of the terminal C-Cl dipole moment. This is somewhat surprising, for unlike the C-Cl dipole which acts across the long molecular axis in the 3'-chloro- isomer, the dipole of the 4'-chloro- substituent acts along the molecular axis. Now, if we consider a layer arrangement (Fig. VIII.6) of parallel molecules, each molecule arranged perpendicular to the layer interfaces, and carrying a terminal dipole moment as in the 4′-chloro- compound (XXXVIII), it would seem logical to assume that the terminal dipoles would repel one another and reduce the *lateral* intermolecular attractions.

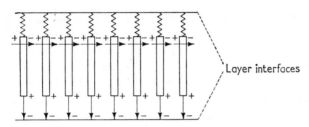

Layer interfaces

FIG. VIII.6. A stratum of molecules arranged perpendicular to the layer interface —reinforcement will occur between dipoles operating across the long molecular axis, and repulsion between those acting parallel to this axis.

The enhanced smectic properties of XXXVIII can be explained only if we imagine that the molecules are tilted at an angle to the layer interfaces. As we tilt the molecules away from the perpendicular arrangement, the separation of the negative and of the positive charges of the C-Cl dipoles does not necessarily increase, but we do bring the positive charge of one dipole nearer to the negative centre of a neighbouring dipole. At some suitable angle, the attractive forces will outweigh the repulsive forces, and the net energy of attraction will enhance the lateral attractions and the smectic properties.

Similarly, enhanced smectic tendencies have been found for the 4′-bromo- and 4′-iodo- derivatives[14] relative to the unsubstituted compound (XXXVII).

We must now postulate that terminal dipoles of this kind, acting in the direction of the long axes of the molecules, may enhance the smectic properties of the compound, provided that the molecules lie tilted to the planes of the smectic strata. The full extent of the enhancement of the smectic properties has not yet been determined by studying compounds such as XXXVIII, but carrying shorter alkyl groups. It is hoped to examine such compounds in the future, for it would be expected that the lower homologues would exhibit nematic properties. That is, the inherent smectic tendencies for XXXVII are already quite marked because of the long alkyl chain, nonyl, and the additional intermolecular attraction, possibly quite small, arising from the dipole of the 4′-chloro- substituent, tips the scales still further in favour of smectic behaviour.

As discussed in Chapter VII, compounds of the type XXXIX have been studied, using R = octyl and methyl.[15]

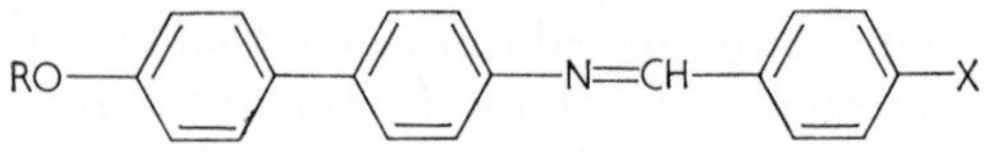

XXXIX

In line with the above discussion, which suggests that a long alkyl group R will play a large part in determining the occurrence of smectic mesophases, irrespective of the nature of X, when R = methyl, the compounds are purely nematic. Even for X = H, however, and R = octyl, the only mesophase exhibited is smectic. This is also the case for X = F, Cl, and Br, but with X = Me, MeO, n-PrO, n-PnO, NO_2, NMe_2, and $NH.CO.CH_3$, both smectic and nematic mesophases are observed. However, the interesting point is whether the substituent X enhances the smectic thermal stability relative to X = H. The order of decreasing smectic thermal stability of the compounds—in terms of the substituent X—is

$$NH.CO.CH_3 > Br > Cl > F > NO_2 > NMe_2 = n\text{-}PnO > n\text{-}PrO > Me > H > MeO$$

This order indicates no simple relationship between strength of dipole and smectic thermal stability. Thus, the nitro- group with its strong dipole acting along the long axis of the molecule yields a smectic mesophase which is less thermally stable than that for X = Cl. Also, with no terminal dipole (X = H), the smectic mesophase is more thermally stable than for X = MeO, for which the dipole acts at an angle *across* the long axis of the molecule. These facts suggest that terminal dipoles contribute to the *terminal* intermolecular attractions, either by polarization or dipole-dipole interactions, as well as to the *lateral* attractions. If such terminal attractions occur, the contribution of the dipole to the lateral attractions will be decreased, and the balance of the lateral and the terminal cohesions will be affected.

Thus, from the above order, the smectic thermal stability for X = Me is greater than for X = MeO. However, from a comparison of the *p*-n-alkoxy- and alkyl-benzoic acids, we find that the octyloxy acid exhibits a smectic mesophase whilst the analogous alkyl acid does not. Therefore, for long alkyl chains the smectic thermal stability for X = alkoxy is greater than for X = alkyl. It may be suggested that with the *longer* alkyl chains, the dipole moment of the alkoxy group participates less in dipole-dipole *terminal* interactions with neighbouring molecules, and therefore contributes more to the lateral attractions. Such factors will be less critical for the more weakly dipolar alkyl groups.

The exact part which terminally situated dipole moments play in

determining the smectic characteristics of molecules is therefore complicated by the possible dual rôle of these dipoles in affecting both terminal
and lateral attractions. That terminal groups with dipole moments
acting parallel to the long axis of the molecule cannot be relied upon to
give sufficiently strong lateral intermolecular attractions for smectic
mesophase formation is shown by the fact that 4-acetamido-3,4″-dinitro-
p-terphenyl (XXX) gives only a nematic mesophase.

NEMATOGENIC SYSTEMS

As we raise the temperature of a smectic mesophase, the thermal
vibrations eventually become great enough to overcome the strong
lateral intermolecular attractions, and the molecules are no longer maintained in their layer arrangement, i.e. the change which occurs at the
smectic-nematic transition is envisaged as a sliding of the molecules, in
the direction of their long axes, out of the smectic strata, the molecules
retaining their parallel orientation, but with no regular arrangement of
their ends, (see Fig. VIII.1 (*a*) and (*b*), page 142).

Since the primary terminal cohesions between the ends of the molecules were overcome at the solid-smectic transition, and the primary
lateral attractions at the smectic-nematic transition, the intermolecular
attractions which maintain the parallel arrangement in the nematic
mesophase must be the residual lateral and terminal cohesions, the
weaker of these two determining the nematic-isotropic transition
temperature.

Before going further, it should be repeated that the smectic-nematic
transition will not occur if the primary lateral attractions in the smectic
mesophase are too high. In such cases, the layer arrangement persists
until quite high temperatures, and when the molecules do become free
to move, the thermal vibrations are sufficient to destroy the parallel
arrangement completely. No nematic mesophase is then observed, and
the smectic mesophase passes direct to the isotropic liquid. This point
is illustrated well on ascending many homologous series of mesomorphic
compounds, when the smectic tendencies become more pronounced as
the lateral intermolecular attractions increase with growing alkyl chain
length, and the nematic tendencies become less pronounced. At a certain
stage in the series, nematic mesophases no longer appear, and we observe
direct smectic-isotropic transitions.

However, what is usually meant by a nematogenic system is a compound which melts to give the nematic mesophase, and not one which
produces the nematic mesophase as a result of the thermal breakdown
of the smectic arrangement. Now, whilst a smectic mesophase can be
produced *only* from a layer crystal lattice comprised of parallel molecules, *two* possible types of molecular arrangement may give rise to a

nematic melt. Whilst in both cases the elongated molecules must be parallel to one another, we may envisage:

(1) A layer crystal lattice which, at the melting point, passes over in one stage to the nematic molecular orientation. If this occurs, the primary lateral and terminal attractions must weaken at the melting point. Therefore, the conditions necessary for such a change are that the strengths of the terminal and lateral attractions must be roughly equal. Thus, we have the converse of the most favourable conditions for smectic mesophase formation, i.e. when the ratio of the strengths of the lateral and terminal attractions is high. Too strong lateral cohesions between the molecules are not therefore likely to lead to nematic mesophase formation.

(2) If the lateral intermolecular attractions are not particularly strong, it is probable that the layer arrangement of the molecules will not be adopted, i.e. the lateral attractions will not assist the molecules into a stratified assemblage. Therefore, as indicated by the X-ray studies of Bernal and Crowfoot,[3] an imbricated molecular arrangement in the crystal lattice is most likely to give rise to the nematic melt (see Fig. VIII.3, page 145).

In such a crystal lattice the parallel molecules are arranged in a regular manner with the ends of the molecules in a set pattern. This set pattern ceases to exist in the nematic melt, and the molecules are free to slide in the direction of their long axes. As in the first case then, the primary terminal and lateral attractions have weakened at the melting point, and as far as the changes which occur in the intermolecular cohesions are concerned, there is no real difference between the production of the nematic melt from a layer or from an imbricated type of crystal lattice.

We may say then, that if our molecule is structurally suitable for mesomorphism, in the sense that it is long and narrow and possesses polarizable aromatic rings or other groups, but contains no very long alkyl chain and no strong dipole moments operating across the long axis, then the compound is most likely to exhibit nematic properties. That is, the absence of the structural characteristics most favourable for smectic mesophase formation is as useful a criterion as any that a structure is potentially nematogenic, and the question of deciding between the possible smectic or nematic tendencies of a compound is indeed a relative one.

We have already seen that dipoles acting across the long axes of molecules contribute to the lateral attractions, and enhance the smectic forming tendencies of the system. Let us now consider two different molecules of almost identical length and shape, e.g. the two acids p-n-octyloxybenzoic acid[1] (XXXIX) and p-n-nonylbenzoic acid[16] (XL). In the dimeric molecules of the ether, there are two dipoles which act at an angle across the long axis of each molecule, but in the alkyl acid, there are no such strong dipoles present. Knowing that the octyloxy acid exhibits both smectic and nematic mesophases, we would predict that the weaker lateral attractions between the molecules of the nonyl acid would reduce the tendency to give a smectic mesophase. In fact, the nonyl acid is purely nematic in its behaviour. However, we should note that the thermal stability of the nematic mesophase of the alkyl acid is considerably lower (by about 40°) than that of the octyloxy acid, and this reminds us that the dipoles of the ether groups play some

XXXIX   XL

part in maintaining the parallel orientation in the nematic melt (see Chapters IX and X). The dipoles of the ether groups probably enhance the *terminal* intermolecular attractions, because the data already given in Table VIII.3 for the 5-substituted 6-n-alkoxy-2-naphthoic acids[10] have shown that the rôle played by the dipoles of the ring substituents are much more important as far as the smectic mesophase is concerned. The 5-substituents do not greatly increase the breadth of the molecule of the parent compound, and we find that the smectic thermal stabilities of the 5-chloro-, bromo-, iodo-, and nitro-6-n-alkoxy-2-naphthoic acids are greater than for the unsubstituted acids. The nematic thermal stabilities also show increases from that of the parent acid, but only in the cases of the 5-chloro- and bromo- substituted acids, and the increases are much smaller than for the smectic mesophase. The 5-iodo- acids have less thermally stable nematic melts than the parent acids, and the 6-n-alkoxy-5-nitro-2-naphthoic acids[10] exhibit no nematic mesophases at any stage in the homologous series, i.e. the ring-NO_2 dipole has so enhanced the smectic characteristics that no nematic orientation persists when the smectic orientation begins to break down. From the above data, it is obvious that dipolar substituents are much more likely to enhance the thermal stability of a smectic mesophase than that of a nematic mesophase.

At this stage, we should consider more closely the effect upon smectic and nematic mesophases of introducing substituents of a dipolar nature into aromatic mesomorphic systems. In most cases, these substituents will substantially broaden the molecule, unlike 5-substitution of the 6-n-alkoxy-2-naphthoic acids, where the 5-substituent is at least partly sheltered by the 4-hydrogen atom. For example, consider the 3-chloro- derivatives[7] of the dimeric p-n-alkoxybenzoic acids.

The dipole moment of each ring-halogen bond will reinforce that of the neighbouring ring-alkoxy group, presumed to lie *trans-* to the chloro-substituent for steric reasons. The molecule is substantially broader than the p-n-alkoxybenzoic acid molecule, and we must consider two effects: (a) the enhancement of the lateral intermolecular attractions arising from the increased polarity and polarizability of the substituted molecules; and (b) the decrease in the intermolecular lateral attractions because of the increased separation of the long axes of the molecules.

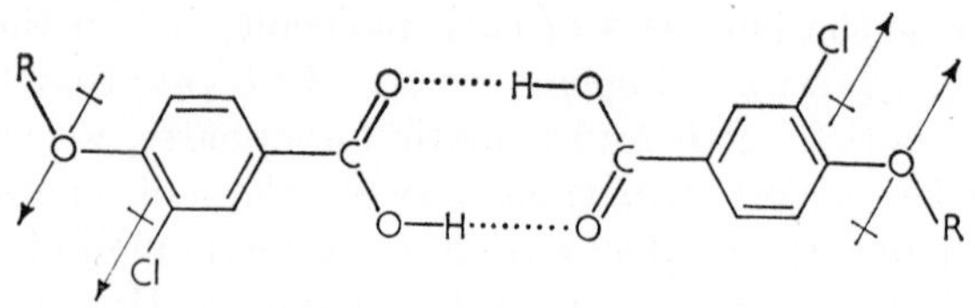

In fact, the 3-chloro-substituent decreases both the nematic and smectic thermal stabilities of the parent acid, and the larger 3-bromo- and 3-iodo- substituents completely eliminate mesomorphic properties. Effect (b) above therefore predominates. Indeed this effect is general for substituents which cause the full breadth-increasing effect, and is found for the 3-substituted *trans*-p-n-alkoxycinnamic acids[17] and 3'-substituted 4'-n-alkoxybiphenyl-4-carboxylic acids,[18] for which the data in Table VIII.4 illustrate the extent of the effect for various substituents.

TABLE VIII.4. *3'-X-4'-n-Octyloxybiphenyl-4-carboxylic Acids*

X	H	F	Cl	Br	I
Smectic-nematic transition temp. (°)	255	254·5	225	214	192·5
Decrease in smectic thermal stability from unsubstituted acid (°)		0·5	30	41	62·5
Nematic-isotropic transition temp. (°)	264·5	255·5	233	224	214
Decrease in nematic thermal stability from unsubstituted acid (°)		9	31·5	40·5	50·5

For both mesophase types, the decrease in thermal stability increases with increasing molecular breadth. This is readily understood in terms of the increase in effect (b) above, effect (a) remaining more nearly constant because of the relatively small fluctuation in dipole moment along the series of ring-halogen bonds. It will be noted that the 3'-fluoro- substituent, the smallest, only just causes a smectic thermal stability decrease, i.e. the increase in the polarity of the system almost overcomes the slightly increased molecular separation caused by the substituent.

From the thermal stability decreases in Table VIII.4, it is clear that the 3'-fluoro-substituent affects the nematic mesophase much more than the smectic mesophase, but this is not generally true for other substituents. With the chloro- and bromo- substituents, the smectic and nematic mesophases are in each case reduced in thermal stability to about the same extent, whilst the 3'-iodo-substituent decreases the smectic thermal stability more than the nematic thermal stability.

In the smectic mesophase, the molecules will be arranged as in Fig. VIII.7 (a),

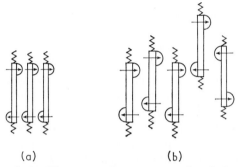

(a)   (b)

FIG. VIII.7 (a) and (b). The rectangles represent the skeleton of a dimeric aromatic carboxylic acid carrying halogeno- substituents (the semi-circles) and alkoxy groups (the zig-zag lines). The arrangements of the molecules in the smectic and nematic mesophases are represented in (a) and (b) respectively.

where the two semicircles on each rectangle represent the halogeno-substituents in the dimeric molecule. The dipoles of all the neighbouring substituents should reinforce and increase the lateral attractions. However, the rectangles, representing the ring systems, the dimerized carboxyl groups, and the alkyl chains are now separated more than in the case of the parent acid, and, as the transition temperatures show, there results a net decrease in smectic thermal stability. In the nematic melt, we have some arrangement such as shown in Fig. VIII.7 (b). The molecules must have moved apart considerably to make it possible for the molecules to slide past one another in the direction of their long axes. Since the ends of the molecules are no longer ordered in their arrangement, repulsions between the dipoles of the substituents must occur quite frequently. Presumably, however, arrangements of the molecules with their dipoles in direct opposition are disfavoured from a potential energy standpoint, and the over-all arrangement will lead to a net dipole-dipole attraction, which may, however, be quite small, and it is obvious that the lateral attractions and in particular the dipole-dipole interactions leading to attraction must be less than for the smectic mesophase. On this basis we might reason that a *large* substituent will lead to weak lateral attractions and to weak residual lateral attractions, and will therefore reduce the thermal stabilities of smectic and nematic mesophases more than will a small substituent. However, for a substituent of given size and polarity, we cannot predict the relative effects that it will have on the thermal stabilities of the smectic and nematic mesophases. For both mesophase types, two opposing effects operate—the dipolar effect increasing and the breadth effect decreasing both lateral and residual lateral attractions—and the relative extents to which the two effects cancel one another in the different molecular orientations of the two mesophase types may differ considerably. Moreover, terminal intermolecular attractions will be shown to influence nematic thermal stability, and possible variations in these cohesive forces from one substituted molecule to another introduce a further complicating feature in assessing relative effects on the two mesophase types. Finally, a rotation or translation of the molecules away from the parallel arrangement is presumably involved at the nematic-isotropic transition. The inertia resisting such movement will increase with the mass of the molecule and higher molecular weight molecules may therefore give rise to higher nematic thermal stabilities than would otherwise be expected, i.e. the effect of a large substituent on the *nematic* thermal stability may be less than that expected on the basis of the decrease in *smectic* thermal stability. The data in Table VIII.4 agree with this suggestion, since the ratio

$$\frac{\text{decrease in smectic thermal stability}}{\text{decrease in nematic thermal stability}}$$

increases with increasing mass of the halogeno- substituent from fluoro- to iodo-. This is also found for the 4-alkoxy-3-halogenobenzoic acids,[7] although the data are more limited. The figures quoted below are for the decyloxy acids.

Decrease in thermal stability (H–F) — smectic mesophase $10°$

nematic mesophase $25·5°$

Decrease in thermal stability (H–Cl) — smectic mesophase $26°$

nematic mesophase $26°$

It has already been stated that the nematic-isotropic transition temperatures for many homologous series of compounds decrease with increasing length of the alkyl chain, and Table VIII.5 presents figures in support of this statement.

TABLE VIII.5

System	Range of alkyl groups	Average decrease in nematic-isotropic transition temp.
p-n-alkoxybenzoic acids	propyl to dodecyl	17°
trans-p-n-alkoxycinnamic acids	methyl to dodecyl	25
4'-n-alkoxybiphenyl-4-carboxylic acids	methyl to decyl	43
4-n-alkoxy-3-fluorobenzoic acids	octyl to dodecyl	6
4-n-alkoxy-3-chlorobenzoic acids	octyl to dodecyl	5
trans-4-n-alkoxy-3-chlorocinnamic acids	hexyl to dodecyl	10
4'-n-alkoxy-3'-chlorobiphenyl-4-carboxylic acids	methyl to decyl	57·5
4'-n-alkoxy-3'-bromobiphenyl-4-carboxylic acids	propyl to decyl	22·5
6-n-alkoxy-2-naphthoic acids	methyl to dodecyl	45
6-n-alkoxy-5-chloro-2-naphthoic acids	propyl to dodecyl	29·5
6-n-alkoxy-5-bromo-2-naphthoic acids	butyl to dodecyl	29·5
6-n-alkoxy-5-iodo-2-naphthoic acids	pentyl to dodecyl	26
7-n-alkoxyfluorene-2-carboxylic acids	methyl to decyl	31
4-p-n-alkoxybenzylideneaminobiphenyls	methyl to decyl	14
2-p-n-alkoxybenzylideneaminofluorenes	methyl to dodecyl	37·5
2-p-n-alkoxybenzylideneamino-fluorenones	ethyl to octadecyl	11·5
2-p-n-alkoxybenzylideneamino-phenanthrenes	methyl to dodecyl	40·5
4,4'-di-(p-n-alkoxybenzylideneamino)-biphenyls	pentyl to dodecyl	91
2,7-di-(p-n-alkoxybenzylideneamino)-fluorenes	propyl to dodecyl	85·5
2,7-di-(p-n-alkoxybenzylideneamino)-fluorenones	pentyl to dodecyl	67·5
N,N'-di-(p-n-alkoxybenzylidene)-p-phenylenediamines	propyl to dodecyl	104

Whilst it should be repeated that several homologous series are known for which the nematic-isotropic transition temperatures *rise* with increasing alkyl chain length, it is considered that these series are anomalous, and they will be considered more fully in the next chapter. In the considerable number of cases for which decreases in the nematic-isotropic transition temperatures are observed as the homologous series is ascended, the smectic-nematic transition temperatures, when they occur, increase with growing chain length. This rise may be interpreted in terms of the stronger lateral intermolecular attractions for the more polarizable long-chain molecules. The decreases in the nematic-isotropic transition temperatures suggest therefore that the *residual* lateral attractions are relatively less important in retaining the arrangement of the molecules in the nematic mesophase than the lateral attractions are in the smectic mesophase. It is possible to explain the decreasing nematic-isotropic transition temperatures in terms of the lower *terminal* intermolecular attractions between the longer chain members of the homologous series. Consider for example the ends of two molecules of 4'-methoxybiphenyl-4-carboxylic acid (Fig. VIII.8).

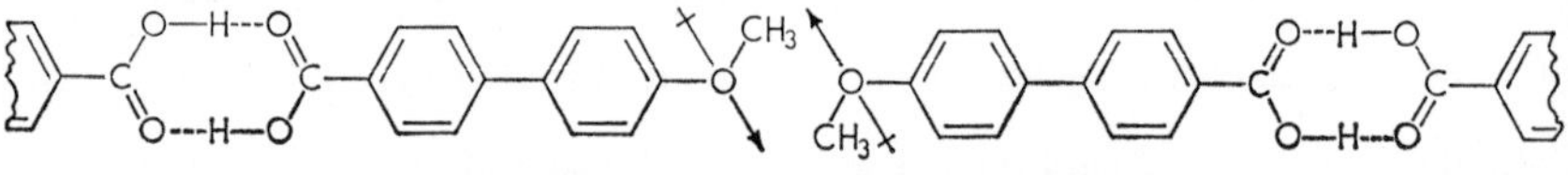

FIG. VIII.8. An end-to-end arrangement of two molecules of
4'-methoxybiphenyl-4-carboxylic acid.

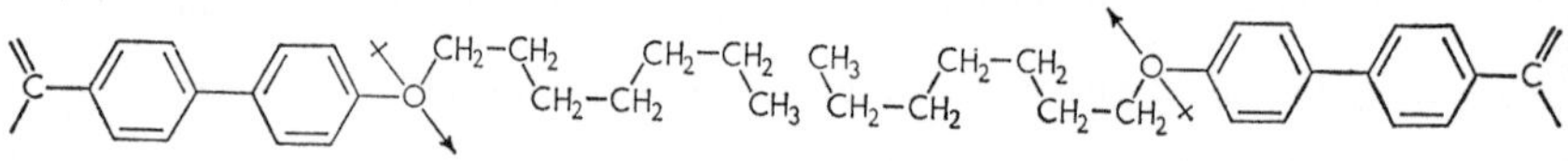

FIG. VIII.9. An end-to-end arrangement of two molecules of
4'-n-heptyloxybiphenyl-4-carboxylic acid.

Dipole-dipole and induced dipole interactions will give a net attraction between the ends of two molecules arranged as in Fig. VIII.8. If we now consider the analogous heptyloxy acid (Fig. VIII.9), the end-to-end attractions—both dipole-dipole and induced dipole—between the molecules will be lower than for the methyl ether. The terminal attractions will therefore fall off with increasing alkyl chain length as the dipolar and polarizable centres of the molecules become further separated from one another. It is not suggested that these terminal attractions are the *sole* factors involved in maintaining the molecular order, for it has already been made clear that residual lateral attractions play some part in this respect, but it *is* suggested that the changes in these residual terminal attractions with increasing alkyl chain length are responsible for the *decreasing* nematic-isotropic transition temperatures. Moreover, as will be pointed out in Chapter IX, a reasonable explanation of the *alternation* of nematic-isotropic transition temperatures, as they fall with increasing alkyl chain length, may be put forward in terms of the terminal attractions between the molecules.

Finally, let us consider other available data which relate to the effects of various terminal groupings on the thermal stabilities of nematic mesophases.

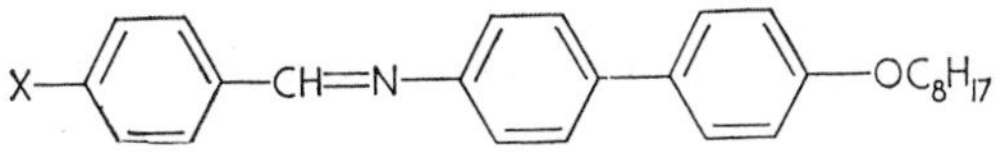

XLI

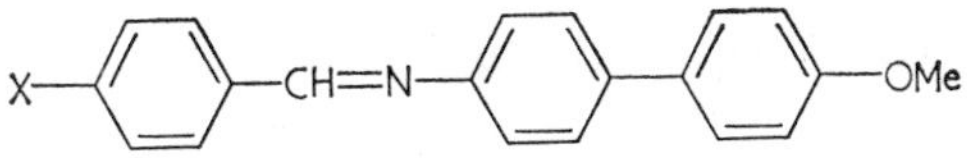

XLII

Schiff's bases of the type XLI and XLII, with terminal substituents $X = MeO-$, n-PrO-, n-PnO-, $NH.CO.CH_3$, Br, Cl, F, NO_2, NMe_2, Me, iso-PrO-, and H, have been examined[15] and the influence of these substituents on the smectic thermal stabilities has already been discussed. The nematic thermal stabilities fall from $X = MeO-$ to n-PrO- to n-PnO- as would be expected. Including only the open-chain alkoxy group $X = MeO-$, the order of decreasing nematic thermal stability for the methyl ethers, XLII, is,

$$NH.CO.CH_3 > MeO > NO_2 > Cl > Br > NMe_2 > Me > F > \text{iso-PrO} > H$$

It will be remembered that the order of terminal group efficiency for nematic mesophase formation in the mixed liquid crystalline systems studied by Dave and Dewar[19] was:

$$NO_2 > MeO > NMe_2 > Me > Cl > Br > H$$

Whilst the two orders are different, it is noteworthy that the replacement of H by any substituent X enhances the nematic properties of the system whether judged by the behaviour of a mixed liquid crystalline system or by the mesomorphic thermal stability of a pure compound. The least effective substituent is $X = \text{iso-PrO-}$. This branched group will increase the side spacing of the molecules and reduce the residual lateral attractions, but despite this, the nematic mesophase is more thermally stable than that for the compound $X = H$, by 80°. The group $X = \text{iso-PrO-}$ also increases the smectic thermal stability relative to $X = H$, in the case of the octyl ethers (XLI), but by a much smaller amount (7.5°). This again emphasizes that the *residual* lateral attractions in the nematic mesophase exert a far less dominant effect than the lateral attractions do in the smectic mesophase, and suggests that the increase in nematic thermal stability on passing from $X = H$ to $X =$

iso-PrO- is explained by the increased residual terminal attractions between the molecules.

It will be remembered that when the compounds XLI are arranged in order of decreasing smectic thermal stability, there is no obvious relationship between the order in which the substituents fall and their dipolar nature. In the case of the nematic mesophases, there is again no simple interpretation of the order for the substituents X, e.g. methyl is higher in the order than fluoro-, but at least the more dipolar groups $NH.CO.CH_3$, MeO, and NO_2 are again at the head of the order.

Of course, if the dipole moments of the terminal substituents X are enhancing the terminal attractions and the nematic thermal stabilities, it must be remembered that the interactions will not be caused solely by dipole-dipole interactions, and that induced dipole interactions operating mutually between the ends of neighbouring molecules will also be important. Bearing this in mind, the combined permanent polarity *and* polarizability of the system ring-X will be the determining factor as far as the terminal intermolecular cohesions are concerned. In this sense, a weakly dipolar substituent may lie higher in the order than a more strongly dipolar one, e.g. Me>F, if the polarizability of the former substituent is greater than that of the latter and can lead to a net increase in the attraction. The shape and size of the terminal substituent will also influence the terminal attractions, and when all these factors are taken into account no simple relationship between the nature of X and the thermal stability of the nematic mesophase is to be expected. Indeed, it is perhaps surprising that the order matches the general trend of combined permanent polarity and polarizability of the substituents X as closely as it does.

Weygand, Gabler, and Biran[20] have studied one further type of terminal substituent, an alkyl chain combining two ether functions, e.g. $CH_3O.CH_2O-$. Rather few compounds have been examined, but the data show that they have lower nematic thermal stabilities than the analogous compounds containing the group $CH_3CH_2CH_2O-$. Attempts have been made to explain this in terms of differences in the linear nature of the two groups, one containing one and the other containing two oxygen atoms, but it is equally likely that the reason lies in some interaction between the two ether dipoles. For example, the effective dipole moment of the group $CH_3O.CH_2O-$ may be a weaker resultant dipole acting along the axis of the chain (Fig. VIII.10).

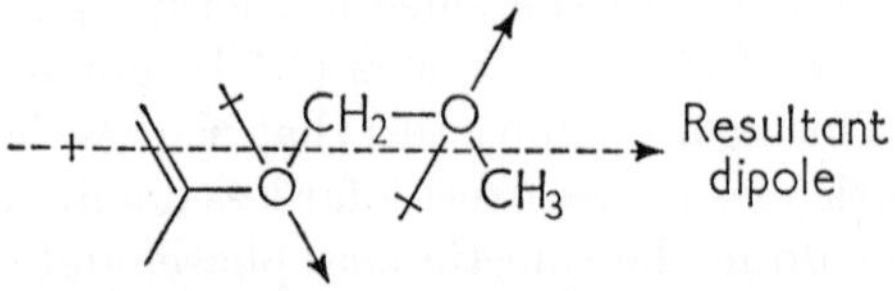

FIG. VIII.10. Partial dipole cancellation in the group $-OCH_2.OCH_3$.

The significance of such interactions is, however, difficult to assess, as, in the first place, their extent will depend upon the conformation adopted by the group $CH_3O.CH_2O$—.

It appears then that a relatively small or compact group situated terminally in a molecule will enhance the nematic properties of the compound. The effect upon smectic thermal stabilities may, however, be quite different. For instance, we may note that in the system XLI, with the exception of X = $NH.CO.CH_3$, X = MeO gives the most thermally stable nematic mesophase, but the least thermally stable smectic mesophase. This fact is emphasized in concluding this section, because, despite the obvious correlations which do exist, many factors must be taken into account when predicting either the type of mesophase to be expected for a compound or the change in mesomorphic thermal stability which will accompany a given change in molecular constitution. For example, consider the case of p-azoxyanisole (XLIII), one of the most well known of all mesomorphic compounds.

XLIII

The stereochemistry of the azoxy group is not represented accurately in XLIII, but obviously a dipole moment associated with this group will act across the long axis of the molecule, together with the dipoles of the two methoxy groups. From a consideration of the lateral attractions which could arise from these dipolar parts of the molecule, one might predict that p-azoxyanisole would be a smectic compound. In fact, p-azoxyanisole is purely nematic, the nematic-isotropic transition temperature being 134°. Our prediction should of course have taken into account the two terminal methoxy groups which we know lie high in the order of group efficiency for nematic mesophase formation, possibly by their influence on terminal intermolecular attractions. Smectic properties do indeed arise later in the homologous series of p-azoxy-phenol ethers, Weygand and Gabler[21] having observed a monotropic smectic mesophase for the hexyl ether and enantiotropic smectic mesophases in the next six homologues. Our rule concerning increased smectic tendencies with increased alkyl chain length does therefore apply to the p-azoxyphenol ethers.

In predicting smectic properties for p-azoxyanisole, we might, of course, have been influenced by the knowledge that n-propyl 4'-ethoxy-biphenyl-4-carboxylate,[5] XLIV, is a purely smectic compound. In this molecule we have again a relatively short alkoxy group, and although there is no dipole moment acting across the molecule in a central position, there is the strong dipole moment of the carboalkoxy group and the polarizability of the propyl chain of the ester group, both of which will lead to increased lateral attractions. The two systems XLIII and XLIV are not therefore so markedly different, and the nematic behaviour of the azoxy compound and the smectic behaviour of the ester may be determined in the first instance by the crystal lattice types adopted by the compounds. Thus, the azoxy group will cause some deviation from the linear representation of the molecule given above in XLIII. This may make it difficult for the system to assume a layer

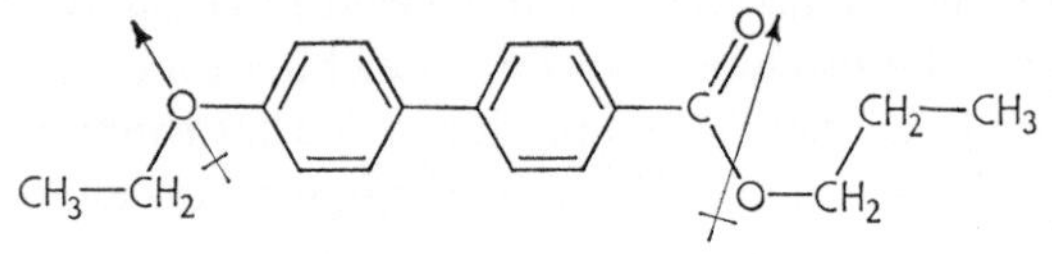

XLIV

crystal lattice conducive to smectic behaviour, and indeed, Bernal and Crowfoot[3] have shown that p-azoxy-anisole and -phenetole adopt an imbricated arrangement of the molecules in the crystal lattice, the basic pattern required for nematic behaviour.

Thus, even if we consider the disposition of the dipoles and their possible influence on terminal and lateral intermolecular attractions, the shape of the molecule is also important and may ultimately forbid the adoption of a molecular arrangement suitable for the type of mesophase we would predict for the system. Certainly it would be much easier to predict the mesophase type likely to arise from a particular system if we knew exactly how the molecules were packed in the crystal lattice, but such knowledge is rarely available except for the more simple mesomorphic systems that have been studied.

It should also be remembered that the oxygen atom of the azoxy group will protrude, beyond the aromatic rings of the molecule of p-azoxyanisole, and exert a broadening effect relative to the analogous azo- compound. This effect will counteract the increased lateral attractions arising from the dipole of the azoxy group. However, we find that p-azoanisole exhibits a monotropic nematic mesophase with an isotropic-nematic transition at 110°, 24° lower than for the azoxy compound. The nematic tendencies are therefore reduced in the azo- compounds. It is interesting, none the less, to compare the analogous azo- and azoxy compounds with alkyl chains containing nine carbon atoms in the alkoxy group, i.e. the nonyl ethers.

	Smectic-nematic *transition temperature* (°)	*Nematic-isotropic* *transition temperature* (°)
azo-	99	107
azoxy	113	121

On passing from azoxy to azo- compound, we see that the nematic and smectic thermal stabilities are reduced to the same extent, suggesting that the dipole moment of the azoxy group does not indeed contribute to the smectic thermal stability as effectively as might have been expected after a casual inspection of the molecular structure. Indeed, a comparison of the azo- and azoxy compounds containing heptyloxy groups reveals an increase in smectic thermal stability and a decrease in nematic thermal stability on passing from the azoxy to the azo- derivative. However, it is suggested that the data for the azo- compounds in particular are not completely reliable, for no mesophases of any kind are reported for the *p*-azophenol octyl ether.

The position is complicated further when we remember that ethyl *p*-azoxycinnamate and ethyl *p*-azoxybenzoate are purely smectic in character. Here, any disadvantages associated with the azoxy group as far as smectic properties are concerned, appear to be overcome, presumably as a result of the lateral attractions arising from the *two* carboethoxy groups in each molecule. These attractions appear to be strong enough to arrange the molecules in a layer crystal lattice, and to maintain this layer arrangement in a smectic mesophase after melting has occurred.

Despite the difficulties and uncertainties which do exist, the following brief summary may usefully be given in connection with the smectic and nematic tendencies of compounds, and the mesomorphic thermal stabilities of systems of differing chemical constitution.

It is clear that if a compound is to be mesomorphic—smectic or nematic—the molecules should be geometrically anisotropic,[27] preferably long and lath-like in shape. The intermolecular attractions must be sufficiently great to hold these molecules in a parallel arrangement after melting has occurred, and dipolar groups are always to be found in mesomorphic systems. These groups may be terminally or centrally situated in the molecule, and the attractions to which they give rise are supplemented by other polarizable groups such as aromatic rings which are frequently present in the molecules of mesomorphic compounds. The way in which the molecules pack together in the crystal lattice is of importance in determining the mesophase type exhibited. Thus, an imbricated arrangement of the parallel molecules may give a nematic mesophase if the melting point of the compound is not too high, but cannot give a smectic mesophase, whilst a layer arrangement in the solid may yield either a smectic or a nematic mesophase dependent on the melting point of the compound. The relative strengths of the lateral and terminal cohesive forces between the molecules are of great importance. A layer crystal lattice in which strong lateral and weak terminal intermolecular cohesions operate will probably give rise to a smectic mesophase, which, if the lateral cohesions are high enough, may persist until the isotropic liquid is formed. Weaker lateral attractions will probably lead to the production of a nematic mesophase from the smectic meso-phase, before the isotropic liquid is formed, and for systems comprised of rod-like molecules between which there is a more equal balance between the lateral and terminal attractions, the nematic mesophase will most probably be formed from the crystalline solid when the compound melts. Substituents which decrease the geometric anisotropy of the molecule will decrease the thermal stabilities of both smectic and nematic mesophases. Whilst dipole moments which operate across the long axes of the molecules appear to enhance smectic tendencies more than nematic, the precise part played by the number and strength of these dipoles in determining whether the system exhibits smectic or nematic properties is not simply defined, because this depends on the distribution of these dipoles in the molecule, i.e. if these dipoles are situated near the ends of the molecule, they may enhance the terminal intermolecular attractions and so favour nematic behaviour. For this reason, long alkyl chains in the ether group favour the occurrence of smectic properties, because the dipolar centres of molecules which are arranged end-to-end must lie far apart, and the terminal interactions will be weak. Conversely, short alkyl chain ethers exhibit nematic properties because of the lower ratio of the lateral to terminal inter-molecular attractions to which they give rise. The presence of the strongly dipolar ester grouping in a potentially mesomorphic system always appears to confer smectic properties upon the compound.

CHOLESTERIC COMPOUNDS

The majority of compounds which exhibit cholesteric mesophases are derivatives of sterols such as cholesterol (XLV). These sterol

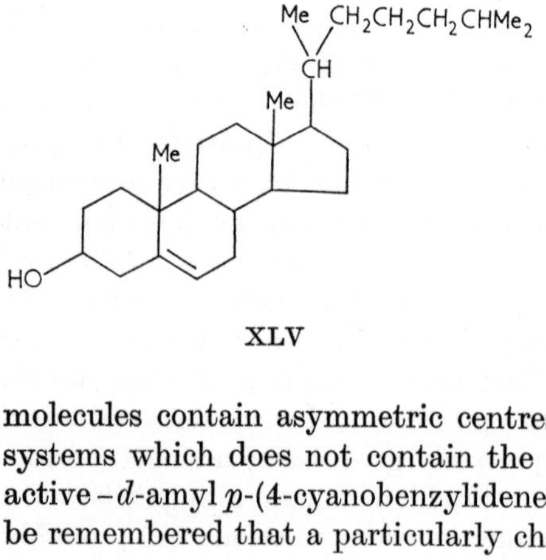

XLV 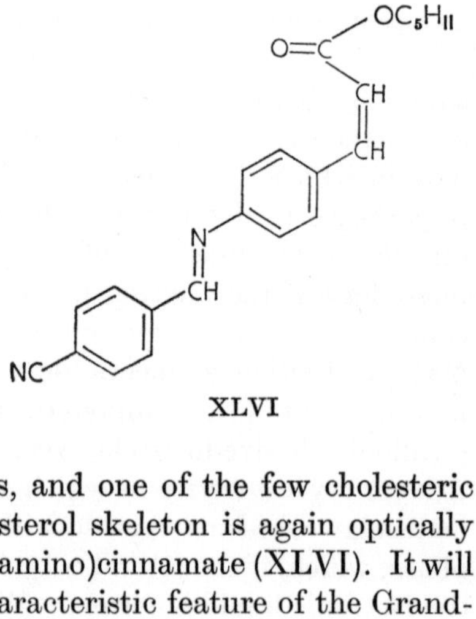   XLVI

molecules contain asymmetric centres, and one of the few cholesteric systems which does not contain the sterol skeleton is again optically active–d-amyl p-(4-cyanobenzylideneamino)cinnamate (XLVI). It will be remembered that a particularly characteristic feature of the Grandjean plane texture of the cholesteric mesophase is the extremely high optical rotatory power which it displays.

The exact nature of the molecular orientation in either the focal-conic or Grandjean plane textures of the cholesteric mesophase is uncertain, although in order to account for the optical and other physical properties of these textures, some sort of layer arrangement comprising a helical or twisted orientation of the molecules would seem to be necessary. Bernal and Crowfoot[3] have in fact shown that the solid states of both cholesteryl chloride and bromide do possess layer crystal lattices. It is often stated that derivatives of cholesterol exhibit cholesteric mesophases because of the broad, *flat*, nature of the molecules which readily pack one on top of the other to give a stratified assembly. Although the molecules may indeed pack in this way, the reason is probably not because the molecules are *flat*, an impression given when we draw a structure such as XLV. Indeed, a space-filling molecular model shows that the molecule is quite a thick, kidney-shaped conglomeration of atoms which does not look at all suitable for mesophase formation of any kind. The concept of a broad, flat molecule is obviously an over-simplification, and really we know nothing more about the relationship between molecular constitution and the tendency of a compound to exhibit a cholesteric mesophase than that a sterol skeleton or some similar molecular configuration such as XLVI is most likely to lead to this type of anisotropic behaviour in the melt. The general observation made in connection with smectic and nematic mesophases, that the molecule must be geometrically anisotropic, obviously still holds for these cholesteric systems, and it is therefore quite reasonable to suggest that the lateral and terminal cohesions between such molecules will differ substantially. The conditions are therefore suitable for melting to occur in stages. It is very doubtful, however, if we can class these molecules as rod-like in shape, and yet we must not forget that open-chain esters such as cholesteryl heptanoate and the higher homologues do exhibit smectic mesophases, which give the cholesteric mesophases only on heating to higher temperatures. The general rule that increasing alkyl chain length increases the smectic tendencies of a potentially mesomorphic compound would again *appear* to be true for cholesteric systems. However, the smectic-cholesteric transition temperatures of the fatty esters of cholesterol[22] increase only up to cholesteryl laurate and then fall steadily through the myristate, palmitate, and stearate. That is, the smectic-cholesteric transition temperature curve does not join the falling cholesteric-isotropic curve and give rise to direct smectic-isotropic transitions for the longest-chain esters which have been examined. It is not therefore true to make the general statement that the smectic thermal stability increases as the length of the ester alkyl chain increases and the thermal stability of the cholesteric mesophase decreases.   Recent work by Kuksis and Beveridge[23] on β-sitosteryl laurate and myristate does, however, appear to show that these long-chain sterol esters are purely smectic. The isotropic-mesomorphic transitions are, however, monotropic and an exact study of the mesophases is not easy; it will be remembered that the cholesteric mesophases of the long-chain cholesteryl esters do not exhibit the characteristic iridescent colours of the lower esters, presumably because the wavelength of the reflected light is beyond the visible region of the spectrum at the ultra violet end, and these cholesteric mesophases may readily be mistaken for smectic mesophases or may escape observation altogether. Indeed, cholesteryl stearate was originally reported[24] as passing direct from the isotropic liquid to the smectic mesophase, because the cholesteric mesophase was not detected.

It is not easy to assess the importance of such observations as long as we remain ignorant of the detailed molecular arrangement in the cholesteric mesophase, in its focal-conic and Grandjean plane textures. Indeed, our knowledge is so scanty that opinions are divided as to whether the cholesteric mesophase should be regarded as a modification of the smectic mesophase or of the nematic mesophase, or whether it is best to regard it as a third and separate type of mesophase.

As in the case of smectic and nematic mesophases, the thermal stability of a cholesteric mesophase, i.e. the cholesteric-isotropic transition temperature, is very sensitive to changes made to the molecular configuration and geometry. Much less work has been done in this connection with cholesteric systems than with smectic and nematic systems, and the available data on which to reach general conclusions are very limited. The work which has been carried out may be divided into the following sections.

(A) THE INFLUENCE OF INCREASING ALKYL CHAIN LENGTH ON THE MESOMORPHIC PROPERTIES OF THE OPEN CHAIN CHOLESTERYL ESTERS

The mesomorphic transition temperatures of the homologous series of cholesteryl esters[22] from cholesteryl formate to decanoate, laurate, myristate, palmitate, and stearate have been obtained. The first six esters of the series exhibit only cholesteric mesophases, and the remainder both smectic and cholesteric mesophases. The smectic-cholesteric and cholesteric-isotropic transition temperatures change in a regular manner as the homologous series is ascended. The cholesteric-isotropic transition temperatures rise to a maximum at the acetate and then fall smoothly with a regular alternation between odd and even carbon-chain esters, and the smectic-cholesteric transition temperatures rise to a maximum at the laurate and then fall off as the chain length grows. Therefore, in common with series of smectogenic and nematogenic compounds, cholesteryl esters give mesomorphic transitions which show regular trends as the homologous series is ascended. The significance of these observations is best discussed along with the behaviour of other homologous series of mesomorphic compounds (Chapter IX), but it is evident that the thermal stability of the cholesteric mesophase is very sensitive to the length of the alkyl chain. Moreover, in view of the alternation of the cholesteric-isotropic transition temperatures, the cholesteric thermal stability is probably partly determined at least by the terminal attractions between the molecules. As will be noted in Chapter IX, the shape of the cholesteric-isotropic transition temperature against chain length curve is very similar to that obtained for the smectic-isotropic transitions of the n-propyl 4'-n-alkoxybiphenyl-4-carboxylates.[5]

(B) THE EFFECT OF MODIFYING THE STEROL SKELETON IN CHOLESTERIC SYSTEMS

The cholesteric-isotropic transition temperatures are again quite sensitive to even small changes in the structure of the sterol skeleton, and the work of Wiegand[25] on esters of cholesterol (XLV), cholestanol (XLVII), and epicholestanol (XLVII) demonstrates this clearly.

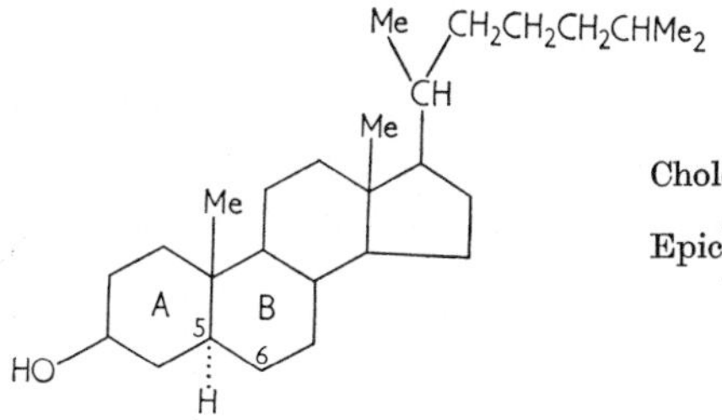

Cholestanol: rings A and B *trans*-, —OH in the
β-position
Epicholestanol: rings A and B *trans*-, —OH in
the α-position

XLVII

The esters studied and their mesomorphic properties are shown in Table VIII.6, where R.CO represents the acyl group which replaces the hydrogen atom of the —OH group in the parent sterol.

The cholesterol and cholestanol esters differ only in the presence of the double bond between the 5,6-positions of the cholesterol derivatives, and if the enhanced polarizability of the more unsaturated esters plays the same part in determining the thermal stability of a cholesteric mesophase as it does for a smectic or nematic mesophase, we would expect a decrease in the cholesteric-isotropic transition temperature on passing from the cholesteryl ester to the analogous cholestanyl ester. Two of the five pairs of esters in Table VIII.6 do not bear this out, but it should be noted that other data[26] for the p-methoxybenzoate of cholesterol indi-

TABLE VIII.6

R.CO	Cholesterol		Cholestanol		Epicholestanol	
	m.p.(°)	chol.-iso. (°)	m.p. (°)	chol.-iso. (°)	m.p. (°)	chol.-iso. (°)
C_6H_5.CO	149–150	178	136·5–137	155	104–105	——
p-MeO.C_6H_4.CO	162·5–163	236	160–160·5	239	104·5–106	——
p-C_6H_5.C_6H_4.CO	177–179	290	171–172	291	115–117	——
p-Me.C_6H_4.CO	179·5–180·5	241	171·5–172·5	225	91·5–92·5	——
o-Me.C_6H_4.CO	120–121	133	122–123	(108)	96–98	——

cate that it has higher transition temperatures than those reported by Wiegand—m.p. 175°, cholesteric-isotropic 258·5°(decomp.). Using this transition temperature of 258·5° and the one reported by Wiegand for cholestanyl p-methoxybenzoate, 239°, we now have a decrease in the cholesteric-isotropic transition temperature on passing from the cholesteryl to the cholestanyl ester, as for three of the other four pairs of esters.

The number of pairs of cholesteryl and cholestanyl esters which have been studied is, however, rather too small for us to be sure whether this is a general trend, and the fact that a change from a β- to an α- configuration of the —OH group destroys the mesomorphic properties of the esters should strike a warning note against making general statements about cholesteric systems on inadequate experimental evidence.

Wiegand also varied the location of (a) the double bond between the 5,6-positions in cholesterol and of (b) the pair of double bonds between the 5,6- and 7,8-positions in cholestadienol, and studied the influence of these changes on the cholesteric-isotropic transition temperatures of the benzoates. The system of numbering of the ring system of cholesterol is shown in XLVIII, and the transition temperatures for the esters are recorded in Table VIII.7.

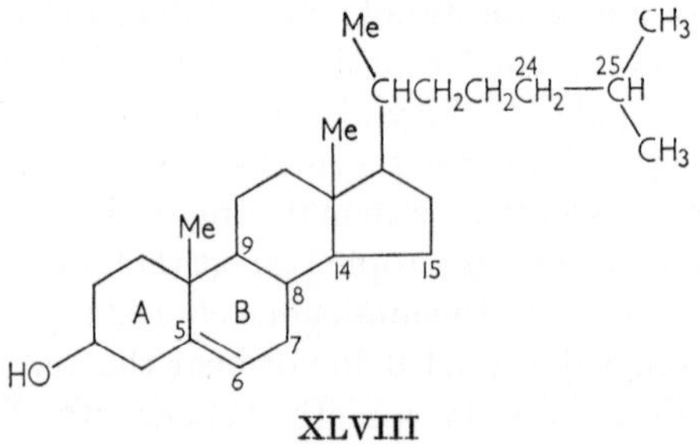

XLVIII

TABLE VIII.7.

| Parent system: cholesteryl benzoate | | | Parent system: cholestadienyl benzoate | | | |
Position of double bond	m.p. (°)	chol.-iso. (°)	Position of double bonds		m.p. (°)	chol.-iso. (°)
5,6	149–150	178	5,6	7,8	142·5–143	188
7,8	157–158	176	6,7	8,9	146	180
8,9	147	174	7,8	14,15	149–150	——
8,14	115	140	8,9	24,25	126–128	138
14,15	169–171	——	14,15	24,25	120–122	——

It is seen from the cholesteric-isotropic transition temperatures for the sterol benzoates, which possess only one double bond, that its position influences the mesomorphic properties quite markedly. Movement of the double bond within ring B has quite a small effect, but when the double bond lies between atoms 8 and 14, the thermal stability of the cholesteric mesophase falls by 38° from the cholesteric-isotropic transition temperature of cholesteryl benzoate. Further, with the double bond between atoms 14 and 15, no mesophase is detected. This last case does not necessarily imply a big reduction in mesomorphic thermal stability, because the melting point of the ester has been raised quite considerably from that of cholesteryl benzoate. The changes in the cholesteric-isotropic transition temperatures for the cholestadienyl benzoates are also difficult to assess. The introduction of a second double bond enhances the cholesteric thermal stabilities in only two cases, and two of the five diolefins in Table VIII.7 give no mesophases at all. It is obvious, however, that the movement of the double bond or bonds will affect the stereochemistry of the molecules quite markedly, and an interpretation of the data in Table VIII.7 would hardly be expected in simple terms.

(C) THE INFLUENCE OF THE NATURE OF THE ACYL GROUP ON THE MESO-MORPHIC THERMAL STABILITIES OF THE CHOLESTERYL ESTERS

Cholesterol is not itself a mesomorphic compound, and, as has been previously discussed, this is not surprising in view of the presence of the free hydroxyl group in the molecule. When hydrogen bonding effects of the free —OH group are eliminated by replacement of the group by say chlorine, we find a monotropic cholesteric mesophase in cholesteryl chloride. Most work has however centred around the acyl esters derived from cholesterol, e.g. the open-chain aliphatic esters referred to under (A) above. A more limited amount of work has been carried out on substituted benzoates of cholesterol, and it is interesting to consider the influence of the various substituents on the cholesteric-isotropic transition temperatures (Table VIII.8). The substituted benzoates are represented in general terms by XLIX.

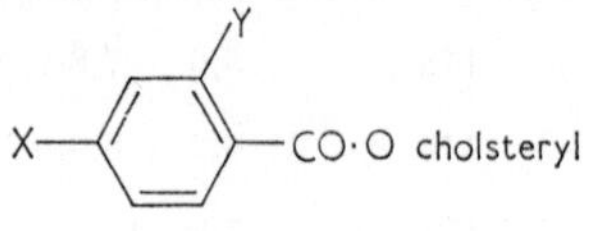

XLIX

TABLE VIII.8

X	Y	Cholesteric-isotropic transition temp. (°)	Ref.
Phenyl	—	290	25
NO$_2$	—	258–9 (decomp.)	26
MeO	—	258·5 (decomp.)	26 (236°(25))
Cl	—	245–6	26
Me	—	241	25
H	H	177·5	—
NO$_2$	NO$_2$	157	26
—	Me	133	25

The points to be noted are:

(1) *Ortho*-substitution of the benzoyl group decreases the thermal stability of the cholesteric mesophase. Thus, it would appear that substituents which broaden a molecule reduce the thermal stabilities of *all three* mesophase types.

(2) All five of the *p*-substituents enhance the thermal stability of the cholesteric mesophase of cholesteryl benzoate. A similar conclusion was obtained by studying the influence of a rather wider range of terminal substituents on the thermal stabilities of *nematic* mesophases. However, a terminal MeO group *reduces* the thermal stability of the smectic mesophase of a parent compound.

(3) In terms of the terminal substituent X, the order of decreasing thermal stability for the cholesteric mesophases is,

$$\text{Phenyl} > \text{NO}_2 \geqslant \text{MeO} > \text{Cl} > \text{Me} > \text{H}$$

Considering only the last five of the above substituents, and assuming that they occupy a terminal position in a molecule, the order of decreasing thermal stability would be (a) for the *smectic* mesophase

$$Cl > NO_2 > Me > H > MeO$$

(b) for the *nematic* mesophase

$$NO_2 > MeO > Me > Cl > H$$

The effect of a series of terminal substituents on the cholesteric-isotropic transition temperatures is therefore more closely similar to that for nematic-isotropic transition temperatures. This may be taken to mean that the cholesteric mesophase resembles the nematic mesophase more closely than it does the smectic mesophase. However, as has been pointed out earlier in this book, there also exist close similarities between the behaviours of smectic and cholesteric mesophases. Until more is known about the molecular orientation in the cholesteric mesophase, it is best to regard this mesophase as a third type of liquid crystalline state, but more could assuredly be learned about this most unusual mesomorphic state by carrying out more comprehensive studies of the influences of changes in chemical constitution on the thermal stabilities of cholesteric mesophases.

DI-ISOBUTYL SILANEDIOL

Although an examination of the structure of a molecule and the intermolecular forces to which it is likely to give rise are of great assistance in reaching a better understanding of whether or not a compound will be mesomorphic, whether the type of mesophase which is produced when the compound melts will be smectic, nematic, or cholesteric, and, relatively speaking, how thermally stable the mesophase will be, it is necessary to point out that at least one unusual example of liquid crystalline behaviour has been brought to light by Eaborn and Hartshorne,[28] who studied several dialkyl silanediols. The di-isobutyl silanediol was found to be mesomorphic, the mesophase persisting between 89·5 and 101·5°. The mesophase is optically negative and exhibits bâtonnet-like structures, but the authors consider that it is neither smectic, nematic, nor cholesteric. It is fair to say that mesomorphic properties would not have been predicted on the basis of a casual inspection of the structure of this molecule, although a system of parallel layers of molecules appears to exist in the solid state. In order to explain the liquid crystalline properties, Eaborn and Hartshorne have proposed that either (a) the system of parallel layers in the solid persists in the mesophase, or (b) the anisotropic melt involves a parallel or nearly parallel association of SiOH chains with a random lateral arrangement of groups so that the crystal structure is not preserved.

It is all the more interesting that none of the other dialkyl silanediols exhibit this mesomorphic behaviour.

This is a most important example of liquid crystalline behaviour to remember, particularly if one is tempted to over-generalize and be too dogmatic about relationships between mesomorphism and chemical constitution.

REFERENCES

1. Gray, G. W. and Jones, B. (1953). *J. Chem. Soc.* 4179.
2. Bryan, R. F. (1960). *J. Chem. Soc.* 2517.
3. Bernal, J. D. and Crowfoot, D. (1933). *Trans. Faraday Soc.* **29**, 1032.
4. Gray, G. W. and Jones, B. (1954). *J. Chem. Soc.* 1467.
5. Gray, G. W., Hartley, J. B. and Jones, B. (1955). *J. Chem. Soc.* 1412; Gray, G. W., Jones, B. and Marson, F. (1957). *J. Chem. Soc.* 393.
6. Weygand, C., Gabler, R. and Hoffmann, J. (1941). *Z. phys. Chem.* (*Leipzig*) **50B**, 124; Maier, W. and Markau, K. (1961). *Z. phys. Chem.* (*Frankfurt*) **28**, 190.
7. Gray, G. W. and Jones, B. (1954). *J. Chem. Soc.* 2556.
8. Gray, G. W., Hartley, J. B., Ibbotson, A. and Jones, B. (1955). *J. Chem. Soc.* 4359.
9. Culling, P., Gray, G. W. and Lewis, D. (1960). *J. Chem. Soc.* 2699.
10. Gray, G. W. and Jones, B. (1954). *J. Chem. Soc.* 683; (1955). 236.
11. Herrmann, K. (1933). *Trans. Faraday Soc.* **29**, 972.
12. Gray, G. W. (1958). *Steric Effects in Conjugated Systems*, Butterworths, London p. 160 (Editor; G. W. Gray).
13. Byron, D. J., Gray, G. W., Ibbotson, A. and Worrall, B. M. Unpublished work.
14. Byron, D. J. and Gray, G. W. Unpublished work.
15. Aaron, C., Byron, D. J. and Gray, G. W. Unpublished work.
16. Weygand, C. and Gabler, R. (1940). *Z. phys. Chem.* (*Leipzig*) **46B**, 270.
17. Gray, G. W., Jones, B. and Marson, F. (1956). *J. Chem. Soc.* 1417.
18. Gray, G. W. and Worrall, B. M. (1959). *J. Chem. Soc.* 1545.
19. Dave, J. S. and Dewar, M. J. S. (1954). *J. Chem. Soc.* 4617; (1955). 4305.
20. Weygand, C., Gabler, R. and Bircon, N. (1941). *J. prakt. Chem.* **158**, 266.
21. Weygand, C. and Gabler, R. (1940). *J. prakt. Chem.* **155**, 332.
22. Gray, G. W. (1956). *J. Chem. Soc.* 3733.
23. Kuksis, A. and Beveridge, J. M. R. (1959). *J. Org. Chem.* **25**, 1209.
24. Friedel, G. (1922). *Ann. Physique* **18**, 273.
25. Wiegand, C. (1949). *Z. Naturforsch.* **4b**, 249.
26. Gray, G. W. Unpublished work.
27. Wiegand, C. (1948). *Z. Naturforsch.* **3b**, 313; (1954). **9b**, 516; (1955). " Methoden der Organischen Chemie ", Houben-Weyl, Vol. III, p. 685.
28. Eaborn, C. and Hartshorne, N. H. (1955). *J. Chem. Soc.* 549.

CHAPTER IX

THE REGULAR TRENDS OF MESOMORPHIC TRANSITION
TEMPERATURES FOR HOMOLOGOUS SERIES

IT has already been pointed out that when the mesomorphic transition
temperatures for an homologous series of compounds are plotted against
the number of carbon atoms in the alkyl chain, e.g. in homologous series
of n-alkyl ethers or esters, certain smooth curve relationships for like
transitions are found. This important behaviour will now be discussed
in greater detail, for its occurrence is general over a wide range of
different homologous series of mesomorphic compounds. It is not to be
denied that the mesomorphic transition temperatures which have been
published in the literature for several homologous series do not give
these smooth curve relationships, but the author has found that when
due regard is paid to the purity of the members of the series, one of a
limited number of smooth curve trends is always obtained. Indeed,
even although only a small portion of an homologous series, e.g. the four
homologues heptyl to decyl, is studied, any reasonable departure from
the smooth curve relationships which should exist for the transition
temperatures is obvious, and allows one to comment on the purity of
the samples being studied. In no case in the author's experience, have
departures from these smooth curve trends not been attributable to
impurity in the compounds, and either repreparation of the samples, or
their more rigorous purification has removed the anomalies in the plots
of the transition temperatures against the number of carbon atoms in the
alkyl chain. Indeed, it is suggested that the attainment of transition
temperatures which give smooth curve plots is as rigorous a criterion as
any for the purity of the compounds under consideration. Mesomorphic transition temperatures are very sensitive to traces of impurity
and are depressed much more than ordinary melting points by the same
concentration of an added component. Quite satisfactory combustion
analyses may be obtained for compounds considered unsatisfactory on
the basis of their transition temperature against chain length plots.

Although the transition temperatures for changes between two different types of mesophase, e.g. smectic-nematic, do give smooth curve
relationships when plotted against the alkyl chain lengths, the mesomorphic-isotropic transitions are the best on which to judge the purity
of the homologues. There are several reasons for this:

(1) The mesomorphic-isotropic change is well defined, and accurate values for the temperature are readily obtained.

(2) The easily detected reversal from isotropic liquid-mesophase at the *same* temperature gives an additional check on both the transition temperature and the purity of the sample.

(3) When extended series, e.g. C_1–C_{10}, C_{12}, C_{16}, C_{18}, are being studied, the range of mesomorphic-isotropic transition temperatures obtained is considerable, i.e. smectic-nematic transitions may occur for only a few of the middle order homologues.

(4) The alternation of mesomorphic-isotropic transition temperatures between members of the homologous series containing odd and even numbers of carbon atoms in the alkyl chain helps to detect any anomalously high or low transition temperatures. For example, let us assume that only four ethers, containing the alkyl groups heptyl–decyl, are being studied, and consider the specific case of the series of 4,4'-di-(*p*-n-alkoxybenzylideneamino)-2,5-dimethylbiphenyls, for which the melting points and transition temperatures are recorded in Table IX.1.

TABLE IX.1

| Alkyl | Temperature of transition to | |
	smectic	nematic
Heptyl	118·5°	230°
Octyl	114	219·5
Nonyl	113·5	208
Decyl	114·5	196·5

Figure IX.1 (*a*) represents the plot of these nematic-isotropic temperatures against the number of carbon atoms in the alkyl chain. The alternation of the transition temperatures is obvious, such that if a straight line is drawn through the points for the octyl and decyl ethers (the transition temperature plots for even carbon chain homologues (ethers) always lie above those for odd carbon chain homologues), the transition temperature for the nonyl ether lies on this line, and that for the heptyl ether below it. If we now join the points for the heptyl and nonyl ethers, the straight line merges with the line joining the points for the even carbon chain members, but does not cross it.

Figure IX.1 (*b*) shows the plot which would be obtained if the transition temperature for the heptyl ether were only 1° lower (229°), and Fig. IX.1 (*c*) is obtained if the transition temperature for the nonyl ether is 2° lower (206°). The plot represented in Fig. IX.1 (*b*) is unsatisfactory, since the line through the points for the odd members tends to cross that for the even members, and this would imply that the higher carbon chain homologues would show an inversion of the alternation. This has never been observed in practice, and is unlikely in principle. Figure IX.1 (*c*) is unsatisfactory because the two lines diverge.   This implies a crossing of the lines earlier in the series, and as discussed above, this is unlikely. Quite small changes from the transition temperatures giving the best plot (Fig. IX.1 (*a*)) are therefore detectable, and would lead one to carry out further purifications on the suspect homologues.

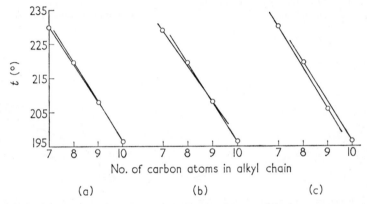

Fig. IX.1. The changes in the nematic-isotropic transition temperatures with increasing alkyl chain length (heptyl–decyl) for the 4,4′-di-(*p*-n-alkoxybenzylidene-amino)-2,5-dimethylbiphenyls.   In (*a*) the actual transition temperatures are used, whilst (*b*) and (*c*) show the trends of the transition temperatures if the nematic-isotropic transition temperature of the heptyl ether is 1° lower and that for the nonyl ether 2° lower respectively.

Some seventy homologous series or parts (at least four homologues) of homologous series of mesomorphic compounds have been examined by the author and his co-workers.   When plots of the mesomorphic transition temperatures against the alkyl chain lengths are made for these series, smooth curve relationships of one kind or another are found in all cases. The seventy series studied give rise in fact to seven general types of transition temperature against chain length plot.   These general types are illustrated in the composite figure (Fig. IX.2 (*a*)–(g)), to which has been added Fig. IX.2 (*h*), a typical plot for a series of polymesomorphic compounds. Each of these figures (Fig. IX.2 (*a*)–(*h*)) is an actual transition temperature plot for a particular homologous series which is noted beneath each diagram. In Table IX.2 are gathered together the various homologous series that have been studied, these being grouped together according to the general type of transition temperature plot to which they give rise. It should be emphasized that,

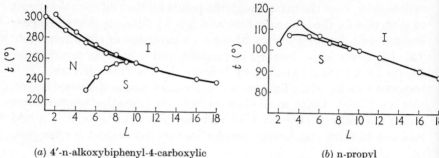

(a) 4'-n-alkoxybiphenyl-4-carboxylic
acids

(b) n-propyl
4'-n-alkoxybiphenyl-4-carboxylates

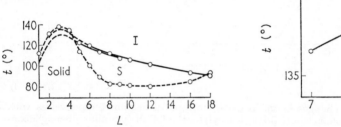

(c) ethyl 4'-n-alkoxybiphenyl-
4-carboxylates

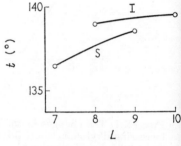

(d) 4-p-n-alkoxybenzylideneamino-
3'-chlorobiphenyls

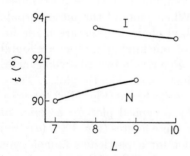

(e) 4-p-n-alkoxybenzylideneamino-
3-chlorobiphenyls

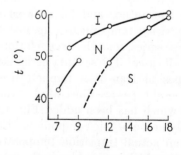

(f) 4-p-n-alkoxybenzylideneamino-
2-methylbiphenyls

Fig. IX.2.

FIG. IX.2.—*continued*

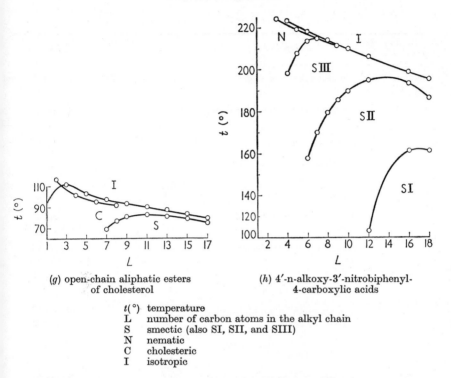

(*g*) open-chain aliphatic esters
of cholesterol

(*h*) 4'-n-alkoxy-3'-nitrobiphenyl-
4-carboxylic acids

$t(°)$ temperature
L   number of carbon atoms in the alkyl chain
S   smectic (also SI, SII, and SIII)
N   nematic
C   cholesteric
I   isotropic

FIG. IX.2. Representative examples of the types of plot of mesomorphic transition
temperature against alkyl chain length which have been obtained in the course of
examining some seventy homologous series or parts of homologous series of
mesomorphic compounds.

within a particular group, the gradients and curvatures of the transition
lines may differ substantially, but the general pattern will be the same,
e.g. for the series which give a plot of the type shown in Fig. IX.2 (*f*),
the gradients of the lines through the nematic-isotropic temperatures
may differ appreciably, but all the lines do rise as the series is ascended.
Table IX.2 also contains a column of general comments, and a column
which shows clearly the range of homologues for which the general pattern of behaviour has been established in each case.

We can assume, therefore, that the occurrence of one of a limited
number of smooth curve relationships is to be expected for the mesomorphic transition temperatures of any homologous series of compounds. The commonest pattern of behaviour is that shown in Fig.
IX.2 (*a*), in which the nematic-isotropic transition temperatures fall
with increasing alkyl chain length, a regular alternation of the temperatures occurring between homologues containing odd and even numbers

TABLE IX.2

S = smectic; N = nematic; M = mesomorphic; I = isotropic

Section and general pattern	Compound type	No. of homologues studied	Comments
Section A Fig. IX.2 (a)	p-n-alkoxybenzoic acids[1]	C_1—C_{10},C_{12},C_{16},C_{18}	S and N C_1,C_2 not M
	trans-p-n-alkoxycinnamic acids[2]	,,	S and N
	4'-n-alkoxybiphenyl-4-carboxylic acids[3]	,,	,,
	6-n-alkoxy-2-naphthoic acids[4]	,,	,,
	7-n-alkoxyfluorene-2-carboxylic acids[5]	C_1,C_3,C_5,C_7–C_{10}, C_{12},C_{16},C_{18}	,,
	4-n-alkoxy-3-fluorobenzoic acids[6]	C_1–C_{10},C_{12},C_{16},C_{18},	S and N C_1–C_5 not M
	4-n-alkoxy-3-chlorobenzoic acids[6]	,,	S and N* C_1,C_5–C_7 not M
	trans-4-n-alkoxy-3-chlorocinnamic acids[7]	,,	S and N C_1–C_5 not M
	4'-n-alkoxy-3'-chlorobiphenyl-4-carboxylic acids[8]	,,	S and N C_1 not M
	4'-n-alkoxy-3'-bromobiphenyl-4-carboxylic acids[8]	,,	S and N C_1,C_2 not M
	4'-n-alkoxy-3'-nitrobiphenyl-4-carboxylic acids[8]	C_1–C_{10},C_{12},C_{16},C_{18}	S and N† C_1,C_2 not M
	6-n-alkoxy-5-chloro-2-naphthoic acids[9]	,,	,,
	6-n-alkoxy-5-bromo-2-naphthoic acids[9]	,,	,,
	6-n-alkoxy-5-iodo-2-naphthoic acids[9]	,,	S and N C_1–C_3 not M
	4-p-n-alkoxybenzylideneamino-biphenyls[10]	,,	S and N
	2-p-n-alkoxybenzylideneamino-fluorenes[10]	,,	,,
	2-p-n-alkoxybenzylideneamino-fluorenones[10]	,,	,, *
	2-p-n-alkoxybenzylideneamino-phenanthrenes[11]	,,	,,
	N,N'-di-(p-n-alkoxybenzylidene)-p-phenylenediamines[10]	,,	,,
	4,4'-di-(p-n-alkoxybenzylidene-amino)biphenyls[10]	,,	,,

TABLE IX.2.—*continued*

Section and general pattern	Compound type	No. of homologues studied	Comments
Section A Fig. IX.2 (*a*) –cont.	2,7-di-(*p*-n-alkoxybenzylidene-amino)fluorenes[10]	C_1–C_{10},C_{12},C_{16},C_{12},	S and N
	2,7-di-(*p*-n-alkoxybenzylidene-amino)fluorenones[10]	,,	,,
Section B Fig. IX.2 (*a*)	4-*p*-n-alkoxybenzylideneamino-3-methylbiphenyls[12]	C_7–C_{10}	Nematic only
	4,4′-di-(*p*-n-alkoxybenzylidene-amino)-2-fluorobiphenyls[13]	,,	S and N
	4,4′-di-(*p*-n-alkoxybenzylidene-amino)-2-chlorobiphenyls[12]	,,	S (C_9,C_{10}) and N
	4,4′-di-(*p*-n-alkoxybenzylidene-amino)-2-bromobiphenyls[12]	,,	,,
	4,4′-di-(*p*-n-alkoxybenzylidene-amino)-2-iodobiphenyls[12]	,,	,,
	4,4′-di-(*p*-n-alkoxybenzylidene-amino)-2-methylbiphenyls[13]	,	S (C_8–C_{10}) and N
	4,4′-di-(*p*-n-alkoxybenzylidene-amino)-2-nitrobiphenyls[13]	,,	S and N
	4,4′-di-(*p*-n-alkoxybenzylidene-amino)-3-chlorobiphenyls[13]	,,	,,
	4,4′-di-(*p*-n-alkoxybenzylidene-amino)-3-bromobiphenyls[13]	,,	,,
	4,4′-di-(*p*-n-alkoxybenzylidene-amino)-3-methylbiphenyls	.,	,,
	4,4′-di-(*p*-n-alkoxybenzylidene-amino)-2,5-dichlorobiphenyls[13]	,,	Nematic only
	4,4′-di-(*p*-n-alkoxybenzylidene-amino)-2,6-dichlorobiphenyls[13]	,,	,,
	4,4′-di-(*p*-n-alkoxybenzylidene-amino)-2,2′-dichlorobiphenyls[13]	,,	,,
	4,4′-di-(*p*-n-alkoxybenzylidene-amino)-2,3′-dichlorobiphenyls[13]	,,	,,
	4,4′-di-(*p*-n-alkoxybenzylidene-amino)-3,3′-dichlorobiphenyls[13]	,,	S (C_8–C_{10}) and N
	4,4′-di-(*p*-n-alkoxybenzylidene-amino)-2,5-dibromobiphenyls[13]	,,	Nematic only
	4,4′-di-(*p*-n-alkoxybenzylidene-amino)-2,6-dibromobiphenyls[13]	,,	,,

TABLE IX.2.—*continued*

Section and general pattern	Compound type	No. of homologues studied	Comments
Section B Fig. IX.2 (a) –cont.	4,4′-di-(p-n-alkoxybenzylidene-amino)-2,2′-dibromobiphenyls[13]	C_7–C_{10}	Nematic only
	4,4′-di-(p-n-alkoxybenzylidene-amino)-3,3′-dibromobiphenyls[13]	,,	S (C_8–C_{10}) and N
	4,4′-di-(p-n-alkoxybenzylidene-amino)-2,5-dimethylbiphenyls[13]	,,	Nematic only
	4,4′-di-(p-n-alkoxybenzylidene-amino)-2,2′-dimethylbiphenyls[13]	,,	,,
	4,4′-di-(p-n-alkoxybenzylidene-amino)-2,3-dimethylbiphenyls[13]	,,	,,
	4,4′-di-(p-n-alkoxybenzylidene-amino)-3,3′-dimethylbiphenyls[13]	,,	,,
	4,4′-di-(p-n-alkoxybenzylidene-amino)-3,3′-di-iodobiphenyls[13]	,,	S (C_8–C_{10}) and N
	4,4′-di-(p-n-alkoxybenzylidene-amino)-2,2′,6-trichlorobiphenyls[13]	,,	Nematic only
Section C Fig. IX.2 (b)	n-propyl 4′-n-alkoxybiphenyl-4-carboxylates[8]	C_1–C_{10},C_{12},C_{16},C_{18}	C_1 not M
	n-propyl 4′-n-alkoxy-3′-nitrobiphenyl-4-carboxylates[8]	,,	C_1,C_2 not M
	6-n-alkoxy-5-nitro-2-naphthoic acids[9]	C_1,C_5,C_8–C_{10},C_{12},C_{16},C_{18}	C_1,C_5,C_8 not M†
Section D Fig. IX.2 (c)	Methyl 4′-n-alkoxybiphenyl-4-carboxylates[8]	C_1–C_{10},C_{12},C_{16},C_{18}	C_1–C_5 not M
	Ethyl 4′-n-alkoxybiphenyl-4-carboxylates[8]	,,	C_1–C_4 not M‡
	n-propyl 7-n-alkoxyfluorene-2-carboxylates[5]	C_7–C_{10}	Smectic only
Section E Fig. IX.2 (d)	7-acetyl-2-n-alkoxyfluorenes[5]	C_7–C_{10}	Slight rise in transition lines
	4-p-n-alkoxybenzylideneamino-3′-chlorobiphenyls[12]	,,	,,
	4-p-n-alkoxybenzylideneamino-3′-bromobiphenyls[12]	,,	,,
	4-p-n-alkoxybenzylideneamino-3′-methylbiphenyls[12]	,,	,, §
Section F Fig. IX.2 (e)	4-p-n-alkoxybenzylideneamino-3-chlorobiphenyls[12]	C_7–C_{10}	$C_7(90°)$,$C_{10}(93°)$

of carbon atoms in the alkyl chain. If the nematic-isotropic transition temperatures for a series of compounds do behave in this way, and if the series also exhibits smectic properties, then the smectic-nematic transition temperatures will be found to rise steeply at first and then more gradually as the alkyl chain lengthens. In most cases, the smectic-nematic curve becomes coincident with the falling nematic-isotropic curve before the former has reached its maximum, although in certain cases which will be discussed later, the smectic-nematic curve begins to fall before it merges with the more steeply falling nematic-isotropic curve. After these two curves have joined together, no nematic properties are observed in the series, and the smectic mesophases pass direct to the isotropic liquid. These smectic-isotropic transitions usually begin at about the decyl or dodecyl ether, and the smectic-isotropic temperatures for say the decyl, dodecyl, hexadecyl, and octadecyl ethers, together with the *nematic*-isotropic transition temperatures for the lower homologues containing an even number of carbon atoms in the alkyl chain, constitute *one* smoothly falling mesomorphic-isotropic transition temperature curve. In Table IX.2 (Sections A and B), there are listed forty-four homologous series or groups of at least four homologues which behave in this general way, with or without the occurrence of smectic mesophases. One other series in Section A, the 4'-n-alkoxy-3'-nitrobiphenyl-4-carboxylic acids, exhibits polymesomorphism of the smectic mesophase, and is also included in Section I of Table IX.2. Two other series in Section A of Table IX.2, i.e. giving the general pattern of behaviour represented in Fig. IX.2 (a), do in fact exhibit certain anomalies. In the first of these, the 4-n-alkoxy-3-chlorobenzoic acids, the smectic-nematic curve does not become coincident with the nematic-isotropic curve, but reaches a maximum at the nonyl ether and then falls through the monotropic points for the decyl and dodecyl ethers. Unfortunately, the exact monotropic nematic-smectic transition temperatures for the hexadecyl and octadecyl ethers could not be obtained, but it appears that the smectic-nematic line must fall with a gradient equal to or less than that of the nematic-isotropic line. This behaviour will be mentioned again later, but for the purpose of this introductory survey, the point to note is that direct smectic-isotropic transitions are not observed at any stage in this series of alkoxyarene carboxylic acids up to the octadecyl ether. The 2-p-n-alkoxybenzyl-ideneaminofluorenones exhibit a somewhat more unusual divergence from the general pattern of Fig. IX.2 (a). The transition temperature against chain length plot for the series is shown in Fig. IX.3. Once more, the smectic-nematic curve does not coincide with the falling nematic-isotropic curve at the longest chain length (C_{18}) so far studied. More extraordinary, however, is the fall to a minimum followed by the rise to a maximum given in the early stages of the series by the nematic-isotropic transition temperatures of both odd and even carbon-chain homologues. The normal decrease, with alternation, is then observed as the alkyl chain is further lengthened. An attempt to explain this behaviour will be made later in this chapter.

There is, however, a great weight of evidence to support the view that the general pattern shown in Fig. IX.2 (a) is the one to be expected for homologous series of compounds which exhibit either nematic or

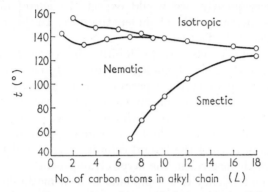

FIG. IX.3. The smectic-nematic and nematic-isotropic transition temperatures of the 2-p-n-alkoxybenzylideneaminofluorenones plotted against the number of carbon atoms in the alkyl chain of the ether group.

smectic and nematic properties. It is therefore worthwhile discussing the general trends shown by the mesomorphic transition temperatures of such series in more detail.

SERIES WHICH GIVE MESOMORPHIC TRANSITION TEMPERATURE AGAINST CHAIN LENGTH PLOTS OF THE TYPE SHOWN IN FIG. IX.2 (a)

In earlier chapters, two suggestions have been made with regard to the factors which determine the thermal stabilities of smectic and nematic mesophases.

(1) The thermal stability of a smectic mesophase, which at a higher temperature is replaced by a nematic mesophase, is determined mainly by the intermolecular attractions which operate between the sides and planes of the molecules, i.e. the strengths of the lateral cohesive forces determine the smectic-nematic transition temperatures.

(2) The molecules in the nematic swarms are maintained in their parallel orientation by the residual *terminal* and *lateral* attractions between the molecules, and the strengths of these cohesive forces must determine the nematic-isotropic transition temperatures.

Let us consider therefore how these cohesive forces will be affected by the successive addition of methylene groups to an alkyl chain, in an attempt to explain the trends in the mesomorphic transition temperatures as the homologous series of compounds is ascended.

As the methylene chain is lengthened, the separation of the aromatic centres, which are highly polarizable and may carry permanently dipolar substituents, is increased, and there should be a decrease in the strength of the *terminal* intermolecular cohesions. However, the addition of a methylene group does increase[16] the over-all polarizability of the molecule, and consequently, we would expect the *lateral* intermolecular attractions to increase as the chain length grows. In this way, we reach an explanation of the fact that

(*a*) in an homologous series exhibiting both smectic and nematic properties, only the lower homologues are purely nematic, i.e. for the shorter chain compounds, the separation of the aromatic nuclei is at a minimum and the terminal cohesive forces are strongest, and

(*b*) in the middle members of the series, e.g. C_6, C_7, C_8, etc., the smectic properties very often make their first appearance, because the alkyl chain is increasing the lateral cohesive forces, and the molecules may maintain themselves in the layer arrangement.

That is, the tendency of a compound to be nematic should decrease as the alkyl chain is lengthened, and at the same time, its tendency to exhibit smectic properties should increase. We would therefore expect a stage to be reached in the homologous series at which no nematic properties would be shown and the system would be purely smectic in behaviour. This is in fact the case for twenty of the twenty-two series of nine or more homologues listed in Section A of Table IX.2—the only two exceptions are the homologous series of 4-*p*-n-alkoxy-3-chlorobenzoic acids and 2-*p*-n-alkoxybenzylideneaminofluorenones to which reference has already been made.

At this stage in the homologous series, the smectic mesophase will pass directly to the isotropic liquid, presumably because the terminal intermolecular attractions are inadequate to maintain the parallel molecular orientation required for the nematic mesophase. It should be emphasized again that a nematic mesophase cannot give rise to a smectic mesophase at higher temperatures. The smectic mesophase is a more highly organized state and therefore represents a system of lower kinetic and potential energy than the nematic mesophase. A nematic-smectic transition occurring with rising temperature is therefore impossible, as it would necessitate a change from a higher to a lower energy system with increasing temperature.

The above discussion explains the general distribution of the mesophases in an homologous series of compounds, but not the regular changes in the mesomorphic transition temperatures as the series is ascended. Let us turn to this aspect of the problem, considering first the nematic-isotropic transition temperatures. For reasons which will be discussed presently, let us assume that the alkyl chains in the molecules of the alkoxyarene carboxylic acids and Schiff's bases adopt the cog wheel rather than the zig-zag arrangement of the carbon chain.

Cog Wheel   Zig-zag

As we move along the series in one or other of the sequences methyl to propyl to pentyl to heptyl (i.e. odd members), and ethyl to butyl to hexyl to octyl (i.e. even members) a constant change is being made to the length of the alkyl chain. If the nematic-isotropic transition temperatures are determined by the terminal intermolecular attractions, we should therefore expect these cohesive forces to change, and in fact to decrease in a regular manner as we pass from one odd member to another or from one even member to another along the series.   That is, the separation of the polarizable aromatic centres is being successively increased by a constant amount.

(*a*) for odd members of the series by the group $-CH_2\diagup^{CH_3}$, and

(*b*) for even members of the series by the group CH_2-CH_3.

The nematic isotropic transition temperatures for the even members should therefore change in a regular way along the homologous series,

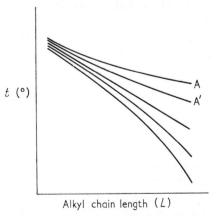

Fig. IX.4 The slopes of the lines represent different possible ways in which the rates of decrease for nematic-isotropic transition temperatures may change as homologous series are ascended.

t (°)

Alkyl chain length (L)

and so also should the transition temperatures for the odd carbon chain members. Therefore, if we plot the nematic-isotropic transition temperatures for the even members of the series against an axis representing the length of the alkyl chain, we should obtain some form of curve or line sloping down from the lower to the higher homologues. Various possibilities are shown in Fig. IX.4. All of the lines or curves except those of the type marked A and A' imply that the terminal interaction energy will fall off linearly or with increasing rapidity as the alkyl chain lengthens. Whilst this may be the case as far as the interaction energy between the polarizable aromatic centres is concerned, we must consider that, even when these centres are infinitely distant from one another, there will still be a residual energy of attraction between the terminal groups of the infinitely long alkyl chains of the two molecules. Hence, the polarizability of the alkyl chains themselves must enter into the picture, and the terminal attractions should fall off and gradually approach a limiting value equivalent to the terminal interaction energy between the ends of the molecules of two open-chain paraffins. The nematic-isotropic transition line would therefore be expected to fall off rapidly at first and then more gradually, levelling off in fact to a more or less constant value, i.e. a curve of the type A would be expected, and is in fact found, c.f. Fig. IX.2 (a).

However, the usefulness of the concept of an increasing physical separation of the aromatic centres ends here, for although it affords an explanation of the fact that two curves exist for the nematic-isotropic transition temperatures, it does not explain why the curve for the even members always lies above that for the odd members. In fact, since the separation is increased most on passing from odd to even, and least from even to odd carbon-chain homologue, we would conclude that the co-hesive forces and the nematic-isotropic transition temperatures would decrease on passing from odd to even member of the series, i.e. that the odd carbon chain members would give the nematic-isotropic transition temperatures which form the uppermost of the two curves.

As inferred above, the polarizability of the alkyl chain must be brought into the argument, but if we consider its polarizability *in the direction of the major axis* of the molecule, we are still concerned with the *terminal* intermolecular cohesions which are considered to play a signifi-cant part in determining the maintenance of the nematic molecular order.

Let us therefore consider the influence of a polarizing field (due to the close proximity of other molecules) on the polarizability of the alkoxy group of one particular molecule, in the direction of its long axis. We may consider that the alkyl chain is lengthened by the replacement of one of the hydrogen atoms of the end methyl group by another methyl group, and the polarizability of the system will be increased largely by the polarizabilities of the C—H bonds of the new terminal methyl group. The three C—H bonds will be arranged symmetrically about the new C—C bond. Now, the spatial distribution of the new C—C bond is deter-mined by the number of carbon atoms in the chain. Using the cog-wheel conformation of the chain, when the number of atoms is made up to an even number by the addition of a —CH_3 group, the terminal C—C bond lies in the direction of the major axis of the chain, but makes an angle of about 70° with this axis when the number of carbon atoms is made up from even to odd. Thus, for an even number of carbon atoms in the new chain, the terminal C—CH$_3$ unit makes a given contribution to the polarizability of the chain, in the direction of its major axis, which is reduced by a factor of cos 70° when the chain contains an odd number of carbon atoms. That is, the polarizability of the alkyl chain in the direction of the major axis of the molecule increases most on passing from an odd to an even member of the series, and the nematic-isotropic transition temperature for the homologues containing an even number of carbon atoms should lie on a curve which is above the nematic-isotropic transition line for the odd members of the series. In these terms, we can explain the alternation of the nematic-isotropic transition temperatures for an homologous series of alkyl ethers. It should be noted that for an alkyl chain linked *directly* to a ring system, the change from an *odd* to an *even* member is the same as that involved on passing from an *even* to an *odd* member of a series of alkoxy compounds (Fig. IX.5). With an alkyl ester, the changes are the same as for an alkyl compound (Fig. IX.5).

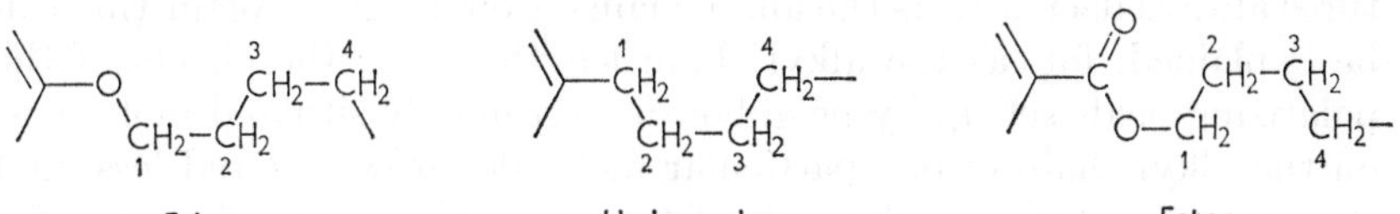

Ether Hydrocarbon Ester

FIG. IX.5. Structural differences arising from the presence of odd and even numbers of carbon atoms in the alkyl chains of alkyl ethers, hydrocarbons, and alkyl esters.

Therefore, the mesomorphic-isotropic transition temperatures for even carbon-chain esters and hydrocarbons lie on a curve below that for the odd carbon-chain homologues.

Although the polarizability of the alkyl chain increases as the chain length increases, we cannot postulate on these grounds that there will be an increase in the terminal attractions between the molecules. The cohesive forces between the ends of the shorter chain homologues will depend *mainly* upon the induced polarization effects operating between the ends of the molecules. These forces of attraction will *decrease* with growing chain length, as the separation of the dipolar aromatic centres of neighbouring molecules is increased and they are forced further away from the alkyl chains of neighbouring terminally situated molecules. The dispersion forces between the ends of chains may *increase* as the chains lengthen, but the increases will be small particularly after, say, the first two members of the series, as the separation of individual methylene units is progressively increased. A net *decrease* in the terminal attractive forces is therefore likely, the interaction energy at infinite chain length approaching that for pure dispersion forces between the molecules of two long open-chain paraffins.

The separation of the dipolar aromatic centres is again brought into the discussion therefore, but this time from the point of view of the polarizing effect of these centres on the alkyl chains of neighbouring molecules, and we would once more postulate a falling nematic-isotropic transition point curve of the type A in Fig. IX.4, i.e. falling rapidly at first, and then levelling off as the cohesive forces begin to approach the limiting value for two long alkyl chains. That the interaction energy between the ends of the molecules is not solely a function of the separation of and interaction between the aromatic centres themselves, but involves the polarizability of the alkyl chain and the effect of the dipolar centres on this chain, is demonstrated by the above arguments, which allow us to explain the observed alternation of the nematic-isotropic transition temperatures in terms of the changes in the polarizability of the alkyl chain, in the direction of its long axis, as we pass from odd to even to odd carbon-chain homologue.

The extent of the alternation of nematic-isotropic transition temperatures always decreases as the alkyl chains grow longer. Again this can be explained, for, as the alkyl chain length grows, the effects of the polarizing fields set up by neighbouring terminally situated molecules, on the alkyl chain of one particular molecule, grow less and less, and the attraction between the ends of two molecules approaches that for the limiting case of the molecules of two open-chain paraffins, between which only dispersion forces operate. The sensitivity of the terminal attractions to the spatial distribution of the terminal methyl group which is added on passing from homologue to homologue, would therefore be expected to grow less, and the extent of the alternation to diminish.

So far, we have discussed the nematic-isotropic transition temperatures only, in so far as they are affected by changes in the terminal attractions between molecules. We do know, of course, that residual lateral interactions between the molecules play some part in determining the thermal stabilities of nematic mesophases. Thirty-four of the forty-seven series or parts of series listed in Sections A and B of Table IX.2 exhibit smectic as well as nematic mesophases. The lateral intermolecular attractions for such series of compounds must therefore be *reasonably strong*. Moreover, the addition of a methylene group to the alkyl chain will increase the residual lateral attractions. Presumably it is the disruption of the weaker residual terminal attractions which determines the temperature of the nematic-isotropic change, and therefore, although the residual lateral interactions increase as the homologous series is ascended, this effect is unlikely to counteract the *decreasing* residual terminal interactions between the molecules to such an extent that the nematic-isotropic transition temperatures rise along the series, particularly in a system for which the primary and residual lateral attractions are quite strong, i.e. in a smectogenic series of compounds. No doubt, the increase in the residual lateral attractions will reduce the rate of decrease of the nematic-isotropic transition temperatures, and gives a further reason for the ultimate levelling off in the nematic-isotropic curve for the longer-chain homologues, for which the residual lateral interactions will be strongest.

It is interesting to note that in Sections A and B of Table IX.2, the thirteen series which do not exhibit smectic properties are comprised of compounds which involve either a steric effect between rings or substituents, or a very large breadth-increasing effect caused by a substituent. In such systems, the lateral and residual lateral intermolecular attractions will be relatively *low* (see Chapter X for a fuller discussion), and the addition of successive methylene groups to the alkyl chains will cause relatively large percentage increases in the residual lateral attractions. The residual lateral attractions should therefore reduce the rate of decrease of the nematic isotropic transition temperature curve more effectively than in a non-sterically affected system. Consider the 4,4'-di-(p-n-alkoxybenzylideneamino)biphenyls (I),

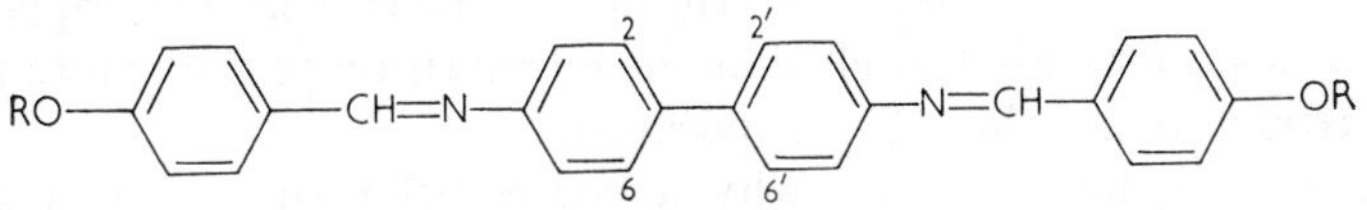

I

and the effect of various substituents on the slope of the nematic-isotropic transition line joining the transition points for the octyl and decyl ethers. In Table IX.3, the slope of this line is recorded as the decrease in nematic-isotropic transition temperature (D°) between these two ethers.

TABLE IX.3. *Substituted 4,4'-Di-(p-n-alkoxybenzylideneamino)biphenyls*

Substituent	$D°$	Substituent	$D°$	Substituent	$D°$
—	29	—	29	—	29
2-chloro-	21	2-bromo-	18	2-methyl	21
2,2'-dichloro-	17·5	2,2'-dibromo-	15	2,2'-dimethyl	19·5
2,2',6-trichloro-	14				

As the steric congestion increases from the unsubstituted Schiff's base to the trichloro-derivative it is evident that the gradient of the transition line decreases. That is, for the most sterically affected system, for which the residual lateral attractions are weakest, the percentage increase in these attractions will be greatest as the chain lengthens, and the transition line will level off most rapidly. The methyl group exerts much the same steric effect as a chloro- substituent and the decreases, D, in column three of Table IX.3 are similar to those in column one. The larger bromo- substituent has a more pronounced steric effect, and the gradient of the line for the dibromo- derivatives is almost as low as that for the trichloro- compounds.

Factors such as these will be considered again when dealing with series of compounds for which the nematic-isotropic transition lines rise as the homologous series is ascended, c.f. Fig. IX.2 (e) and (f). Residual lateral intermolecular attractions do therefore play some part in determining the trends in nematic-isotropic transition temperatures along homologous series, and the actual slopes of the lines obtained. The combined effect of the residual terminal and residual lateral interactions is obviously important, but in series for which the intermolecular lateral attractions are not too weak, the decreasing intermolecular terminal attractions determine the decreases in the nematic-isotropic transition temperatures and explain the alternation of the transition temperatures as the series is ascended, such that the curve through the points for the even carbon chain ethers lies uppermost.

We should now consider why a cog-wheel rather than a zig-zag conformation of the alkyl chain has been presumed to occur in these

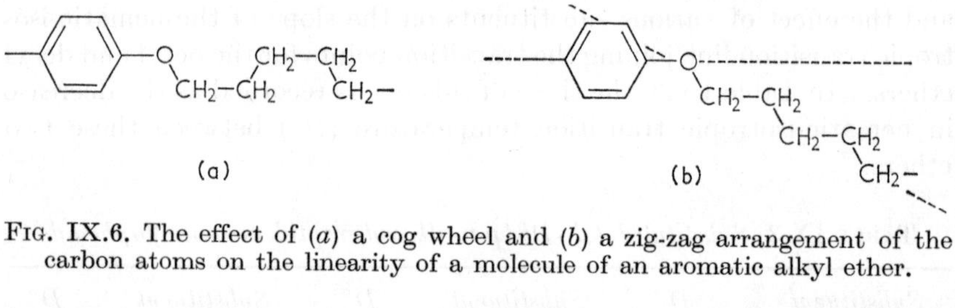

FIG. IX.6. The effect of (a) a cog wheel and (b) a zig-zag arrangement of the carbon atoms on the linearity of a molecule of an aromatic alkyl ether.

systems. The reasons are that: (a) its occurrence allows us to explain the alternation of the transition temperatures—the zig-zag conformation would lead to identical changes in polarizability both in the direction of the major molecular axis and at right-angles to this, and would not explain the alternation effect; and (b) although the cog-wheel conformation is considered to be of higher potential energy than the zig-zag arrangement which occurs in the crystalline states of n-paraffins and open-chain fatty acids, this confers a more linear over-all structure on the molecules of alkoxyarene carboxylic acids and Schiff's bases of the type listed in Table IX.2—see Fig. IX.6 (a) and (b).

The alkyl chain is of course flexible, and the zig-zag form shown in Fig. IX.6 (b) could possibly be distorted such that the axis of the chain and that of the rest of the molecule become parallel. However, this distortion may increase the potential energy to an extent such that the zig-zag form is energetically unfavourable in the mesophase compared with the cog wheel form.

At this point it should be remembered that the nematic melt is subject to intense movements. These movements probably involve the swarms as units, however, and it is reasonable to assume that we have a relatively tranquil arrangement of the molecules within the swarms. It is of course recognized that molecules may break away from a swarm, gradually changing the direction of orientation of their major axes, before joining up with another swarm. In this sense, our picture of the end-to-end arrangement of the molecules is an over-simplification. However, we are really concerned with an over-all or average picture for the system, and it is quite reasonable to apply our model of geometrically anisotropic molecules held together by the residual lateral cohesions and the weaker residual terminal cohesions even to a flowing nematic melt, i.e. we can imagine strings or bundles of strings of molecules sliding and slipping past one another like fibres. The connection between the anisotropic behaviour of nematic melts and the phenomenon of streaming birefringence is of course obvious.

Maier and Baumgartner[16,17] have also addressed themselves to the problem of explaining the alternation of nematic-isotropic transition temperatures, with specific reference to the lower homologues of the series of 4,4'-di-n-alkoxyazoxybenzenes. It was demonstrated[17] that the dipole moments of the seven homologues, methyl–heptyl, are virtually constant. The permanent dipole rises somewhat on passing from the methyl to the ethyl ether (2·36–2·42 D), remains virtually constant

TABLE IX.4

n-Alkyl	Nematic-isotropic temp. (°)	P_M at 120° (cm.^{3})
Methyl	135·3	−2·1
Ethyl	165·2	−5·8
Propyl	122·2	−4·2
Butyl	135·4	−7·8
Hexyl	129·3	−8·8

(2·41 D) for the propyl ether, and then falls slightly to 2·35–2·36 D on passing through the butyl–heptyl ethers. It is pointed out therefore that the permanent polarizations of the molecules afford no obvious explanation of the alternation of the transition temperatures, but it was shown that, at a given temperature, the dielectric anisotropies ($\Delta\epsilon = \epsilon_1 - \epsilon_2$) of the nematic melts (orientated by magnetic fields) did alternate. Maier suggests that ϵ_1 is the dielectric constant of the orientated melt parallel to the major axes of the molecules, and ϵ_2 the dielectric constant perpendicular to the major axes of the molecules. Since we may relate the molecular polarization (P_M) to the dielectric constant (ϵ) by the usual expression, this means that the anisotropy of the molecular polarization (ΔP_M) at a given temperature also alternates as we ascend the homologous series—see Table IX.4, which also includes the transition temperatures (nematic-isotropic) for compounds.

Maier has concluded that the dielectric constant, and therefore the polarization, is greatest at right-angles to the major axis of the molecule, and argues that it is the differences in the polarization effects between the *sides* of the molecules containing even and odd numbers of carbon atoms in the alkyl chains which explain the alternation effects. The writer, on the other hand, assumes that the polarizability of the alkyl chain will be greatest in the direction of its long axis, and that the alternation of the transition temperatures is explained by the alternation of the polarization effects in this direction, on passing from odd to even to odd carbon-chain homologue, i.e. the terminal interactions will be weaker than the lateral interactions, the nematic-isotropic transition temperature will be predetermined by the weaker interactions, and the alternation of the strengths of the weaker interactions as the series is ascended will impose an alternation on the nematic-isotropic transition temperatures. The approximate constancy of the dipole moments of the 4,4′-di-n-alkoxyazoxybenzenes does not affect this interpretation, because it is not implied that direct dipole-dipole interactions play any great part in determining the strengths of these terminal attractions, which are assumed to have their origin in induced polarization and polarizability effects. Whilst the writer and Maier both seek to interpret the alternation of the transition temperatures in terms of polarization and polarizability effects, their conclusions differ. However, the difference between the two approaches to this problem may well be differences of degree rather than of kind, for the writer recognizes in the arguments used throughout this chapter that residual lateral intermolecular attraction may also play their part in determining the temperatures of nematic-isotropic transitions.

It is interesting to note that Maier[17] points out that the approximate constancy of the dipole moments, and the increasing anisotropy of the molecular polarization as the series of 4,4′-di-n-alkoxyazoxybenzenes is ascended, suggest that the hindrance to rotation of the alkyl chains in the orientated nematic melt is considerable, despite the fact that we normally regard an alkyl chain as very flexible. This provides some evidence in support of the author's use of a regularly changing pattern for the alkyl chain as the homologous series is ascended.

Let us turn our attention now to the transitions involving smectic mesophases in the series in Sections A and B of Table IX.2. Smectic mesophases usually make their appearance in the middle members of the series, but there is little significance in the actual homologue for which smectic properties are first observed in a series. The reason is that the smectic-nematic transition temperature curve rises very steeply at the beginning, and if extrapolated back, may cut the line formed by joining the solid-mesomorphic transition temperatures for the series (Fig. IX.7). That is, the smectic mesophase becomes monotropic with

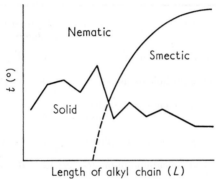

Fig. IX.7. A hypothetical plot showing how widely melting points may fluctuate along an homologous series. Bearing this in mind, and also the steepness of the smectic-nematic line for the lower homologues, the alkyl chain length at which smectic properties are first observed in a series is of little significance.

respect to the solid. The detection of such a monotropic mesophase depends on whether the melt will supercool below the melting point, and the tendency of anisotropic melts to supercool may vary considerably, even for structurally related homologous series. Moreover, the solid-mesomorphic transition temperatures for homologous series do not change regularly with increasing length of the alkyl chain, and sudden and irregular rises or falls in the melting points frequently occur. This variation in the melting points can quite easily determine whether or not we observe a smectic mesophase for a particular homologue. The onset of smectic properties in a series is therefore influenced by (a) the melting points of the compounds and (b) the supercooling tendencies of the melts. Both of these factors are related to the crystal structures of the compounds, and even within an homologous series, the crystal lattice types may vary considerably and irregularly as the series is ascended.[15]

Regular changes in the smectic-nematic transition temperatures do occur as the alkyl chain is lengthened, however, and when these temperatures (t) are plotted against the chain length (L), a single smooth curve is obtained for the series. This curve rises steeply at first and then levels off before merging with the nematic-isotropic transition temperature curve, which falls as the molecules are lengthened. Exceptions to this general behaviour should be noted, and these are:

(a) Those series for which the smectic-nematic transition temperature curve falls somewhat before it merges with the nematic-isotropic transition temperature curve. Six of the twenty-two homologous series listed in Section A of Table IX.2 behave in this way, and these are listed separately in Table IX.5.

TABLE IX.5

Series	Decrease (°) in smectic-nematic transition temperature (C_x–C_y)		
6-n-alkoxy-5-chloro-2-naphthoic acids	1	(C_{10}–C_{12})	
6-n-alkoxy-5-bromo-2-naphthoic acids	0·5	(C_{10}–C_{12})	
N,N'-(di-p-n-alkoxybenzylidene)-p-phenylene-diamines	4	(C_{10}–C_{12})	
4,4'-di-(p-n-alkoxybenzylideneamino)biphenyls	13	(C_9–C_{12}); 10·5	(C_{10}–C_{12})
2,7-di-(p-n-alkoxybenzylideneamino)fluorenes	12	(C_7–C_{12}); 8	(C_{10}–C_{12})
2,7-di-(p-n-alkoxybenzylideneamino)fluorenones	2	(C_{10}–C_{12})	

(b) Those series for which the smectic-nematic transition temperature curves do not merge with the nematic-isotropic transition temperature curves at the longest chain homologues (C_{18}) so far studied. Two such series are known. For the 2-p-n-alkoxybenzylideneamino-fluorenones, the smectic-nematic transition temperature rises 2° on passing from the hexadecyl to the octadecyl ether, and these two ethers exhibit nematic mesophases which persist respectively over temperature ranges of 9° and 6°. The thermal stability range of the nematic mesophase is therefore decreasing quite quickly, and it is obvious that the two curves would coincide for long alkyl chain derivatives. The behaviour of the series would then be quite normal.

For the other series, the 4-n-alkoxy-3-chlorobenzoic acids, the mono-tropic nematic-smectic temperatures rise to a maximum at the nonyl ether and then fall slightly (0·5°) for the decyl ether, and more rapidly (2·5°) on passing to the dodecyl ether. Although monotropic smectic mesophases occur for the hexadecyl and octadecyl ethers, accurate nematic-smectic temperatures cannot be obtained. However, if we extrapolate the smectic-nematic line through the points for the decyl and dodecyl ethers, bearing in mind the fact that the nematic meso-phases for these two members of the series persist over the same tempera-ture range (4·5°), we obtain monotropic nematic-smectic transition temperatures for the hexadecyl and octadecyl ethers. The extrapolated nematic-smectic curve either lies parallel to or may approach very gradu-ally the nematic-isotropic transition line. It is impossible to say which is the case, but even if it is the latter, nematic mesophases will be eliminated only at extremely long alkyl chain lengths.

Summarizing the position for smectic-nematic transition tempera-ture curves, the general pattern is an initial steep rise, levelling off to a greater or lesser extent as the alkyl chain is lengthened. In the majority of series (fourteen out of twenty-two) the curve merges with the nematic-isotropic transition point curve before or at its maximum, although in a few cases (six out of twenty-two series) the curve falls again before joining the nematic-isotropic curve. In only two cases have the two curves not merged on reaching the octadecyl ether.

The initial increase in smectic-nematic transition temperatures may be explained by the over-all increase in the polarizability of the mole-cules as each successive methylene group is added to the alkyl chain. This effect will increase the cohesive forces operating between the sides and planes of the molecules which lie parallel to one another, with their ends in line, forming the smectic layers. The increasing molecular weight of the molecules will also tend to make it more difficult for thermal vibra-tions to cause a sliding of the molecules out of the layers to give the imbricated orientation of a nematic fluid. The increasing molecular mass and polarizability do not, however, explain the levelling off in the smec-tic-nematic curves, or their tendency to fall again in certain cases. To explain this behaviour, we must not simply consider the over-all in-creasing lateral attractions between the molecules, but also the effect of the increasing alkyl chain length on the arrangement of the ends of alkyl chains across the smectic strata, and the fact that the residual terminal cohesions between the ends of chains will progressively de-crease as the series is ascended. Consider now in greater detail the mole-cular arrangements on either side of the smectic strata (Fig. IX.8).

Although the intermolecular forces which operate between the ends of the molecules, across the smectic strata, are relatively weak, since the layers may slide over one another, these residual attractions will tend to locate the ends of molecules near to one another across the strata, when slipping is not taking place. Therefore, the forces which tend to resist the sliding of a molecule in the direction of its long axis, from one stratum into another will be (a) the lateral cohesive forces between the molecules, and (b) the residual terminal cohesive forces operating across the strata.

Now, although the over-all intermolecular lateral attractions will increase with increasing alkyl chain length, the average intermolecular lateral attraction/unit length of the molecule will not increase. That is, the attractions between the highly polarizable aromatic rings carrying dipolar substituents, and represented by the rectangles in Figs. IX.8 and IX.9, contribute most to the lateral intermolecular attractions.

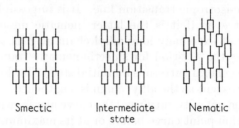

Smectic   Intermediate   Nematic
state

Fig. IX.8. Possible stages in the interpenetration of smectic strata.

Fig. IX.9. A more detailed representation of the arrangement of the molecules in the intermediate state in Fig. IX.8.

As the chain lengthens, it should therefore become more easy to interpose a molecule between these flexible chains, between which the cohesive forces are relatively low, leaving the aromatic centres still more or less strongly attracted to one another (Fig. IX.9).

Therefore, as the chain lengthens, (a) the residual terminal attractions, which tend to hold the ends of the molecules together across the strata, become weaker and offer less resistance to this interpenetration, and (b) the distortions of individual bonds in the alkyl groups necessary to achieve this interpenetration become less.

The intermediate state represented in Fig. IX.8 may then be formed. This is not the molecular orientation we usually have in mind for a nematic mesophase, for the ends of the molecules are still in line, but its formation will certainly mark the end of the smectic mesophase's existence and its characteristic properties (layer flow, focal-conic groups, etc.). Moreover, the difference between the intermediate state and a true nematic state is one of degree and not kind. The interpenetration of the chains will, as it grows more profound with rising temperature, tend to force apart the aromatic centres giving eventually the imbricated nematic orientation shown on the right of Fig. IX.8.

The dislocation of the residual terminal intermolecular cohesions at the smectic-nematic transition is probably only temporary, and as the interpenetration of the layers becomes greater and the normal imbricated arrangement of the molecules of a nematic melt is approached, the ends of the molecules will once more become associated, and the terminal interactions may again come into play and influence the thermal stability of the nematic melt.

Again then, we have two opposing tendencies as the alkyl chain lengthens, (1) an increasing molecular mass and polarizability tending to increase the resistance to a sliding of the molecules from one layer to another, and (2) an increasing tendency for interpenetration of the layers as the alkyl chains grow longer and more flexible, and the terminal attractions between them grow weaker.

These two effects will in themselves explain the shape of the smectic-nematic transition temperature curves, their rise to a maximum when (1) predominates, their levelling off when (1) and (2) are roughly balanced, and their gradual fall when (2) begins to exert the larger effect.

The levelling off in the smectic-nematic transition temperature curve should therefore occur only when the alkyl chain is reasonably long and the residual terminal cohesions are quite weak. This is, in fact, the case and when the levelling off does occur, we are normally near to the stage in the homologous series at which the smectic-nematic and nematic-isotropic transition temperature curves merge, and nematic properties cease to be observed, i.e. when the re-formed residual terminal cohesions (*a*) are so weak that they are able to maintain the nematic order over only a small temperature range, or (*b*) are unable to maintain this order at all, and the smectic mesophase passes direct to the isotropic liquid.

The direct passage of the smectic mesophase to the isotropic liquid is therefore brought about because of the weakening terminal intermolecular attractions. Smectic-isotropic transition temperatures should therefore depend upon the same factors which determine nematic-isotropic transition temperatures, i.e. they should decrease with increasing alkyl chain length, and they should alternate between odd and even carbon-chain homologues. Further, the nematic-isotropic and smectic-isotropic transition temperature curves should merge and form one continuous curve, as shown in Fig. IX.2 (*a*). In this way, we obtain a reasonable explanation of the shape of the over-all mesomorphic-isotropic transition temperature curve and its continued descent after nematic mesophases cease to appear in the homologous series. The diagram for the 4′-n-alkoxybiphenyl-4-carboxylic acids does not show the alternation of the *smectic*-isotropic transition points, and this would be true for most of the series in Section A of Table IX.2. The reason for this is quite simple. The homologues usually studied have been C_1–C_{10}, C_{12}, C_{16}, and C_{18}, and the smectic-nematic curves do not normally merge with the nematic-isotropic curves until the C_{10} or even the C_{12} homologue is reached. The smectic-isotropic transitions then involve only even carbon-chain homologues, and the alternation would not arise. To obtain evidence for the alternation of smectic-isotropic transition temperatures we must either study a purely smectic series (see on), or a series in which nematic properties cease to appear at an early stage. The 4'-n-alkoxy-3'-nitrobiphenyl-4-carboxylic acids afford an example of the latter kind. The last member of the series which exhibits a nematic mesophase is the hexyl ether, and smectic-isotropic transition temperatures are obtained for the heptyl, octyl, nonyl, decyl .... octadecyl ethers. When the smectic-isotropic transition temperatures of the first four of these ether acids are plotted against the alkyl chain length, a slight but obvious alternation is shown, continuing the alternation of the nematic-isotropic transition temperatures of the propyl, pentyl, and hexyl ethers.

It is interesting to note that there is no detectable alternation of the smectic-nematic transition temperatures in any of the series which have been studied. If we assume that the cog wheel conformation of the alkyl chain is also adopted in the smectic mesophase, then the arguments used to explain the alternation of nematic-isotropic transition temperatures would have to be reversed. That is, if the lateral intermolecular attractions are the attractive forces which maintain the order of the smectic mesophase, then the change from an even to an odd carbon-chain homologue would result in the most marked contribution, from the increase in the polarizability of the alkyl chain, to the lateral attractions. The smectic-nematic transition temperatures of the odd carbon-chain homologues should then be higher than those of the even. However, for many of the series, it is not easy to say *conclusively* that no alternation occurs, for the following reasons: (a) smectic-nematic transitions do not occur for a sufficient number of the homologues, and (b) when smectic-nematic transitions appear relatively early in the series, e.g. for the hexyl ether, the portion of the curve involving odd and even members of the series is rising extremely steeply, such that the alternation would have to be very marked to be detectable.

When the smectic-nematic transition temperature curves do level off and a less marked degree of alternation might be detectable, we are, however, at a stage in the homologous series at which the flexibility of the alkyl chains and the residual terminal attractions between the ends of the molecules are beginning to play their part in determining the temperature of the smectic-nematic transition. It is difficult to imagine how the change from an odd to an even carbon-chain homologue is likely to affect the over-all flexibility of the alkyl chain and the relative ease of interpenetration of the smectic strata. However, we have already argued that the intermolecular terminal cohesions will decrease less on passing from an odd to an even carbon-chain homologue, than vice versa. That is, the alternation effect likely to arise from the effect of the residual *terminal* attractions on the smectic-nematic transition temperatures is likely to oppose that arising from the polarizability increases of the added methylene groups on the *lateral* intermolecular attractions.

The position regarding the possible alternation of smectic-nematic transition temperatures is therefore complicated by several factors. If, of course, the carbon chain adopts the zig-zag conformation in the smectic state, no alternation of the smectic-nematic transition temperatures arising from the relative polarizability effects of odd or even alkyl chains on either the lateral or residual terminal cohesions would be expected. Moreover, it is unlikely that the density effects which explain the alternation of the melting points (solid-isotropic liquid) of open-chain paraffins or paraffinic acids play any part in determining the smectic-nematic transition temperatures, because the statistical variation in the arrangement of the molecules within the smectic layers and across the layer interfaces is probably quite great throughout the bulk of the mesophase. If our explanation of the alternation of nematic-isotropic transition temperatures is correct, and if the absence of any alternation of smectic-nematic transition temperatures is caused by the adoption of the zig-zag conformation of the alkyl chain, then we must postulate a change from the zig-zag to the cog wheel arrangement of the alkyl chain at the smectic-nematic transition, and indeed at some stage before the smectic-*isotropic* transition, since smectic-isotropic transition temperatures alternate as do nematic-isotropic temperatures. It may be that such changes in the conformation of the alkyl chain are possible, but so many arguments may be brought into play that any ideas concerning the absence of alternation of smectic-nematic transition temperatures remain purely speculative.

Within the framework of the group of homologous series or parts of homologous series listed in Sections A and B of Table IX.2.—i.e. giving rise to transition temperature against chain-length plots of the general type shown in Fig. IX.2 (*a*)—there is, of course, a considerable variation in the shapes of the curves. Thus, the gradients of the nematic-isotropic, smectic-nematic, and smectic-isotropic lines vary greatly; in certain series the smectic-nematic lines begin to fall before merging with the nematic-isotropic lines, the position in the series at which merging of the smectic-nematic and nematic-isotropic lines occurs varies widely, and in two series, these two curves have not merged even when the alkyl chain contains eighteen carbon atoms. No pretence can be made to explain these differences of detail, because so many factors having their origin in particular features of the molecular constitution may alter the relative strengths of the lateral and terminal cohesive forces which are presumed to determine the exact shapes of the curves. However, it is satisfying to be able to offer some explanation of the general trends shown by the transition temperature plots of the series in Sections A and B of Table IX.2, and it is of interest to consider now whether these ideas which have been used in reaching these explanations help us to understand the general trends shown by the series listed in the other sections of Table IX.2, i.e. series giving rise to transition temperature against chain length plots of the types shown in Fig. IX.2 (b)–(g).

TRANSITION TEMPERATURE PLOTS OF THE TYPE SHOWN IN FIG. IX.2 (b), (c), and (d)

Figure IX.2 (b) illustrates the transition temperature plot for the n-propyl 4'-n-alkoxybiphenyl-4-carboxylates, which exhibit only smectic mesophases. The smectic-isotropic transition temperatures lie on two curves, clearly indicating an alternation between the odd and the even carbon chain homologues. The curve for the even carbon chain (i.e. in the alkoxyl group) homologues lies uppermost, as for the nematic-isotropic transitions. This suggests that terminal intermolecular attractions are playing their part in determining the smectic-isotropic transition temperatures, just as they do for homologous series of the type shown in Fig. IX.2 (a), after nematic mesophases cease to appear. That is, the destruction of the smectic molecular order is determined by the fact that the terminal attractions are becoming weaker, so allowing interpenetration of the layers to occur more easily as the alkyl chains grow longer. This explains the falling smectic-isotropic transition temperature curves for the higher homologues of the series, but not the rise to a maximum, before this fall occurs, for the transition lines of both odd and even carbon-chain members of the series. For these early members of the series which give increasing smectic-isotropic transition temperatures as the alkyl chain lengthens, the terminal intermolecular attractions will be at their strongest, but the lateral intermolecular attractions will be at their weakest. The smectic-isotropic transition temperatures of the first members of the series must therefore be determined by the weak lateral attractions. These attractions will increase as the chains grow longer, and the smectic mesophases will increase in thermal stability, but only up to a point, for as the alkyl chains lengthen still further, the terminal cohesions grow weaker and the probability of interpenetration of the smectic strata at a lower temperature increases. For the higher homologues, therefore, the weakening terminal cohesions determine the thermal stabilities of the smectic mesophases, and explain the subsequent fall in the smectic-isotropic transition line as the series is ascended. The shape of either one of the two smectic-isotropic transition temperature lines in Fig. IX.2 (b) is very similar to that of the combined smectic-nematic and smectic-isotropic transition temperature plots for many of the series in Section A of Table IX.2, and obviously, the same explanations have been used to account for both—increasing lateral attractions determining the initial rise of the curve, and decreasing terminal attractions the subsequent fall. The difference between the two cases lies solely in the fact that the terminal intermolecular attractions in the early stages of the homologous series of esters are not sufficiently strong to reform and produce a nematic mesophase, after the lateral attractions have disrupted.

A transition temperature against chain-length plot of the type shown in Fig. IX.2 (b) has been obtained for only three homologous series, the n-propyl 4′-n-alkoxybiphenyl-4-carboxylates (see above), the 6-n-alkoxy-5-nitro-2-naphthoic acids, and the n-propyl 4′-n-alkoxy-3′-nitrobiphenyl-4-carboxylates. The smectic-isotropic transition temperature plot for the nitronaphthoic acids is very similar to Fig. IX.2 (b), but, because of the monotropic nature of the smectic mesophases, is obtained for only a portion of the homologous series (C_9–C_{18}). However, for the even members, the rise to a maximum and then the fall after the dodecyl ether is clearly demonstrated, and the low smectic-isotropic transition temperature of the nonyl ether implies that an alternation does occur. The nitrobiphenyl esters again give two smectic-isotropic transition curves with the usual alternation. Both curves rise steadily as the series is ascended, and reach a maximum only at the hexadecyl ether, the smectic-isotropic transition temperature of the octadecyl ether being only 0·5° lower than that of the hexadecyl ether. The unusual feature here is the late stage in the series at which levelling off in the smectic-isotropic curve takes place. The analogous compounds with chloro-(II) instead of nitro- (III) as substituent are not mesomorphic,

II   III

and the occurrence of mesophases in the series represented by III, which depicts a broader molecule than II, is explained by the strong ring-NO_2 dipole moment. That is, despite the breadth and shape of the molecules of the nitro- esters, relatively strong lateral attractions must operate. The terminal intermolecular attractions must therefore weaken considerably before they begin to cause a decrease in the smectic-isotropic transition temperatures, and in these terms, the continued rise in the smectic-isotropic curves to such a late stage in the homologous series as the hexadecyl ether is understandable. It will be noted too, that for the nitronaphthoic acids, which should again involve relatively strong lateral cohesions, the maximum in the smectic-isotropic curve is attained only at the dodecyl ether.

In one other homologous series, the ethyl 4'-n-alkoxybiphenyl-4-carboxylates, the occurrence of maxima in the smectic-isotropic transition point curves can be implied although not definitely proved. The transition temperature against chain-length plot for this series is represented in Fig. IX.2 (c). The alternation of the smectic-isotropic temperatures is quite marked, and the first homologue to exhibit a mesophase is the pentyl ether. The distribution of the melting points of the first four, non-mesomorphic ethyl esters is interesting, for these rise to a maximum at propyl and then fall to butyl. Therefore, if we extrapolate the *smectic*-isotropic transition point curves in such a way that they conform to the shape of a normal nematic-isotropic transition point curve (Fig. IX.2 (a)), the methyl and ethyl ethers, and perhaps also the propyl and butyl ethers, should exhibit enantiotropic smectic meso-

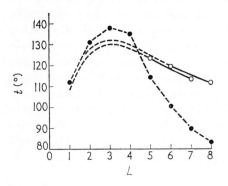

FIG. IX.10. A more detailed picture of the changes in m.p. (●) and smectic-isotropic transition temperature (O) for the earlier members of the homologous series of ethyl 4'-n-alkoxybiphenyl-4-carboxylates (see also Fig. IX.2 (c)).

phases. The position is shown more clearly in Fig. IX.10, where the full circles represent the melting points (solid-smectic or -isotropic) and the open circles the smectic-isotropic transition temperatures. Since enantiotropic smectic-isotropic transitions are not in fact observed for the methyl to butyl ethers, it must be implied that their melting points are higher than the maximum temperatures at which mesophases could exist for these ethers, i.e. their " mesophases ", if they could be detected, would be monotropic. The inference is that these " monotropic transition temperatures " (isotropic-smectic) lie below the melting points in each case, so that the completed smectic-isotropic transition point curves for the series can be envisaged only by extrapolating (broken curves) as shown in Figs. IX.2 (c) and IX.10.

These " monotropic smectic mesophases " are not in fact observed, because the isotropic liquids do not supercool sufficiently before crystallization occurs. In fact, the melts of the ethyl–butyl ethers crystallize within 0·5° of their melting points, and that of the methyl ether only

4° below the melting point. Therefore, although the shape of the broken section of the curves is purely conjectural, it is legitimate to draw the two extrapolated portions fairly close to the melting points (full circles). Bearing in mind the alternation of these hypothetical points, we therefore infer that the two curves rise to a maximum and then fall as the series is ascended.

It is possible that a similar state of affairs occurs for the methyl esters, but in this series, the melting points fall steadily from the methyl ether to the hexyl ether, which is the first mesomorphic member of the series, and this possibility cannot be confirmed.

It is evident then that data are available to show that the smectic-isotropic transition lines for homologous series of purely smectic compounds may be expected to rise to a maximum and then fall again as the series is ascended. The stage in the series at which the maximum is reached is obviously determined by the chemical constitution of the molecules involved, and structures giving rise to strong lateral inter-molecular attractions will tend to delay the attainment of the maximum until longer alkyl chain lengths. In addition to the series of esters discussed above, the smectic systems grouped together in Section E of Table IX.2 further substantiate the tendency of smectic-isotropic transition point curves to give an initial rise to a maximum. The four systems in Section E each constitute a part of an homologous series, and in each case the smectic-isotropic transition lines rise, though to quite a small extent, as the chain length grows. Only four ethers (heptyl–decyl) have been examined so far for these four systems, but it is obvious that, if the alkyl chains were extended, maxima in these smectic-isotropic transition lines would quickly be achieved. The transition temperature against chain-length plot for one of these series is shown in Fig. IX.2 (d), but there is in fact no real distinction between such a series and say the n-propyl 4'-n-alkoxy-3'-nitrobiphenyl-4-carboxylates which give a transition temperature plot of the type shown in Fig. IX.2 (b). In fact, only two series of purely smectic compounds have been studied which do not give direct evidence for the initial rise of smectic-isotropic transition lines. One of these cases, the methyl 4'-n-alkoxybiphenyl-4-carboxylates, has already been discussed, and here it is merely the distribution of the melting points of the lower homologues which makes it impossible to say whether or not maxima in the transition lines occur. In the other case, the n-propyl 7-n-alkoxyfluorene-2-carboxylates, only four ethers (heptyl–decyl) have been examined. The smectic-isotropic transition temperatures for these four ethers fall gently as the chain is extended, but when the lower homologues are studied, it is quite likely that a transition temperature against chain-length plot of the type shown in Fig. IX.2 (b) will be obtained.

TRANSITION TEMPERATURE PLOTS OF THE TYPE
SHOWN IN FIG. IX.2 (e) AND (f)

The case for smectic-nematic and smectic-isotropic transitions and the regular trends to which they give rise in homologous series is therefore quite straightforward, and this discussion now moves to nematic-isotropic transition temperature plots of the type shown in Fig. IX.2 (e) and (f). Parts of twelve different homologous series of nematogenic compounds—with or without accompanying smectic mesophases—which give nematic-isotropic transition lines which rise with increasing alkyl chain length, are grouped in Sections F and G of Table IX.2. The compounds in these two sections fall into two groups:

(a) 4-p-n-alkoxybenzylideneaminobiphenyls carrying a substituent in one or other of the two sterically affecting 2- or 2'- positions in the biphenyl ring system, c.f. IV.

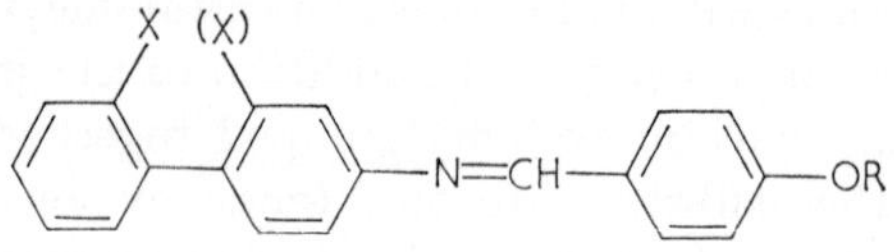

IV

Because of their size, these substituents may prevent the two aromatic rings of the biphenyl nucleus from being coplanar.

(b) 4-p-n-alkoxybenzylideneaminobiphenyls substituted in the 3-position, c.f. V and VI.

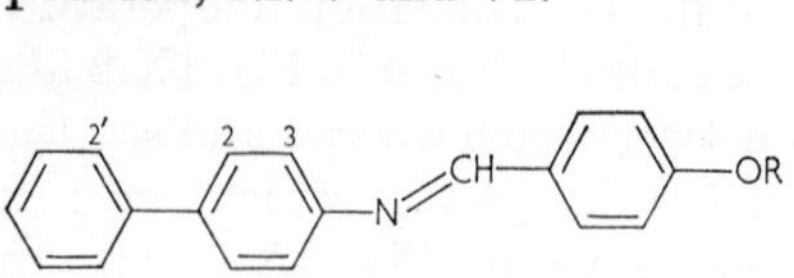

V 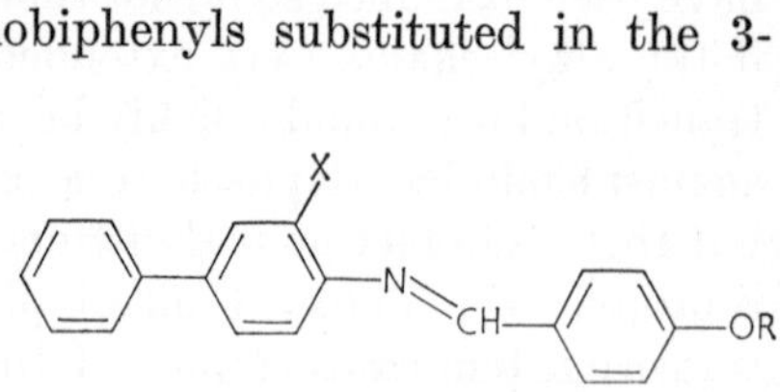   VI

In the cis- structure of the molecule (V), this 3-substituent may interfere with the hydrogen atom of the azo-methine linkage, and prevent the attainment of a coplanar arrangement of the biphenyl nucleus and the p-n-alkoxybenzylideneamino- group. A fuller discussion of the validity of postulating a steric effect in this type of system is given in Chapter X.

Thus, all the compounds in Sections F and G of Table IX.2 may be sterically affected in one way or another. The effect of these steric influences will be to increase the thickness of the molecules. This should make it more difficult for the molecules to pack economically side by side in a parallel arrangement, and should result in a weakening of the lateral intermolecular cohesions. Even if the 3-substituted mono-anils adopt the *trans-* configuration (VI), for which there is no steric effect, the molecule is far from rod-shaped. Economical packing of the molecules therefore will again be difficult. Indeed, only five of the group of twelve compounds in Sections F and G of Table IX.2 exhibit smectic mesophases, and in none of these series does the smectic-nematic curve merge with the nematic-isotropic transition point curve even when the alkyl chain contains ten carbon atoms. More striking is the series of 4-*p*-n-alkoxybenzylideneamino-2-methylbiphenyls for which alkyl chains such as heptyl–decyl, dodecyl, hexadecyl, and octadecyl have been employed. Even for the octadecyl ether, the two curves have not merged, although a nematic mesophase of thermal stability range equal to only 1° separates the two. These factors concerning the smectic mesophases of these compounds stress that the lateral intermolecular attractions between such sterically affected or awkwardly shaped molecules are anomalously low. Now our immediate concern is the nematic melt and the nematic-isotropic transition point curve, and we should therefore consider the effect of anomalously low *residual* lateral attractions on the thermal stability of the nematic mesophase.

For what may be termed normal series of compounds, i.e. those listed in Sections A and B of Table IX.2, and giving a transition temperature against chain length plot of the general form shown in Fig. IX.2 (*a*), it will be remembered that the shape of the nematic-isotropic transition line has been explained in terms of the decreasing intermolecular terminal attractions. These terminal interactions explain the alternation of nematic-isotropic transition temperatures, and the decreasing gradient of the falling nematic-isotropic transition curve with increasing alkyl chain length is explained by: (*a*) the tendency of the terminal attractions to become equivalent to the interactions between long paraffin chains, and not to fall to zero; and (*b*) the modifying effect of the increasing residual lateral attractions, which will assist in the maintenance of the nematic molecular order.

Now, if the lateral attractions between the molecules are extremely weak relative to the intermolecular terminal attractions, the nematic thermal stability may be determined by the former of these two effects. Thus, if we imagine a nematic molecular orientation in which the long molecules are extremely firmly linked together by their ends, then, in the absence of adequate lateral interactions, chains of these molecules may split off from the swarm and assume coiled or otherwise random orientations with respect to other similar chains and neighbouring swarms. Presumably of course, as soon as a chain of molecules begins to dissociate itself from the swarm, thermal vibrations will quickly break up the chain into individual molecules, for in practice, our molecules are not, as assumed above, *extremely* firmly linked together by their ends. We are saying that very weak lateral intermolecular attractions may

expect then, that on passing from a small to a large substituent, the lateral intermolecular attractions would become weaker, the terminal intermolecular attractions should be less able to counteract the increasing lateral attractions as the homologous series is ascended, and the nematic-isotropic transition line should rise more steeply. The gradient of the nematic-isotropic transition line is recorded in Table IX.6 as the increase in the nematic-isotropic transition temperature on passing from the heptyl to the nonyl ether. By reference to models of the *cis*- configurations of the molecules, substituents in the 3- position are found to cause smaller twisting effects than they would in the 2- or 2'- positions. We find therefore that the smallest increases in the nematic-isotropic transition temperatures in Table IX.6 are for the 3-chloro- and 3-bromo- derivatives. As will be discussed in Chapter X, an alternative suggestion is that the 3-substituted anils adopt the *trans*- configuration which does not involve a steric effect, but confers an awkward shape

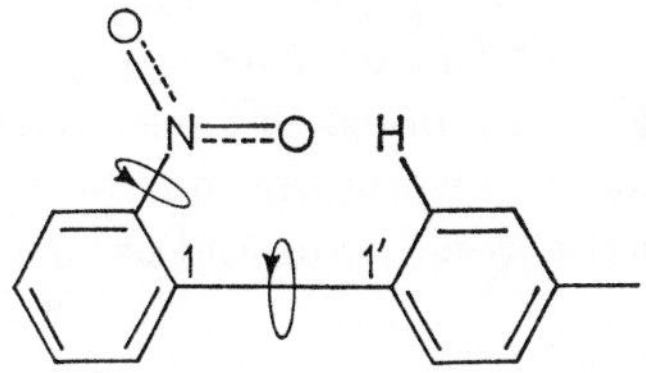

FIG. IX. 11. Rotation about the ring-NO_2 bond may lessen the extent of the twist about the 1,1'-bond between the rings in 2-nitrobiphenyls.

upon the molecule. Taking chloro- as an example, this substituent causes increases (Table IX.6) in the transition temperatures of 1, 7·5 and 7·5° when it occupies the 3-, 2-, and 2'- positions respectively. It will be noted that the 3-bromo- substituent has a larger effect on the gradient than the smaller 3-chloro- substituent. The effects are therefore much more noticeable with 2-substituents, a marked increase in gradient of the transition line occurring on increasing the substituent's size from fluoro- to chloro- to bromo- to iodo-. The 2'-chloro-, bromo-, and iodo- substituents show a similar effect. The 2'-nitro- group, despite its size, increases the gradient of the line by only 7·5°, the effect which might be expected from a substituent equal in size to chloro-. In this case, of course, we may argue that the dipole moment of the substituent is high and will enhance the lateral attractive forces, so counteracting the bulk effect of the substituent. However, there is a further factor to consider, namely that the steric effect of a nitro- group in the 2- or 2'- position, and its effect on the twisting of the phenyl rings from coplanarity, may be reduced considerably by rotation of the nitro- group about the ring-NO_2 bond—see Fig. IX.11. Such a rotation decreases the interplanar angle, and the 2'-nitro-derivatives are not simple cases to discuss. A 2-methyl group has a very similar effect to that of a 2-chloro- substituent, and this is in agreement with the fact that the two substituents are of similar size. The smaller effect of the 2'-methyl group is not, however, easily explained.

Only five of the twelve series of compounds mentioned in Table IX.6 and taken from Sections F and G of Table IX.2 exhibit smectic properties, and there are insufficient facts on which to base any discussion of the gradients of the smectic-nematic curves (Fig. IX.2 (f)). These five smectic-nematic curves, in keeping with those for the series listed in Sections A and B of Table IX.2, reveal no alternation of the transition temperatures. The nematic-isotropic transition temperatures for all the series in Sections F and G of Table IX.2 do, however, alternate. This again implies that the rupture of terminal intermolecular attractions is involved at this type of transition. This fact has been recognized in the above arguments, and does not weaken the proposal that the transitions to the isotropic liquids are first brought about by the weakening of the *lateral* intermolecular attractions. That is, the terminal cohesions become involved as a secondary effect, and are therefore still able to impose an alternation on the transition temperatures as the series is ascended through odd and even carbon-chain members.

THE TRANSITION TEMPERATURE PLOT SHOWN IN FIG. IX.2 (g)

At this stage, we may consider Fig. IX.2 (g), the transition temperature against chain-length plot for the open-chain aliphatic esters of cholesterol. The smectic-cholesteric transition line rises to a maximum at cholesteryl laurate and then falls, and the approach of this transition line to the falling cholesteric-isotropic transition line for the longer-chain homologues is extremely gradual—the thermal stability ranges of the cholesteric mesophases of the myristate, palmitate, and stearate are respectively 5·5, 4·5, and 4°. We may infer therefore that the two curves will coincide at sufficiently great alkyl chain lengths. The cholesteric-isotropic transition temperatures constitute two curves, showing an alternation. In this case, the esters with an uneven number of carbon atoms in the alkyl chain give rise to the uppermost of the two curves, for the extra carbon atom in the carboalkoxy group makes such esters equivalent to ethers containing an even number of carbon atoms in the alkyl group. The curve through the transition points for the acetate, butyrate, and other esters with an odd number of carbon atoms in the alkyl chain rises to a maximum at the butyrate and then falls smoothly to the stearate. Considering the esters with an even number of carbon atoms in the alkyl group, and beginning with cholesteryl propionate, the transition line falls quite rapidly at first and then more gradually as the alkyl chain is extended. If we consider zero to be an even number, and include cholesteryl formate with the esters containing an even number of carbon atoms in the alkyl chain, then this transition line too will rise to a maximum (at the propionate), for the monotropic isotropic-cholesteric transition temperature for the formate occurs at $60 \cdot 5°$, compared with the enantiotropic cholesteric-isotropic transition temperature of $116°$ for the propionate. However, the transition point for the formate has not been included in Fig. IX.2 (g), since the terminal cohesions arising from the formate grouping will not be comparable with those originating from carboalkoxy groups containing an even number of atoms in the alkyl chain.

However, the other cholesteric-isotropic transition temperature curve is similar in shape to the smectic-isotropic curve for the n-propyl 4'-n-alkoxybiphenyl-4-carboxylates (Fig. IX.2 (b)). It is therefore tempting to consider whether cholesteric-isotropic and smectic-isotropic transitions may not be related, and whether the cholesteric mesophase may not simply be a polymesomorphic modification of the smectic mesophase, i.e. that the smectic-cholesteric transition line is similar to a smectic I–smectic II or smectic II–smectic III transition line, as shown in Fig. IX.2 (h) for the polymesomorphic series of 4'-n-alkoxy-3'-nitrobiphenyl-4-carboxylic acids. However, as emphasized in earlier chapters, the characteristic properties of the cholesteric mesophase allow one to draw analogies with *both* smectic and nematic mesophases, and it would be unwise to interpret this similarity between the shapes of the cholesteric-isotropic and smectic-isotropic transition lines of two series as proof of the similarity of smectic and cholesteric mesophases. Indeed, a particular note of caution in interpreting the above results may be struck now that it is realized that nematic-isotropic transition lines may rise with increasing alkyl chain length. Admittedly, for such series (Sections F and G of Table IX.2), the rising nematic-isotropic transition lines have barely reached a maximum at the longest alkyl chains (C_{18}) so far studied. However, it is possible that a certain balance between the terminal and lateral attractions may result in a rapid increase in a nematic-isotropic transition line early in an homologous series, followed by a normal fall in this line as the molecule is lengthened. If this were possible, then of course the cholesteric mesophase could be identified with the nematic mesophase. The full significance of the shapes of the cholesteric-isotropic transition lines in the plot for the cholesteryl esters remains therefore in considerable doubt.

TRANSITION TEMPERATURE PLOTS OF THE TYPE SHOWN IN
FIG. IX.2 (h)

Turning now to the last of the transition temperature against alkyl chain length plots in the composite Fig. IX.2, i.e. Fig. IX.2 (h), this illustrates the type of transition temperature plot obtained for polymesomorphic compounds, with particular reference to the 4′-n-alkoxy-3′-nitrobiphenyl-4-carboxylic acids. There is nothing unusual about the nematic-isotropic, smectic-isotropic, or smectic III-nematic transition lines for this series. The polymesomorphic transition lines are: (a) the smectic II–smectic III curve, which rises smoothly from the hexyl to the dodecyl ether, and then falls to the octadecyl ether; and (b) the smectic I–smectic II curve which rises steeply from the dodecyl to the hexadecyl ether, and then levels off to the octadecyl ether.

However, since we remain ignorant of the changes in the molecular organization which occur at such polymesomorphic transitions, it is obviously impossible to comment on the significance of the shapes of these transition lines. Polymesomorphism of the smectic mesophase is

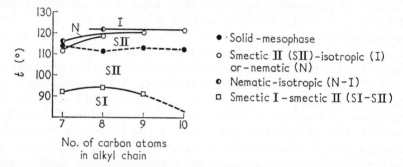

FIG. IX.12. The various transition temperatures for the 4-p-n-alkoxybenzylidene-amino-3′-methylbiphenyls plotted against the number of carbon atoms in the alkyl chain of the ether group.

also known to occur in the 6-n-alkoxy-5-nitro-2-naphthoic acids and the 3′- and 4′- methyl derivatives of the 4-p-n-alkoxybenzylideneamino-biphenyls. For the nitronaphthoic acids, the smectic-smectic changes are monotropic for all the ethers (nonyl, decyl, dodecyl, hexadecyl, and octadecyl) for which the polymesomorphism has been observed, and even approximate temperatures for the transformations are not available. Only one ether (alkyl = nonyl) has been examined for the 4-p-n-alkoxybenzylideneamino-4′-methylbiphenyls, and although the various transition temperatures may be determined accurately (solid-smectic I, 130°; smectic I–smectic II, 166°; smectic II–nematic, 184°; nematic-isotropic, 233°), until other homologues are studied, we cannot say whether the smectic I-smectic II transition temperatures change regularly along the homologous series. In the case of the 3′-methyl isomers, the heptyl–decyl ethers have been prepared, and the transition temperature against alkyl chain length plots for the four homologues are shown in Fig. IX.12.

The melting points are rather irregularly disposed, and it will be noted that smectic mesophase I is monotropic for all four homologues.

The smectic II-smectic I transformation was too far below the melting point of the decyl ether to obtain an actual temperature for the change. The mesomorphic-isotropic transition temperatures alternate as usual, and the plot shows that the nematic-isotropic temperatures increase as the series is ascended. The two smectic II-nematic transitions (heptyl and octyl) obviously comprise the latter part of a normal rising smectic-nematic curve before it becomes coincident with the nematic-isotropic curve. However, the main point is that the three monotropic smectic II-smectic I transition temperatures appear to lie on a curve with its maximum at the octyl ether, a curve which then falls steeply to the point for the decyl ether.

The limited data available do therefore suggest that not only do polymesomorphic transitions between smectic mesophases occur at definite temperatures, but also that these temperatures change in some regular way as an homologous series is ascended. Smoothly rising curves reaching their maxima and then levelling off or falling steeply again appear to describe these smectic-smectic transition lines. Whatever the changes involved at these polymesomorphic transitions may be, they appear to be quite sensitive to the changes in the intermolecular cohesions which occur as the alkyl chain is progressively lengthened. These regular trends in polymesomorphic transition temperatures emphasize once more that these changes are real, and involve some fundamental modification to the molecular order in the smectic mesophases.

One question alone remains to be discussed, and this is the behaviour of the series of 2-p-n-alkoxybenzylideneaminofluorenones. These compounds have been included in section A of Table IX.2, and are listed as giving a general plot of mesomorphic transition temperature against alkyl chain length of the general type shown in Fig. IX.2 (a). However, as the series is ascended, the trends shown by the nematic-isotropic transition temperatures of the lower homologues (C_1–C_7) are seen to be anomalous. The form of the transition temperature plot has already been illustrated in Fig. IX.3 (p. 207), but in general terms, the unusual features are that (a) for the homologues containing an even number of carbon atoms in the alkyl group, the nematic-isotropic transition temperatures fall from ethyl to butyl, rise again slightly to hexyl, and then fall in the usual way through the points for the remainder of the series; and (b) for the homologues containing an odd number of carbon atoms in the alkyl group, the nematic-isotropic transition temperatures fall from methyl to propyl, rise again from propyl to heptyl, and remain constant for the nonyl ether.

Now that we have discussed nematic-isotropic transition lines which rise as a homologous series is ascended, it is interesting to examine whether an explanation of this behaviour can be reached. It would seem reasonable to suggest that if molecules are arranged in a regular orientation by both lateral and terminal intermolecular attractions of different relative strengths, then the weaker of the two types of cohesive force should determine the temperature at which thermal vibrations finally cause the breakdown of the molecular order. This general concept has been used throughout the discussions in this chapter. However, if the lateral intermolecular attractions are *weak*, and relatively speaking, the terminal attractions are *very strong* then it is possible that the strong terminal cohesions delay the breakdown in the molecular order, i.e. that the terminal attractions may maintain the order after the lateral attractions have been disrupted. Now the 2-*p*-n-alkoxybenzylideneaminofluorenones appear to give rise to weak lateral attractions, because the thermal stability of the smectic mesophase is very low, and merging of the smectic-nematic and nematic-isotropic transition lines is delayed until alkyl chain lengths in excess of eighteen carbon atoms. On this basis, a rising nematic-isotropic transition line might be expected for this series. Now, for those series which do give rise to rising nematic-isotropic transition lines, lower homologues have not been studied, i.e. the series has usually been restricted to the heptyl-decyl ethers. If these four homologues alone had been studied for the above fluorenone derivatives, their behaviour would have fitted with any of the series in Section B of Table IX.2. If the pentyl–decyl ethers had been studied, the pattern of behaviour would have been that shown by the compounds listed in Section G of Table IX.2. Thus, the high nematic-isotropic transition temperatures of the methyl and ethyl ethers are the anomalous feature of this series. Now, relative to the other homologues of the series, the terminal interactions for the methyl and ethyl ethers will be strongest and the lateral interactions will be weakest. If these strong terminal attractive forces are able to maintain the molecular order despite the very weak lateral attractions, then on passing to the propyl and butyl ethers, for which weaker terminal attractions will operate, decreases in the nematic-isotropic transition temperatures may occur. If after the butyl ether, the terminal interactions are unable to override the lateral interactions, then the temperature at which the nematic order breaks up will be determined by the weak lateral attractions. These lateral attractions increase as the alkyl chain lengthens and the nematic-isotropic transition line will begin to rise. As discussed earlier in this chapter, these lateral attractions increase rapidly at first and then more gradually as the alkyl chain grows longer. Therefore a stage will be reached in the series at which the weakening terminal attractions begin to determine the nematic-isotropic transition temperatures, and the nematic-isotropic transition lines will then level off and fall.

Of course, behaviour such as this can be explained only for series of compounds for which the lateral intermolecular cohesions are weak. In the above 2-*p*-n-alkoxybenzylideneaminofluorenones (VI), the weakness of these cohesions must be

VI

explained by the substantial breadth increase, compared with the analogous fluorene and biphenyl compounds, caused by the bulky C=O group. Indeed, the effectiveness of the dipole of the carbonyl group in enhancing the lateral attractions appears to be completely eliminated by the breadth increase. A transition temperature plot of the type shown in Fig. IX.3 would therefore be expected only for series of compounds for which the nematic-isotropic transition line tends to rise for the middle members of the series—an effect again caused by weak lateral attractions. It is quite clear that the lower members of several of the series in Sections F and G of Table IX.2 should be prepared in order to ascertain whether the nematic-isotropic transition lines show these trends which are at the moment peculiar to the 2-*p*-n-alkoxybenzylidene-aminofluorenones. It should be emphasized that particularly stringent precautions were taken to ensure the purity of the lower homologues of the series of fluorenone monoanils, and the possibility that contamination of the products explains the anomalous behaviour may be eliminated.

This unusual behaviour is not encountered for the 2,7-di-(*p*-n-alkoxybenzylideneamino)fluorenones. For these molecules, the second benzylideneamino- group will greatly augment the lateral intermolecular attractions and counteract the breadth effect of the carbonyl group. The pattern of behaviour is therefore normal for a series giving a plot of the type shown in Fig. IX.2 (*a*).

A fairly full discussion of the trends shown by mesomorphic transition temperatures as homologous series of compounds are ascended has been given. This has been done in order to emphasize that smooth curve relationships of one or other of a limited number of types are to be expected between the mesomorphic transition temperatures and the alkyl chain lengths, and that the occurrence of irregular trends indicates that the compounds may not be pure. Of course, many of the arguments that have been put forward to explain these trends have their weaknesses. However, the fact that regular trends occur so frequently, and that arguments may be proposed to explain them is in itself satisfying and encouraging, and if in the future, some of the arguments used in this chapter are shown to be wrong, it is of small significance provided that what has been said stimulates thought about these regular trends and leads to better, and finally to the correct explanations of them.

REFERENCES

1. Gray, G. W. and Jones, B. (1953). *J. Chem. Soc.* 4197.
2. Gray, G. W. and Jones, B. (1954). *J. Chem. Soc.* 1467.
3. Gray, G. W. Hartley, J. B. and Jones, B. (1955). *J. Chem. Soc.* 1412.
4. Gray, G. W. and Jones, B. (1954). *J. Chem. Soc.* 683.
5. Gray, G. W. and Ibbotson, A. (1957). *J. Chem. Soc.* 3228.
6. Gray, G. W. and Jones, B. (1954). *J. Chem. Soc.* 2556.
7. Gray, G. W., Jones, B. and Marson, F. (1956). *J. Chem. Soc.* 1417.
8. Gray, G. W., Jones, B. and Marson, F. (1957). *J. Chem. Soc.* 393
9. Gray, G. W. and Jones, B. (1955). *J. Chem. Soc.* 236.
10. Gray, G. W., Hartley, J. B., Ibbotson, A. and Jones, B. (1955). *J. Chem. Soc.* 4359.
11. Gray, G. W. (1958). *J. Chem. Soc.* 552.
12. Gray, G. W. (1958). " Steric Effects in Conjugated Systems ", Butterworths, London, p. 160 (Ed. G. W. Gray).
13. Byron, D. J., Gray, G. W., Ibbotson, A. and Worrall, B. M. Unpublished work.
14. Gray, G. W. (1956). *J. Chem. Soc.* 3733.
15. Bryan, R. F. (1960). *J. Chem. Soc.* 2517.
16. Maier, W. and Baumgartner, G. (1952). *Z. Naturforsch.* **7a**, 172.
17. Maier, W. (1947). *Z. Naturforsch.* **2a**, 458.

CHAPTER X

THE EFFECTS OF SUBSTITUENTS AND OF STERIC FACTORS ON MESOMORPHIC* THERMAL STABILITIES

In discussing different facets of the problem of relating mesomorphic properties to chemical constitution, it has already been necessary to say a certain amount about the effects of substituents on mesomorphic thermal stabilities, and indeed, the influence of terminal substituents has been discussed in detail. As far as substituents which occupy positions along the sides of the long molecules are concerned, it has been made clear that these decrease the thermal stabilities of both mesophase types (smectic and nematic). For example, consider the effect of introducing a chloro- substituent[1] into the 3-position of a *p*-n-alkoxy-benzoic acid (I).

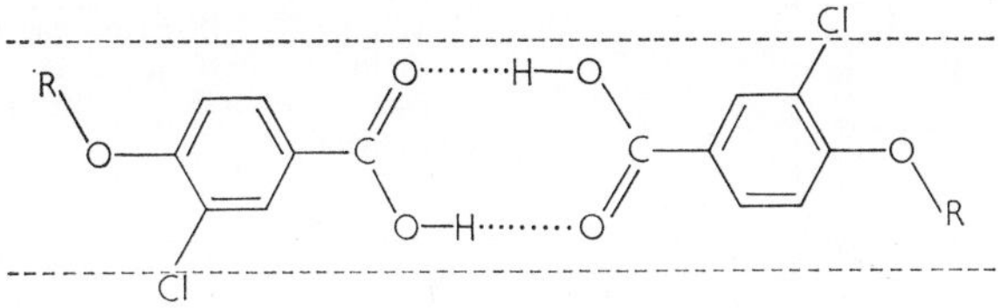

I

The *trans-* configuration of the dimer has been drawn above, because this represents the most symmetrical structure for the molecule. If we define the breadth of a molecule as the diameter of the smallest cylinder through which the molecule will pass, flexible parts such as alkyl chains being assumed not to interfere, then the breadth of a *p*-n-alkoxybenzoic acid molecule will be equivalent to the distance between the two parallel, broken lines shown in I. It is obvious that the 3-chloro- substituent increases the breadth of the unsubstituted molecule, and this will be generally true for any substituent larger than a hydrogen atom, i.e. for all substituents. Therefore, the effect of substitution which leads to an increase in molecular breadth, is that the long narrow molecules will be forced further apart, so reducing the strength of the intermolecular lateral attractions. Both smectic and nematic mesophases depend to a greater or lesser extent on these cohesive forces to maintain the parallel

---

* In this chapter, we are concerned only with smectic and nematic mesophases. The effects of substituents on cholesteric thermal stabilities have been but scantily studied, and the work which has been carried out has been discussed in Chapter VIII.

orientations of the molecules. Therefore, substitution leading to an increase in molecular breadth will decrease the smectic and nematic thermal stabilities, i.e. the smectic-nematic, smectic-isotropic, and nematic-isotropic transition temperatures.

However, the replacement of the hydrogen in the 3-position of the p-n-alkoxybenzoic acids by chloro- and other substituents introduces an additional dipole moment into the molecule. This dipole may reinforce both the lateral and terminal intermolecular attractions, provided that it is suitably directed in the molecule, and will therefore counteract the breadth-increasing effect of the substituent. The increased polarizability of the substituted molecule will act in the same way, reinforcing the permanent dipolar effect of the substituent. The introduction of a substituent into a side position in the molecule of a mesomorphic compound has therefore two opposing effects: (1) the substituent will de-

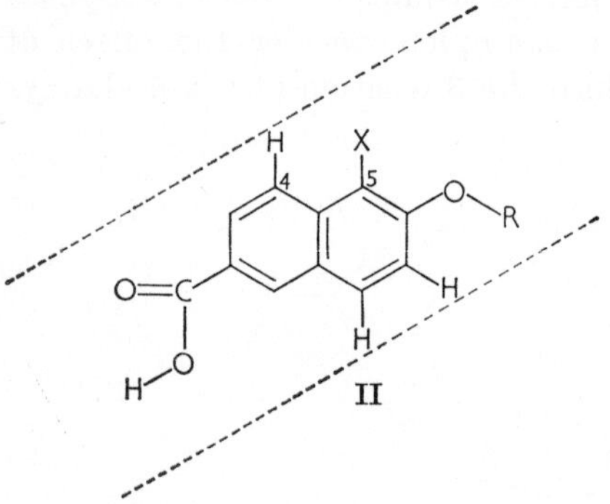

When X = Cl, the breadth of the 5-chloro- derivative is virtually the same as that of the unsubstituted molecule.

crease both smectic and nematic thermal stabilities by increasing the separation of the long axes of the molecules; and (2) the substituent will increase both smectic and nematic thermal stabilities because of its polarization effects which will enhance the intermolecular cohesions.

In the case of the 5-substituted 6-n-alkoxy-2-naphthoic acids[2] (II), for which effect (1) is greatly reduced by the protective effect of the protruding 4-hydrogen atom (the broken lines shown in II represent the breadth of the unsubstituted molecule), effect (2) predominates, and the mesomorphic thermal stabilities are frequently higher than those of the parent 6-n-alkoxy-2-naphthoic acids.

However, in most systems, the substituent exerts its full breadth increasing effect on the molecule, and when this occurs, effect (1) predominates, and there is a marked decrease in the smectic and nematic thermal stabilities on passing from unsubstituted to substituted system.

A considerable body of data for the effect of substituents such as fluoro-, chloro-, bromo-, iodo-, nitro-, and methyl on different parent mesomorphic compounds is now available, and some of this is summarized in Table X.1. The effects of these substituents on a particular system have usually been examined for a group of at least four homologues. However, to simplify the presentation of the data in Table X.1, transition temperatures and changes in mesomorphic thermal stabilities are recorded for only one homologue, usually the decyl ether. When average transition temperatures for a number of homologues are considered, the general trends are the same, and only the extents of the increases or decreases in the mesomorphic thermal stabilities are altered.

For most of the compounds in Table X.1, well-defined decreases in mesomorphic thermal stability occur when substituents are introduced into the sides of the molecules, and several other examples of this type could be quoted, e.g. 3- and 3,3′-substituted 4,4′-di-(p-n-alkoxy-benzylideneamino) biphenyls,[3] the acids and Schiff's bases of the type shown in Table X.1, but containing branched alkyl chains, the Schiff's bases of 4-aminobiphenyl with 3-substituted p-n-alkoxybenzaldehydes, and the 4-n-alkoxy-1-naphthoic acids[4] (III). In this last case, we have

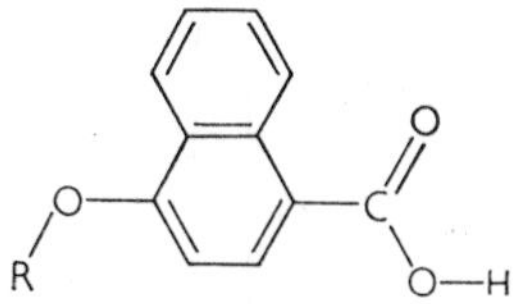

III

effectively a p-n-alkoxybenzoic acid with a side-substituent which bridges the 2- and 3- positions. The bulk of this substituent is so great that the compounds are not in fact mesomorphic. Similar considerations apply to the non-mesomorphic 4-n-alkoxy-3-bromo-benzoic acids.

In the range of side-substituted mesomorphic compounds which have been studied, the 5-substituted 6-n-alkoxy-2-naphthoic acids stand almost alone in having greater mesomorphic thermal stabilities than the unsubstituted compound. This is not surprising, because it is difficult to imagine many molecules whose stereochemistry will lend such protection to a position into which a substituent may be readily introduced. Only one other example of this kind springs to mind, and this involves mesomorphic compounds derived from fluorene (IV).

Unlike the molecule of 2-methylbiphenyl (V) which is linear, but non-planar because of the twisting of the phenyl rings about the 1,1′-bond, the molecule of fluorene is planar, but strained, in the sense that the axes of each of the phenyl rings are inclined at a small angle (11°) to the interannular bond[5] (IV). The structure of a Schiff's base derived from 2-aminofluorene is shown in VI, and the breadth of this molecule may be considered as the separation of the two parallel broken lines, of which the uppermost is drawn tangential to the surface of the hydrogen atom occupying the 3′- position in ring B. Compared with the biphenyl

TABLE X.1

System*	Substituent (X)	S—N(°)	N—I(°)	Change† in mesomorphic thermal stability (°) from parent compound (X=H)	
				smectic	nematic
RO—⟨X⟩—CO_2H	H	122	142		
	F	112	116·5	−10	−25·5
	Cl	(86)‡	(90·5)	−36	−51·5
**RO—⟨X⟩—$CH{=}CH{\cdot}CO_2H$	H	157	165		
	Cl	133·5	134	−23·5	−31
	Br	(<127)	128	>−30	−37
***RO—⟨X⟩—⟨⟩—CO_2H	H	255	264·5		
	F	254·5	255·5	−0·5	−9
	Cl	225	233	−30	−31·5
	Br	214	224	−41	−40·5
	I	192·5	214	−62·5	−50·5
	NO_2	214††	214††	−41	−50·5‡‡
HO_2C—(naphthalene X, OR)	H	147	181		
	Cl	186·5	192·5	+39·5	+11·5
	Br	182·5	189·5	+35·5	+8·5
	I	(164·5)	178·5	+17·5	−2·5
	NO_2	(166·5)	—	+19·5	—
X—⟨⟩—⟨⟩—N=CH—⟨⟩—OR	H	157·5	159·5		
	Cl	139·5††	—	−18	—
	Br	129·5††	—	−28	—
	Me	122††	—	−35·5	—
⟨⟩—⟨X⟩—N=CH—⟨⟩—OR	H	157·5	159·5		
	Cl	—	93	—	−66·5
	Br	—	85	—	−74·5
	Me	—	99·5	—	−60

S—N smectic-nematic transition temp. N—I nematic-isotropic transition temp.

*   Unless otherwise stated, R = n-decyl ($C_{10}H_{21}$)

†   A decrease in mesomorphic thermal stability is recorded as a negative temp. change, and an increase as a positive change.

‡   Transition temps. in parenthesis are for monotropic mesophases.

†† Smectic-isotropic transition temp.

‡‡ Since the smectic-nematic and nematic-isotropic transition temps. are coincident, this may be taken as a measure of the decrease in nematic thermal stability.

** R = n-dodecyl ($C_{12}H_{25}$)   ***R = n-octyl (C_8H_{17})

analogue, the slope of the lower broken line with respect to the 1,4 -axis of ring A has been increased by the straining of ring B relative to ring A. The gradient of the upper parallel line is increased therefore, and the more this gradient is increased, the greater is the chance of accommodating the bridging CH_2 group without its projecting beyond the upper broken line. Molecular models show that the hydrogens of the methy-

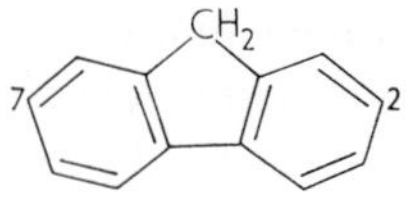

IV 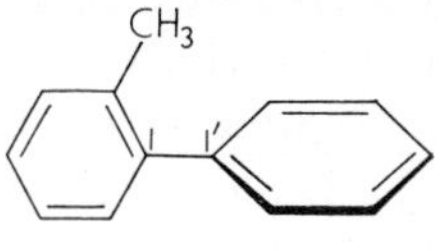   V

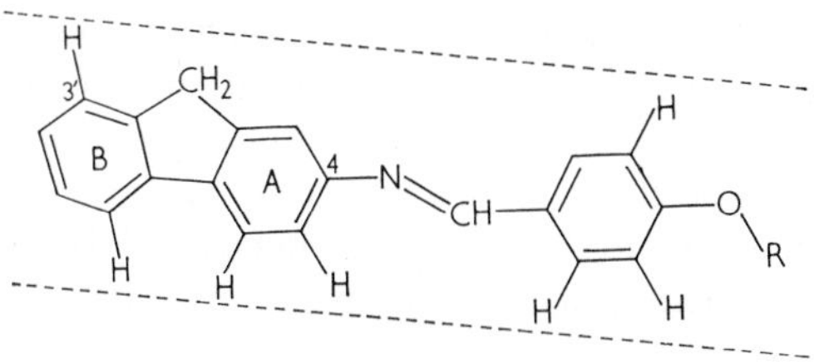

VI

lene bridge do in fact project beyond this line, but the breadth increase compared with the biphenyl analogue is less than would have been obtained had the fluorene ring system been linear. We have then some protection of the substituent methylene group. Compared with biphenyl, the molecule of fluorene has (a) a higher polarizability (arising from the methylene group itself, and the more extensive conjugation in the molecule) and (b) a permanent dipole moment (0·65 D). Factors (a) and (b)

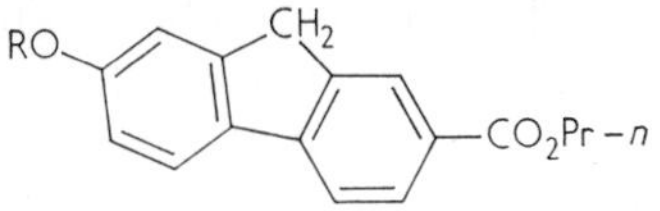

VII 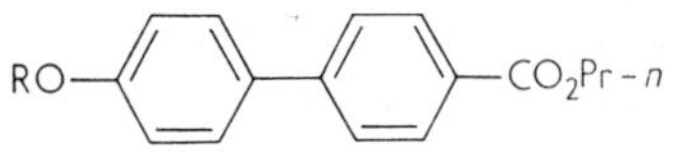   VIII

will enhance the intermolecular attractions, and it is found experimentally that the mesomorphic thermal stabilities of the fluorene monoanils are slightly higher than those of the biphenyl monoanils. That is, the minimizing of the molecular broadening effect of the methylene bridge makes it possible for factors (a) and (b) to predominate and give rise to a net increase in the thermal stabilities of the mesophases. Similar considerations apply to the n-propyl 7-n-alkoxy-fluorene-2-carboxylates[7] (VII) which exhibit smectic mesophases of greater thermal stability than those of the analogous biphenyl esters (VIII).

The above examples serve to warn us against attaching too much importance to the linearity of the system. In the fluorene systems, the slight deviation from linearity minimizes the breadth-increasing effect of the substituent (the methylene bridge) which enhances the polarizability and polarity of the molecule. The net effect is that the mesomorphic thermal stabilities are increased. All conceivable factors must therefore be taken into account before deciding in what way a change in molecular structure will affect the mesomorphic properties.

Table X.2 contains data which make it possible to compare the mesomorphic transition temperatures of the above fluorene and biphenyl compounds. Figures for the corresponding fluorenone derivatives[6, 7] are included in the Table. Oxidation of the CH_2 to the $C{=}O$ group increases the molecular breadth, but also the dipole moment of the system. It is possible, however, that conjugation of the benzylideneamino- group with the $C{=}O$ group greatly decreases the effective dipole moment of the carbonyl group. Contributions from structures such as IX, in which the positive charge is no longer localized on the carbonyl carbon atom, will give rise to two effects which are complementary. Because of the orientation of the dipole in IX, the influence of the *resultant* dipole moment of the *hybrid* molecule on the lateral attractions will be de-

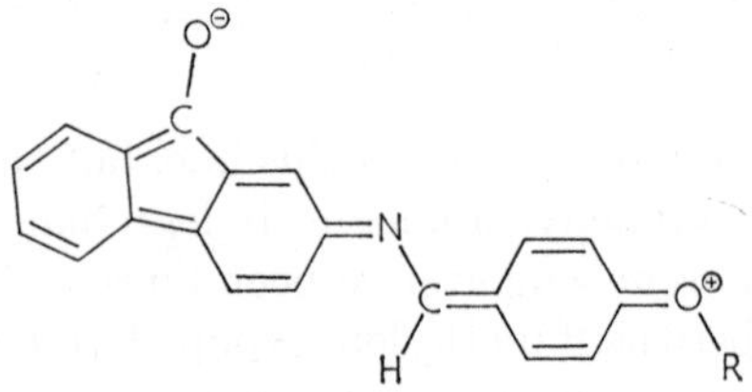

IX

creased, and on the terminal attractions will be increased. In this way, one can explain (*a*) the large decrease in smectic thermal stability and the smaller reduction in nematic thermal stability on passing from a biphenyl to a fluorenone monoanil, and (*b*) the fact that the n-propyl 7-n-alkoxyfluorenone-2-carboxylates[7] are not mesomorphic.

TABLE X.2

Molecule type		Average transition temp. $(C_7-C_{10})(°)$			
		Fluorene		Biphenyl	Fluorenone
Esters	smectic-isotropic	111	9 $\longrightarrow$	102	>22 $\longrightarrow$ <80*
Monoanils	{ smectic-nematic	166	10·5 $\longrightarrow$	155·5	82 $\longrightarrow$ 73·5
	nematic-isotropic	186·5	24·5 $\longrightarrow$	162	22 $\longrightarrow$ 140

* Not mesomorphic.

This work on fluorene and fluorenone monoanils and esters was extended to the dianils (2,7-di-(*p*-n-alkoxybenzylideneamino)-fluorenes (X) and -fluorenones[6]) and the acids (7-n-alkoxy-fluorene- (XI) and -fluorenone-2-carboxylic acids[7]) analogous to the 4,4'-di-(*p*-n-alkoxy-benzylideneamino)biphenyls and 4'-n-alkoxybiphenyl-4-carboxylic acids respectively. The order of decreasing mesomorphic thermal stability, fluorene>biphenyl>fluorenone, established for the monoanils and esters was found to be partly inverted for the acids and dianils, for which the order was biphenyl>fluorene>fluorenone. Detailed arguments offering a qualitative explanation of this inversion of the order have been given elsewhere,[6, 7] and a chapter of this kind which deals with the

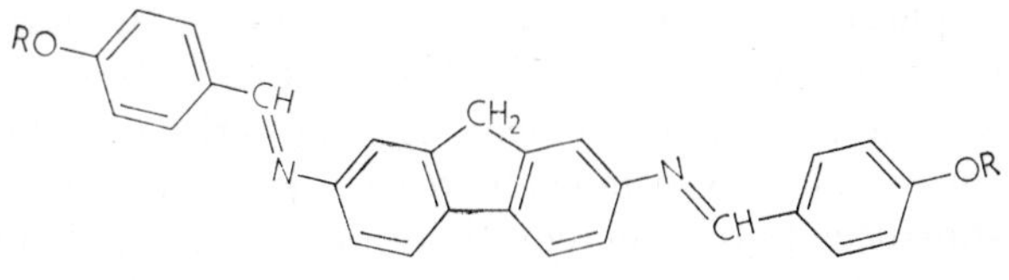

X

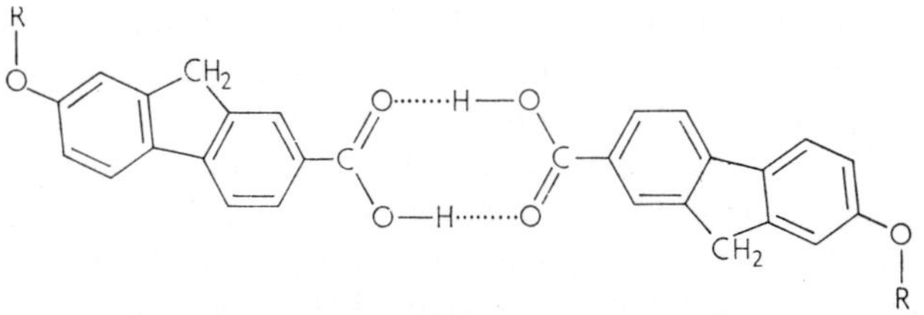

XI

general effects of substituents is no place in which to repeat them. The essence of these arguments was that the effect of the non-linear nature of the fluorene ring system is magnified because of the presence of elongated groups at both ends of the fluorene ring system. Assuming a *trans*- arrangement of the —N=CH— links in the dianils, and of the fluorene rings in the dimeric acid molecules, structures such as X and XI are obtained. The molecules are either S-shaped or saucer-shaped, and it is suggested that difficulties in achieving economical packings of such molecules explain the lower smectic-nematic and nematic-isotropic transition temperatures of the fluorene analogues of the more linear biphenyl systems. An attempt has also been made to assess the rôle which conjugation plays in determining the relative mesomorphic thermal stabilities of such systems.

When a substituent is introduced into the side of the molecule of a mesomorphic compound, and this substituent exerts a molecular broadening effect in keeping with its size, the normal effect is, however, that the thermal stabilities of both the smectic and nematic mesophases are decreased. Attention has already been drawn to the fact that we cannot generalize as to whether the nematic or the smectic mesophase will be the more affected. Small substituents such as fluoro- appear to affect the smectic mesophase less than the nematic mesophase, substituents such as chloro- and bromo- reduce the thermal stabilities of both mesophases to about the same extent, and larger substituents such as iodo- have the most pronounced effect on the smectic mesophase. It has been suggested that if the mass of the substituent is high, the energy required to rotate the molecule out of the nematic orientation should be high also, and that the nematic mesophase will therefore decrease in thermal stability less rapidly with increasing substituent size, than will the smectic mesophase. Data on which such conclusions are based must of necessity be restricted to a range of substituents of different size, but of more or less constant dipole moment, e.g. the series of halogeno- substituents. There is, however, much more to be learned about the relative effects of substituents of different types on the thermal stabilities of smectic and nematic mesophases.

The effects of a given substituent on different mesomorphic systems also show considerable variation. Let us consider some examples. The *decrease* in thermal stability of the smectic mesophase on passing from parent compound to fluoro-compound (Δt (H–F) smectic) for 3′-substituted 4′-n-octyloxybiphenyl-4-carboxylic acid n-propyl ester[8] is 43·5°, for 3-substituted 4-n-decyloxybenzoic acid[1] 10°, and for 3′-substituted 4′-n-octyloxybiphenyl-4-carboxylic acid[8] 0·5°. Similarly, Δt (H–Cl) smectic for the 3-substituted 4-n-decyloxybenzoic acid[1] is 36°, for the 3-substituted *trans-p*-n-dodecyloxycinnamic acid acid[9, 10] 23·5°, and for the 3′-substituted 4′-n-octyloxybiphenyl-4-carboxylic acid[11] 30°. The Δt (H–Cl) nematic values for these last three systems are respectively 51·5, 31, and 31·5°. Turning to the 3′-substituted 4-*p*-n-decyloxybenzylideneaminobiphenyl,[12] we find that Δt (H–Cl) smectic is low (18°), whereas for the 3-substituted 4-*p*-n-decyloxy-benzylideneaminobiphenyl,[12] Δt (H–Cl) nematic is high (66·5°). The large decrease in nematic thermal stability in this last case suggests that a steric effect may operate between the chloro- substituent and the hydrogen of the —N=CH— group, in the *cis*-configuration of the molecule. However, the molecule may adopt the *trans*-configuration, and if it does, the large decrease in nematic thermal stability may be caused simply by the awkward shape of the substituted molecule. The 3-substituted 4-*p*-n-alkoxybenzylideneaminobiphenyls will be discussed in more detail later.

Even if this last case is discounted because a steric effect may operate, the other examples show clearly that a variation in the Δt (H–X) values is to be expected for both smectic and nematic mesophases as we

the 3-position of the 4-n-alkoxybenzoic acids and in the 3'-position of the 4'-n-alkoxybiphenyl-4-carboxylic acids may vary a little, because of the slightly different gradients of the lines defining the minimal breadths of the molecules with respect to the ring-substituent bonds. Effects such as these will of course be small, but as shown by the first two examples, the effects of variations in breadth increase for a given substituent may be considerable, and explain some of the variations in the Δt (H–X) smectic and nematic values for different systems.

(b) On passing from X = H to X = F, for example, the increase in the intermolecular attraction arising from the ring-F dipole moment and the higher polarizability of the substituted molecule will depend on the total polarizability of the parent molecule. In fact, the higher the polarizability of the molecule, the greater will be the increase in intermolecular attraction due to both induced dipole attraction and dispersion forces, and the smaller will be the over-all effect of the substituent in decreasing the smectic thermal stability. The values quoted above for Δt (H–F) smectic bear this out, for these decrease from 43·5 to 10 to 0·5° as the polarizabilities of the molecules increase from the monomeric fluoro- ester to the dimeric benzoic and biphenyl carboxylic acids. On passing from the chlorobenzoic acid to the chlorobiphenyl acid, the decrease in Δt (H–Cl) smectic is not, however, very great—from 36° to 30°.

(c) It is possible therefore that a third factor plays a part in determining the variation in the effect of a substituent X upon the smectic and nematic thermal stabilities of different systems, namely the degree of change in the geometrical anisotropy of the molecule. Thus, the introduction of a chloro-substituent into the 3-position of a p-n-alkoxybenzoic acid or the 3'-position of a 4'-n-alkoxybiphenyl-4-carboxylic acid broadens each molecule to roughly the same extent. However, the breadth/unit length of the benzoic acid molecule is increased more by substitution than is that of the biphenyl acid molecule, i.e. the rod-like nature of the benzoic acid molecule is more markedly reduced.

It is obviously difficult to assess the relative importance of the various factors which will affect the thermal stabilities of the mesophases of *different* compounds when a ring hydrogen is replaced by a substituent X. However, it is of interest to note that, within the group of halogeno-substituents, there is evidence to show that a more or less constant change in mesomorphic thermal stability occurs on passing from fluoro- to chloro-, chloro- to bromo-, or bromo- to iodo-, *irrespective of the system* in which the substituents are present, provided that both substituents are exerting a breadth-increasing effect on the molecule, i.e. systems such as the 5-substituted 6-n-alkoxy-2-naphthoic acids would be expected to give anomalous results if one of the pair of substituents under consideration could be accommodated within the two parallel lines defining the minimal breadth of the unsubstituted molecule. The bromo- and iodo-naphthoic acids can, however, be used to give Δt (Br–I) smectic and nematic values. The available data are summarized in Table X.3.

TABLE X.3

System	Δt (F–Cl)		Δt (Cl–Br)		Δt (Br–I)	
	smectic	nematic	smectic	nematic	smectic	nematic
3-substituted 4-n-alkoxybenzoic acids*	26°	26°	—	—	—	—
3'-substituted 4'-n-alkoxybiphenyl-4-carboxylic acids	29·5	22·5	11°	9°	21·5°	10°
3-substituted *trans*-4-n-alkoxycinnamic acids	—	—	—	6	—	—
5-substituted 6-n-alkoxy-2-naphthoic acids	—	—	—	—	18	11
3'-substituted 4-p-n-alkoxybenzylidene-aminobiphenyls	—	—	11·5	—†	—	—
3-substituted 4-p-n-alkoxybenzylidene-aminobiphenyls	—	—	—‡	8	—	—
3-substituted 4,4'-di-(p-n-alkoxybenzyl-ideneamino)biphenyls	—	—	—§	10	—	—
Average decreases	27·75	24·25	11·25	8·25	19·75	10·5

* The bromo- and iodo- derivatives are not mesomorphic.
† No nematic mesophases.
‡ No smectic mesophases.
§ The smectic properties of these compounds will be discussed later in this chapter.

The number of available Δt (X_1–X_2) values is of course limited, but the following points may be noted in support of the idea of relatively constant changes in the mesomorphic transition temperatures, irrespective of the system, on passing from one substituent to another, provided that X_1 is not hydrogen.

(a) In certain cases such as the 3,3'-disubstituted 4,4'-di-(p-n-alkoxybenzylideneamino)biphenyls,[3] each of the substituents exerts a breadth-increasing effect, and we find that Δt (Cl–Br) nematic is 18° for the decyl ethers, i.e. approximately twice the normal Δt (Cl–Br) nematic average shown in Table X.3 above. In this connection, it should be noticed that the 3-chloro-4-n-alkoxybenzoic acids and 3'-chloro-4'-n-alkoxybiphenyl-4-carboxylic acids are dimeric systems, and we would normally expect the molecules to adopt a *trans*- arrangement as shown in XIV.

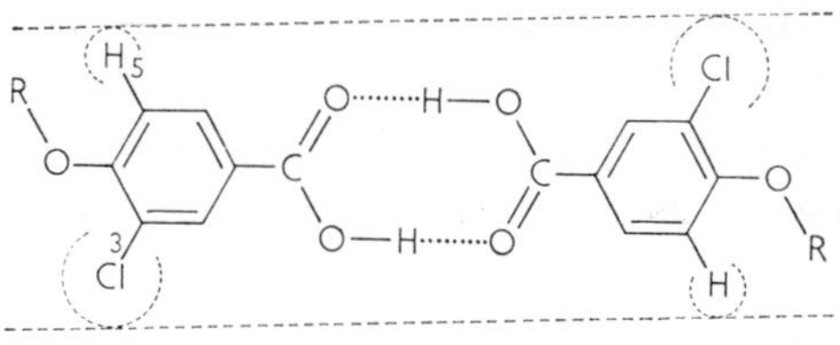

XIV

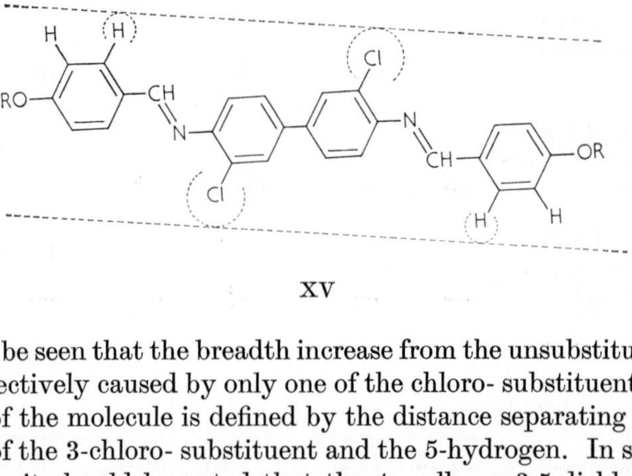

XV

It can be seen that the breadth increase from the unsubstituted molecule is effectively caused by only one of the chloro- substituents, i.e. the breadth of the molecule is defined by the distance separating the outer surfaces of the 3-chloro- substituent and the 5-hydrogen. In support of this point, it should be noted that the 4-n-alkoxy-3,5-dichlorobenzoic acids are not mesomorphic. For the 3,3'-disubstituted 4,4'-di-(p-n-alkoxybenzylideneamino)biphenyls (XV), drawn again with a *trans-trans*- configuration, molecular models show that both chloro- substituents exert breadth increasing effects. For this reason, we would expect Δt (Cl–Br) for XV to be double that for XIV, despite the fact that both molecules contain two chlorines. It should also be noted that Δt (H–Cl) nematic for XV is approximately double the Δt (H–Cl) nematic value for the monosubstituted systems, i.e. the 3-substituted 4,4'-di-(p-n-alkoxybenzylideneamino)biphenyls.

(b) The nematic-isotropic transition temperatures of isomeric methyl and chloro- substituted compounds are always closely similar, i.e. Δt (Me–Cl) nematic is almost constant, and always has a very small value.

It is not easy to explain why Δt (H–X) values vary so much, whilst Δt (halogen$_1$–halogen$_2$) and Δt (Me–Cl) values should be more or less constant. Differences in the breadth-increasing effects on passing from hydrogen to X in different systems of course explain some of the variations in Δt (H–X), but factors (b) and (c), discussed on page 248, should apply equally to the changes from halogen to halogen or methyl to halogen. We should, of course, remember that whilst the change from H to X involves a large change in breadth, polarizability, and polarity of the system, the change from halogen to halogen involves only a breadth-increasing effect and a polarizability increase (the ring-halogen dipoles are more or less the same), and the change from methyl to chloro- only a dipolar and polarizability change (the sizes of the methyl and chloro- substituents are more or less the same). That is, the changes in interaction energy imposed upon the system by the different substituents for which more or less constant Δt values are found, are much smaller than those involved on changing from H to X.

The data available for substituents other than the halogens and methyl are unfortunately limited. A few mesomorphic nitro- compounds have been studied, and in these the bulky, polarizable and dipolar nitro- group is involved. Here, indeed, the change from halogeno- to nitro- substituent does not appear to be constant, e.g. for smectic mesophases Δt (Br–NO$_2$) = 16° for the 5-substituted 6-n-decyloxy-2-naphthoic acids,[2] and = 5·5° for the 3′-substituted 4′-n-decyloxy-biphenyl-4-carboxylic acids.[11] If it is safe to generalize on the limited information available, the Δt (halogeno–NO$_2$) and Δt (H–X) smectic and nematic values appear to be the only ones which vary substantially. Certainly there is evidence for the constancy of Δt (X$_1$–X$_2$) values, where halogeno- or methyl substituents are involved, and on the assumption that this constancy is general, it is possible to make interesting analyses of the behaviour of sterically affected mesomorphic compounds. This feature is dealt with in the second section of this chapter.

It is obvious, of course, that there are many gaps in our knowledge concerning the relationship between a given change in a substituent and the effect which it produces upon the mesomorphic thermal stabilities. It is, however, of interest to examine the effects of a series of different substituents on a particular mesomorphic system. The number of systems which lend themselves to such a study is unfortunately limited. The p-n-alkoxybenzoic acids[1] and the trans-p-n-alkoxycinnamic acids[10] lose their mesomorphic properties if a substituent larger than chloro- is introduced into the 3-position, the 5-substituted 6-n-alkoxy-2-naph-thoic acids[2] are anomalous because of the protected nature of the 5-position, the 3′-substituted 4-p-n-alkoxybenzylideneaminobiphenyls[12] exhibit no nematic properties, and mono- and di-anils derived from other substituted 4-aminobiphenyls and benzidines[12] probably involve steric effects. The 3'-substituted 4'-n-alkoxybiphenyl-4-carboxylic acids (XVI)[11] are in fact the only compounds which give sufficient data with a wide enough range of substituents to make worthwhile comparisons possible.

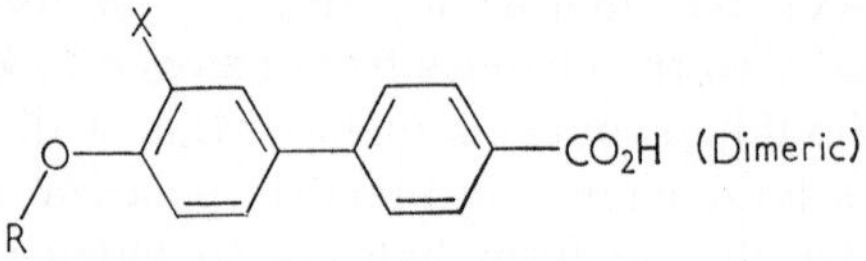

XVI

The mesomorphic transition temperatures and the Δt (X_1–X_2) values are recorded for the octyl ethers (R = n-C_8H_{17}) in Table X.4. The octyl ether of the 3'-nitro- derivative exhibits no nematic mesophase, and the smectic-isotropic transition temperature, 214°, is used in both sets of figures in the Table. This figure may obviously be compared with the other smectic-nematic transition temperatures, but at first sight it should not be comparable with the *nematic*-isotropic transition temperatures for the other derivatives. However, when nematic properties are no longer shown by a particular homologue in a series, the smectic-nematic and nematic-isotropic transition temperature curves coincide, i.e. the smectic-isotropic curve is a continuation of the nematic-isotropic curve, and the smectic-nematic and nematic-isotropic transitions are coincident. Regarded in this way, smectic-isotropic transition temperatures may be compared.

TABLE X.4 *3'-X-4'-n-Octyloxybiphenyl-4-carboxylic Acids*[11]

X	H	F	Cl	Br	I	NO$_2$
Smectic-nematic transition temp. (°)	255	254·5	225	214	192·5	214*
Decrease in transition temp. from unsubstituted acid (°)		0·5	30	41	62·5	41
Nematic-isotropic transition temp. (°)	264·5	255·5	233	224	214	214*
Decrease in transition temp. from unsubstituted acid (°)		9	31·5	40·5	50·5	50·5

* Smectic-isotropic transition temperature.

Using the transition temperatures in Table X.4, we may place the substituents in order of their increasing effect upon the thermal stabilities of the smectic and nematic mesophases.

Smectic Mesophase

$$H < F < Cl < Br = NO_2 < I$$

Nematic Mesophase

$$H < F < Cl < Br < I = NO_2$$

In support of this last sequence for the *nematic* mesophase, obtained using a *smectic*-isotropic transition temperature for $X = NO_2$, the order obtained for $X = H$, Cl, Br, and NO_2 by comparing average *nematic*-isotropic transition temperatures for the n-propyl to n-hexyl ethers is

$$H < Cl < Br < NO_2$$

The group $X = NO_2$ has a smaller effect upon the thermal stability of the smectic mesophase than on that of the nematic mesophase, and it is likely that this is explained by the strong ring-NO_2 dipole moment, which augments the lateral intermolecular attractions and counteracts the separation of the axes of the molecules arising from the bulk of the nitro- group.

It is interesting to assess the effects of the sizes of the substituents upon the thermal stabilities of the smectic and nematic mesophases. To make this possible, the breadths of the molecules (defined as the

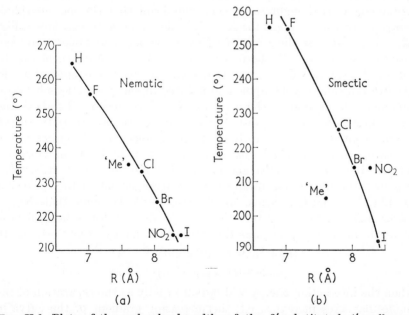

(a)   (b)

FIG. X.1. Plots of the molecular breadths of the 3′-substituted 4′-n-alkoxy-biphenyl-4-carboxylic acids against (a) their nematic-isotropic transition temperatures and (b) their smectic-nematic transition temperatures.

diameters of the smallest cylinders through which the dimerized molecules of the biphenyl carboxylic acids would pass, the flexible alkyl chains being assumed not to interfere) of the 3'-substituted biphenyl acid dimers have been calculated, and these breadths (R) have been plotted in Fig. X.1 (*a*) and (*b*), against the nematic and smectic transition temperatures (*t*) taken from Table X.4.

For the nematic-isotropic transition temperatures, which are plotted against R in Fig. X.1 (*a*), a reasonably smooth decrease in transition temperature is obtained as R increases, and it seems that the order

$$H < F < Cl < Br < I = NO_2$$

is determined mainly by the separation of the long axes of the molecules. It is unfortunate that it has not been possible to obtain a satisfactorily pure sample of 3'-methyl-4'-n-octyloxybiphenyl-4-carboxylic acid, but a predicted nematic-isotropic transition temperature ("Me") has been included in Fig. X.1 (*a*). In seven cases in which isomeric methyl and chloro- substituted mesomorphic compounds have been studied, the average increase in the nematic-isotropic transition temperature on passing from chloro- to methyl derivative is only 2°. The predicted transition temperature for the 3'-methyl acid used in Fig. X.1 (*a*) is therefore 235°, 2° higher than the nematic-isotropic transition temperature for the 3'-chloro- acid. Using a molecular breadth R = 7·6 Å for the 3'-methyl acid, a point lying fairly close to the curve in Fig. X.1 (*a*) is obtained. It is thought to be very significant that the mesomorphic-isotropic transition point for X = NO$_2$ lies so close to the curve (Fig. X.1 (*a*)), and that the large ring-NO$_2$ dipole moment appears to have little influence upon the thermal stability of the nematic mesophase. In the solid state, we would expect that such a strong dipole moment would lead to powerful dipole-dipole and induced dipole interactions between the molecules, but since the point for X = NO$_2$ does not lie above the curve in Fig. X.1 (*a*), we must infer that interactions of these two types do not contribute significantly to the intermolecular attractions in the nematic melt. This means that dispersion forces arising from molecular polarizability effects must account for the intermolecular attractions which maintain the essentially parallel arrangement of the molecules within the nematic swarms. If the assumption be made that the gas phase relation for the interaction energy for such forces holds for the nematic mesophase, i.e. that the interaction energy is proportional to

$$\frac{(\text{molecular polarizability})^2}{(\text{molecular separation})^6} = \frac{\alpha^2}{r^6}$$

then the interaction energy will fall off rapidly as the separation of the molecular axes increases, c.f. the increasing gradient of the curve in Fig. X.1 (*a*) as R increases.

Of course, Fig. X.1 (*a*) merely shows a relationship between the molecular breadths (as influenced by the sizes of the substituents X) and the nematic-isotropic transition temperatures (t), and not a relationship between t and the polarizabilities of the molecules or the interaction energies between them. However, if the polarizabilities of the molecules increase smoothly as the breadths of the molecules are increased, then the changes in the polarizabilities (α) which occur when X is changed will not interfere with a smooth curve relationship between t and R, i.e. the increases in α will merely reduce the gradient of the curve in Fig. X.1 (a). That the molecular polarizabilities will increase reasonably smoothly with increasing R is shown by the plot in Fig. X.2, which demonstrates that the C–X bond refractions change quite regularly as the size of the substituent is increased.

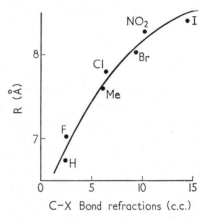

FIG. X.2. The molecular breadths of the 3'-substituted (X) 4'-n-alkoxy-biphenyl-4-carboxylic acids plotted against the C–X bond refractions.

Turning now to Fig. X.1 (b), it is obvious that no simple relationship exists between the smectic thermal stabilities and the molecular breadths of the 3'-substituted 4'-n-octyloxybiphenyl-4-carboxylic acids. The first point to note is that the fluoro- substituent has only a very small effect in reducing the smectic-nematic transition temperature of the unsubstituted acid (X = H). This suggests that the breadth increasing effect of the fluoro- substituent must be counteracted by the increase in the intermolecular attractions which stem from the increase in the permanent polarization of the molecule on passing from X = H to X = F. In Fig. X.1 (b), a curve has been drawn through the points for X = F, Cl, Br, and I, and it is presumed that such a curve exists because there are no great fluctuations in dipole moment as we pass along the sequence of halogeno- substituents. However, for X = NO$_2$, the transition point is displaced from this curve by some 13°, and it is reasonable to propose that, compared with the ring-halogen dipole moments, the much larger ring-NO$_2$ dipole moment leads to an enhanced thermal stability of the smectic mesophase.

Unfortunately, information relating to the thermal stabilities of the smectic mesophases of methyl compounds is very limited, but from the behaviour of the isomeric methyl and chloro- substituted compounds which have been studied, a smectic-nematic transition temperature of about 205° is predicted for the unknown 3'-methyl-4'-n-octyloxy-biphenyl-4-carboxylic acid, i.e. Δt (Cl–Me) = 20·5°. When this point ("Me") is included in Fig. X.1 (b), it lies some 27° below the curve. The lowness of this transition temperature relative to the curve through the points for the 3'-halogeno- acids, may be explained by the fact that the methyl-ring dipole moment is much weaker than the average ring-halogen dipole moment.

It would appear therefore that intermolecular attractions arising from dispersion forces are augmented in the smectic mesophase by attractions which depend upon the permanent dipolar properties of the molecules, i.e. by dipole-dipole and induced dipole interactions. That is, if substitution leads to an increase in molecular breadth, the thermal stabilities of the smectic and nematic mesophases will be reduced, but this effect will be counterbalanced to a greater or lesser extent *for both mesophase types* by the increased polarizability of the substituted molecule (which enhances both the dispersion forces and the induced dipole interactions), and in the case of the smectic mesophase only, by the dipole moment of the ring-substituent bond (which enhances the dipole-dipole and induced dipole interactions). The above facts are understandable in terms of the generally accepted orientations of the molecules in the smectic and nematic mesophases. In the smectic mesophase, the molecules are arranged parallel to one another, with their ends in line, forming layers, and strong interactions are clearly possible between dipoles which act across the long axes of the molecules. At the transition from the smectic to the nematic mesophase, thermal effects weaken these intermolecular attractions and the dipolar effects are unable to maintain the molecules in the stratified arrangement. The molecules therefore become free to slide out of the layers, in the direction of their long axes, still retaining the over-all parallel orientation. We therefore envisage an imbricated arrangement of the parallel molecules in the nematic melt, i.e. the ends of the molecules are now randomly arranged. In such a state, attraction between dipoles operating across the long axes of the molecules is much less likely to occur, for the simple reason that the dipoles will not lie sufficiently close to one another. Moreover, it is often the case that two dipoles act in opposite directions to one another at opposite ends of the long molecules, and it is likely that the dipoles in neighbouring molecules will lead to repulsion as often as to attraction, resulting therefore in a low, over-all, average dipole-dipole interaction in the nematic melt. In this way we can explain the apparent unimportance of permanent dipoles in relation to the thermal stability of the nematic mesophase.

As mentioned earlier in this chapter, no other systems lend them-selves to a similar study with such a wide range of substituents as the 3'-substituted 4'-n-alkoxybiphenyl-4-carboxylic acids, and no con-firmation of these ideas can be obtained from the substituted p-n-alkoxybenzoic acids, trans-p-n-alkoxycinnamic acids, or 6-n-alkoxy-2-naphthoic acids which have been studied. It would therefore be worth-while seeking other systems into which a range of substituents of diverse size and polarity could be introduced without destroying the mesomorphic properties of the compounds, because if quantitative relationships between mesomorphic and molecular properties are ever to be realized, it is vital to know the exact nature of the intermolecular attractions which operate in the different types of mesophase.

From the above discussions, the importance of the data obtained from mesomorphic derivatives of biphenyl is obvious. Now, the meso-morphic properties of compounds are clearly dependent upon the shape and stereochemistry of the molecules, but in discussing the mesomorphic transition temperatures of biphenyl derivatives in relation to their structures, the assumption has been made that the biphenyl nucleus is planar (XVII). That is, no allowance has been made for the possibility that rotation may occur about the interannular, 1,1'-bond (XVIII), resulting in either a fixed, non-planar conformation for the molecule, or, if *free* rotation about the bond were possible, in an average non-planar conformation.

XVII   XVIII

If we imagine two mesomorphic derivatives of biphenyl, in one of which the biphenyl rings adopt the planar arrangement represented in XVII, and in the other, either a fixed, non-planar, or a freely rotating arrangement as represented in XVIII, then there is no doubt that the second derivative, involving the non-planar molecules, would exhibit mesophases of much lower thermal stability, i.e. the non-coplanarity of the two phenyl rings would increase the molecular thickness, interfere with the close packing of the molecules, and decrease the average inter-molecular attractions of all kinds. It is therefore of obvious importance to establish whether the biphenyl ring system is planar or non-planar in the mesomorphic states, and whether the conformation of the bi-phenyl rings is the same in the smectic and nematic states. Thus, the above assessment of the mesomorphic thermal stabilities of the 3'-substituted 4'-n-octyloxybiphenyl-4-carboxylic acids in terms of the molecular breadths (R) would be without foundation if the interplanar angles (θ) differed from one substituted biphenyl acid to another. The arguments would, however, stand if the biphenyl ring systems for all the acids were coplanar, or if all were non-coplanar but possessed the same interplanar angle (θ), or if all involved *free* rotation about the 1,1′-bond. However, in the absence of definite information about the conformation of the biphenyl ring system in the mesomorphic melts, the interpretation of the effects of substituents on the mesomorphic thermal stabilities of biphenyl derivatives in general is open to question.

It is well known that the rotation of small groups of atoms may occur about single bonds, even in the solid state. However, of all the physical states of matter, the molecules will be most nearly at rest in the solid state, and certainly the rotation of entire, large molecules, as distinct from parts of molecules, is unlikely in the crystalline state. It is also considered that the rotation of whole molecules about their long axes is unlikely in the smectic and nematic states.

In the crystalline state, crystal forces maintain the molecules in a rigid, three-dimensional packing, so restraining any movement of whole molecules or parts of molecules, and maintaining the energy of the system at a minimum. Now, the smectic and nematic mesophases are

XIX   XX

not crystalline states, but a considerable degree of molecular organization still persists in them. This means that residual crystal forces must still persist, otherwise the molecular organization would break down and give the isotropic liquid, and these residual crystal forces will tend to resist any movement of whole molecules or parts of molecules. The ability of these residual crystal forces to combat the tendency for rotation to occur will, of course, be less than for the solid state in which the true crystal forces are stronger. Moreover, the temperatures at which mesophases exist are quite elevated, and conditions will therefore be more favourable for rotation. However, let us consider some experimental facts, and in particular the two systems 3-fluoro-4-n-octyloxy-benzoic acid (XIX)[1] and 3,5,-difluoro-4-n-octyloxybenzoic acid (XX).

The monofluoro- acid (XIX) is mesomorphic, melting at 117° and giving a nematic melt which clears at 120·5°, whilst the difluoro- acid (XX) is not mesomorphic. If we assume that the molecules of these acids do not rotate about their long axes in the nematic state, then the absence of mesomorphic properties for the difluoro- acid is explained by the fact that the molecules are considerably broader than those of the monofluoro- acid (XIX). Therefore, although a second polarizable fluoro-substituent has been introduced into the system, the breadth-increasing effect should predominate, as it does on passing from the unsubstituted acid to XIX, and we would expect a marked decrease in thermal stability of the nematic melt on passing from XIX to XX. The nematic mesophase of XIX persists over only 3·5°, and it is not difficult to imagine that the decrease in the mesomorphic potential of the system on passing to XX may result in the disappearance of mesomorphic properties. The same results and arguments apply on passing from a p-n-alkoxybenzoic acid to the 3-chloro- and 3,5-dichloro- derivatives.[1]

However, if the monosubstituted molecules (XIX) and the disub-stituted molecules (XX) freely rotate about their long axes, then the effective rotation diameters or breadths of the two types of molecule are identical. Under these conditions, we would expect the disubstituted system (XX) to exhibit the more thermally stable nematic mesophase, since the molecules are more polarizable and would give rise to stronger intermolecular attractions. Since the difluoro- and dichloro- acids are not in fact mesomorphic, it seems unlikely that free rotation of the molecules occurs about their long axes.

Moreover, it would be thought that if whole molecules did in fact rotate in the mesophases, then kinking and coiling of long alkyl chains would occur. However, regular trends in smectic-nematic and nematic-isotropic transition temperatures are known to occur as the alkyl chains are lengthened. This suggests that the alkyl chain maintains a regular and extended form in the mesomorphic states, and implies that no violent movements of whole molecules occur in the anisotropic states. This and other information, (Chapter IX. pp. 216–217) leads to the view that, although smectic and nematic states often exist at quite elevated temperatures, the residual crystal forces which maintain the molecular order also restrain the molecules in such a way that they do not rotate about their long axes. Undoubtedly, small and compact parts of mole-cules may rotate about single bonds in the mesomorphic states, just as they do in the solid states, and indeed the extent of such rotations is probably more marked than in the more rigid crystal lattice, but in general, the evidence points to the view that the state of the molecules in the smectic mesophase and in the nematic swarms is probably quite tranquil.

Having reviewed the evidence for rotation of whole molecules in the mesophases, and arrived at the conclusion that this is unlikely, let us now return to the specific case of the biphenyl ring system and consider any relevant data which may help us to decide whether the phenyl rings are coplanar, non-coplanar, or freely rotating about the 1,1′-bond in the mesomorphic states.

Foweather and Hargreaves[13] have shown that the molecule of biphenyl is planar in the crystalline state, and more recently Firag and Kader have obtained X-ray data which show that the phenyl rings are also coplanar in 4,4'-dihydroxybiphenyl.[14] However, in the gas phase[15] and in solution,[16] the molecule of biphenyl is non-planar, and the interplanar angle would appear to be about 45°. We see therefore, that in solution and in the gas phase, where the molecules of biphenyl lead a fairly free existence, their natural tendency is to adopt a non-planar conformation. In the solid state, however, the crystal forces which attract the molecules close to one another to give the solid crystal lattice, constrain the phenyl rings into a coplanar arrangement so that the packing of the molecules is as close as possible and the lattice energy is a minimum. Indeed, the potential energy curve for biphenyl, arising from resonance between the π-electrons of the two phenyl rings has minima at the coplanar configurations, whilst the potential energy curve representing steric repulsions between the hydrogen atoms has minima at orthogonal configurations. The minima for the resultant potential energy curve will therefore lie intermediate between these configurations, and an interplanar angle of 45° is to be expected for biphenyl and its derivatives in the gas phase or solution. However, when crystal forces operate between the molecules of biphenyl derivatives, the constraint imposed upon the molecules seems to be sufficiently great to make them adopt a planar conformation (interplanar angle $\theta = 0°$ in the solid state), despite the steric repulsions between the hydrogen atoms in the 2- and 2'-positions. As far as the degree of order of the molecules is concerned, the smectic and nematic mesophases may be regarded as intermediate between the solid state and the isotropic liquid, but there is no available information about the interplanar angles for biphenyl derivatives which exist as isotropic liquids. However, we may make the reasonable assumption that the interplanar angle is at least not greater than 45° in the liquid state, in which the molecules must be more closely associated than they are in the gas phase or in solution. On this basis, the interplanar angles for the mesomorphic states of biphenyl derivatives would be expected to lie between 0° and 45°, and the angle for the smectic mesophase, which is the more highly ordered of the two liquid crystalline states, may be smaller than that for the nematic mesophase.

In an attempt to obtain experimental evidence in support of these ideas, the effect of non-coplanarity of a molecule on the mesomorphic thermal stability was studied by preparing mesomorphic biphenyl derivatives containing 2- or 2'- substituents. The 4-p-n-alkoxybenzylideneaminobiphenyls (XXI)[6] were chosen as the parent compounds.

Molecular models show that even one simple substituent such as chloro-, bromo-, or methyl in either of the 2- or 2'- positions of a biphenyl derivative considerably restricts rotation about the 1,1'-bond, and that the unstrained molecule would be most likely to adopt a non-planar structure. Larger, and more numerous substituents, i.e. in the 2-, 2′-, 6-, or 6′- positions, are of course necessary for optical resolution of a suitable biphenyl derivative. However, although it is not possible to resolve simple 2-substituted biphenyl derivatives, this does not mean that such derivatives consist of coplanar molecules, but simply that rotation of these molecules through a planar state is periodically possible. Rotation about the 1,1′-bond in the mesomorphic state should be less easy than in solution, and the work was begun by preparing the 4-*p*-n-alkoxybenzylideneamino-3′-, 2′-, 2-, and 3-methylbiphenyls.[12]

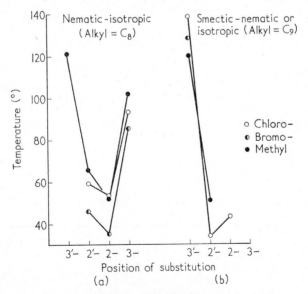

XXI

The results for the methyl derivatives suggested that the steric effects operating in the 2- and 2′-substituted derivatives were in fact having an effect upon the mesomorphic properties, and the analogous 3′-, 2′-, 2-, and 3-chloro- and bromo-derivatives[12] were therefore prepared. For each substituent in any one position, four ethers (R = n-heptyl to n-decyl)

4-*p*-n-alkoxybenzylideneaminobiphenyls

FIG. X.3. The influence of the position of a given substituent on (a) the nematic and (b) the smectic thermal stabilities of the mono-substituted 4-*p*-n-alkoxy-benzylideneaminobiphenyls.

TABLE X.5. *Substituted 4-p-n-alkoxybenzylideneaminobiphenyls*

	Temperature (°)			
Methyl	3'-	2'-	2-	3-
Average* s—n or s—i transition temp.	117·9	56·2‡	—	—
Average n—i transition temp.	118·8†	63·9	49·5	99·7
Δt (H–Me) smectic	37·5	101·1	—	—
Δt (H–Me) nematic	45	98	112·4	62·2
Chloro-				
Average s—n or s—i transition temp.	138·4	39‡	43·5‡	—
Average n—i transition temp.	—	59	52·1	91·9
Δt (H–Cl) smectic	17	118·3	113·8	—
Δt (H–Cl) nematic	—	102·9	109·8	70
Bromo-				
Average s—n or s—i transition temp.	127·5	—	—	—
Average n—i transition temp.	—	44·1	33·7	83·9
Δt (H–Br) smectic	27·9	—	—	—
Δt (H–Br) nematic	—	117·8	128·2	78

s—n smectic-nematic   s—i smectic-isotropic   n—i nematic-isotropic

* Unless otherwise stated, all averages are for the heptyl–decyl ethers.
† Average of heptyl and octyl.
‡ Average of nonyl and decyl.

were prepared, but, as will be clear from the subsequent discussion, it was not always possible to use the average of the four transition temperatures to compare the mesomorphic properties of the isomers. The mesomorphic transition temperatures for these compounds derived from XXI are contained in Table X.5.

The substituted anils have lower smectic and nematic thermal stabilities than the parent compound, but it is obvious that the decreases in mesomorphic thermal stability are much greater for the 2′- and 2-isomers than for the 3′- and 3-isomers. This is illustrated diagrammatically in Figs. X.3 (a) and (b) (see page 261).

The breadths of the molecules (defined earlier in this chapter) of the 3′-, 2′-, and 2-substituted anils for a given substituent are the same within about ± 0·1 Å irrespective of whether the molecules are *cis*- or *trans*-, and the differences in mesomorphic thermal stability between the 2- and 2′- isomers and the 3′- isomers cannot be attributed to molecular breadth effects. The 3-substituted isomers are broader if the molecules adopt a *trans*- configuration (XXII)—the *cis*- configuration is illustrated in XXIII—and the behaviour of these compounds may be anomalous.

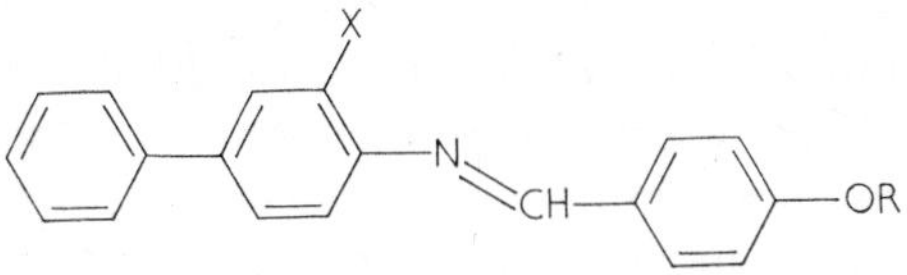

XXII

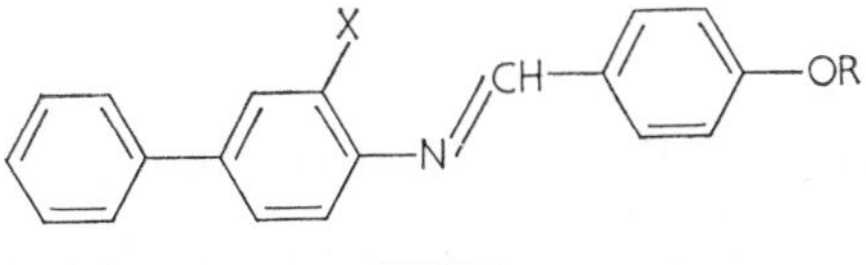

XXIII

The lower transition temperatures for the 2- and 2′- substituted anils must be caused by some significant structural effect which distinguishes them from the 3′- and 3-substituted isomers, and this must be the steric effect of the substituent forcing the ring system into a non-planar state.

In this connection, it is interesting to compare the mesomorphic properties of the 2- and 2′- methyl monoanils with those of the 2-*p*-n-alkoxybenzylideneaminofluorenes.[6] The average smectic-nematic and nematic-isotropic transition temperatures for the two methyl isomers are given in Table X.5, and it is obvious that these transition temperatures are very low compared with the average (C_7–C_{10}) smectic-nematic and nematic-isotropic transition temperatures of 166° and 186·4° respectively, for the fluorene compounds. This again points to a non-planar molecular structure for the 2- and 2′-substituted biphenyl monoanils.

It seems clear therefore that a single 2- or 2′-substituent in the biphenyl ring system is sufficient to achieve a steric effect, despite the fact that a much greater degree of steric congestion would be required to make possible the optical resolution of a suitable biphenyl derivative. These 2- or 2'-substituents will decrease the mesomorphic thermal stability of the parent compound in two ways, (1) by broadening the molecules, and (2) by twisting the phenyl rings relative to one another about the 1,1'-bond, so thickening the molecules.

Both these effects will interfere with the close packing of the molecules, increasing in effect the molecular separation, and decreasing the strength of the intermolecular attractions of all types. Effects (1) and (2) will of course increase with increasing size of the 2- or 2'-substituent, and if we are to assess the full importance of effect (2), effect (1) must be known. Now it has already been made clear that the introduction of a substituent into a molecule will reduce the thermal stabilities of the mesophases, provided that the substituent increases the breadth of the parent molecule. However, on passing from hydrogen to a substituent X, we know that the decrease in mesomorphic thermal stability is dependent to some extent on the nature of the parent molecule. For this reason, the 3'- and 3-substituted monoanils were studied in the hope that their behaviours would demonstrate the effect of a given substituent on the mesomorphic thermal stability of the parent compound, in the absence of a steric effect about the 1,1'-bond. However, the 3'- and 3-substituted monoanils exhibited certain unexpected features, and the anomalous properties shown by the compounds will now be discussed.

3'-CHLORO-, BROMO-, AND METHYL MONOANILS

As might have been expected from the number and the distribution of the dipole moments in the molecules of the 3'-substituted monoanils, e.g. the 3'-chloro-compound (XXIV), the chloro- and bromo- derivatives exhibit purely smectic properties. The thermal stabilities of the smectic mesophases are, of course, lower than for the parent compound, because the halogeno- substituent broadens the molecule. The 3'-methyl

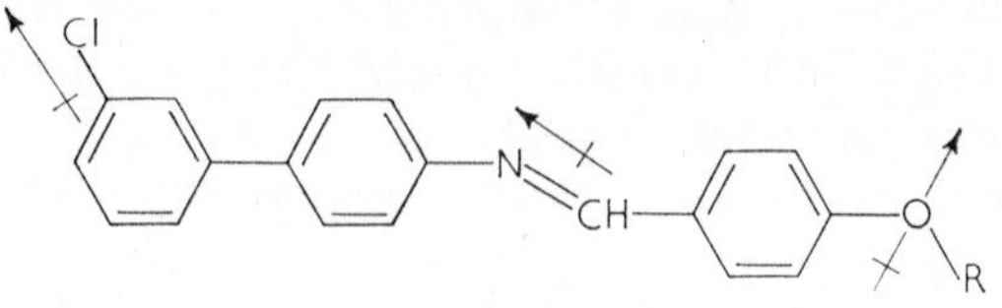

XXIV

isomers exhibit nematic mesophases which persist for only a few degrees when R = heptyl and octyl, but with longer alkyl chains, the compounds are again purely smectic. A comparison of Δt (H–Me) smectic = 37·5° with Δt (H–Cl) smectic = 17° again underlines the fact that the 3'-methyl isomers are less smectogenic than the 3'-halogeno- isomers, and this must be associated with the weaker Me-ring dipole moment which contributes less to the lateral intermolecular attractions. It will be remembered that, earlier in this chapter, reference was made to this Δt (H–Cl) smectic value of 17°, and the fact that it is low compared with the decrease of some 30° and more for the smectic mesophases of systems such as the chloro-substituted p-n-alkoxybenzoic acids. This has been explained by the partial protection of the 3'-position by the perimeter of the unsubstituted molecule, such that a 3'- substituent exerts less than its normal breadth-increasing effect. In this way, the smectogenic tendencies of the 3'- substituted monoanils will be further enhanced. At any rate, the predominantly *smectic* behaviour of these 3'- substituted monoanils means that their transition temperatures cannot be used for an analysis of the *nematic* properties of the 2- and 2'-substituted monoanils.

3-Chloro-, Bromo-, and Methyl Monoanils

The *cis*-configuration of the 3-substituted monoanil (XXIII) has approximately the same molecular breadth as the 3'-, 2'-, or 2-substituted analogues, whilst the *trans*- configuration (XXII) is broader by some 0·2–0·3 Å. However, if the molecules adopt the *cis*- configuration, there will be a steric interference between the 3-substituent and the hydrogen of the anil (—N=CH) linkage. If this occurs, the thickness of the molecule will be increased. A further result of the adoption of the *cis*- configuration will be a substantial cancellation of the ring-halogen and —CH=N—dipole moments. Consequently, whether the molecules of the 3-substituted monoanils adopt a *cis*- or a *trans*- configuration, the thermal stabilities of their mesophases would be expected to be quite low. Indeed, the Δt (H–X) nematic values for the compounds are quite large, and no smectic mesophases are exhibited, suggesting that some feature of the molecular structure is reducing the mesomorphic potential of the 3-substituted monoanils. 3-substituted 4,4'-di-(p-n-alkoxybenzyl-ideneamino)biphenyls (dianils) were later prepared[3] in order to throw more light on the effect which the presence of a substituent *ortho*- to the anil linkage has on the mesomorphic properties, and this work will be discussed later in this chapter.

Since the 3'-substituted monoanils are predominantly smectic in character, and the 3-isomers are in some way anomalous, the effects of substituents in the 3- and 3'-positions on the mesomorphic thermal stabilities cannot reasonably be used to estimate the steric effects of 2- and 2'- substituents on the mesomorphic properties. The data for the sterically affected monoanils must therefore be analysed separately, and to assist such an analysis, three further substituted monoanils were prepared (Table X.6).

TABLE X.6

Fluoro- and Iodo-substituted 4-p-n-alkoxybenzylideneaminobiphenyls[12]

2′-Iodo-	Nematic-isotropic transition temp.				
	(C_7-C_{10})	21·1°	$\varDelta t$ (H–I)	nematic	140·8°
2-Iodo-	Nematic-isotropic transition temp.				
	(C_7-C_{10})	14·9	$\varDelta t$ (H–I)	nematic	147
2-Fluoro-	Smectic-nematic transition temp.				
	(C_9-C_{10})	96	$\varDelta t$ (H–F)	smectic	61·3
	Nematic-isotropic transition temp.				
	(C_7-C_{10})	113·2	$\varDelta t$ (H–F)	nematic	48·7

Let us concentrate first on the 2-substituted monoanils (XXV), for which data concerning mesomorphic thermal stabilities are available for the substituents X = H, F, Cl, Br, I, and Me. In these 2-substituted systems, the unsubstituted ring A may be considered to be rotated from the plane of the rest of the molecule.

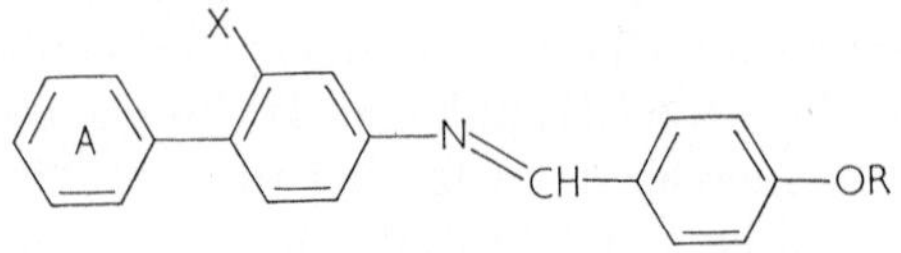

XXV

As noted earlier in this chapter, although $\varDelta t$ (H–X) may vary, for a given substituent, from one system to another, a reasonable constancy of $\varDelta t$ (X_1–X_2), where X_1 is not H, has been observed for both smectic and nematic mesophases, irrespective of the parent system. For example, $\varDelta t$ (Cl–Br) nematic may be given an average value of 8·25°, but for the 2-substituted monoanils, $\varDelta t$ (Cl–Br) nematic is 18·4°, more than double the normally observed value. The difference of some 10° between the two decreases must arise from the greater steric effect of the bromo-substituent which will give rise to a larger interplanar angle θ for the biphenyl nucleus. Unfortunately, there are no available X-ray data relating to the difference in θ between crystalline derivatives of 2-chloro- and 2-bromo- biphenyl, but the interplanar angles for the four 2-halogenobiphenyls and 2-methylbiphenyl have been calculated, on a purely mathematical basis.[17] These calculations show that the angle θ should increase from 55·9° to 60·2° on passing from a 2-chloro- to a 2-bromo- monoanil. An attempt was therefore made to analyse the changes in the mesomorphic thermal stabilities for the 2- substituted monoanils in terms of the changes in the interplanar angles θ. Table X.7 summarizes data relevant to such an analysis—the van der Waal's radii of the substituents X, the interplanar angles (θ) calculated for the 2-substituted biphenyl, the average smectic-nematic and nematic-iso-tropic transition temperatures for the 2-substituted monoanils, and the related Δt (H–X) smectic and nematic values.

TABLE X.7

2-Substituted 4-p-n-Alkoxybenzylideneaminobiphenyls

Substituent	H	F	Cl	Br	I	Me
van der Waal's Radius (Å)	1·08	1·35	1·80	1·95	2·15	2·0
θ (°)	23·2*	42·3	55·9	60·2	64·7	62·4
Average transition temps. (°)						
Smectic-nematic (C_9–C_{10})	157·3	96·0	43·5	—	—	—
Nematic-isotropic (C_7–C_{10})	161·9	113·2	52·1	33·7	14·9	49·5
Δt (H–X) smectic		61·3	113·8			
Δt (H–X) nematic		48·7	109·8	128·2	147·0	112·4

* It will be noted that the calculations do not give an interplanar angle of 0° for the unsubstituted biphenyl ring system. Thus, some steric interaction between the 2- and 2'- hydrogens is indicated and the crystal forces must overcome this by steric compression, or by stretching of the 1,1'-bond, in order to give a planar ring system in the solid state.

The Δt (H–X) values are the decreases in the mesomorphic thermal stabilities caused by (1) the increase in molecular breadth due to the size of the substituent and (2) the increase in thickness of the molecule caused by the steric effect of the 2-substituent, which rotates phenyl ring A—see XXV—from the plane of the rest of the molecule. Let us assume that $x°$ is the decrease in nematic thermal stability caused by effect (1) for a fluoro- substituent. When no steric phenomena occur, it is known that the decreases in nematic thermal stability which are observed on passing from fluoro- to chloro-, chloro- to bromo-, bromo- to iodo-, and methyl to chloro- substituted systems are more or less constant and may be assigned average values of 24·25, 8·25, 10·5, and 2° respectively.

On passing from the unsubstituted monoanil to the 2-substituted system, the *decreases* in nematic thermal stability due to the steric effects of the 2-substituents, $\Delta t'_s$ (H–X) nematic, may therefore be written as

F $(48\cdot7{-}x)°$ Cl $(85\cdot55{-}x)°$ Br $(95\cdot7{-}x)°$

I $(104{-}x)°$ Me $(90\cdot15{-}x)°$

If we now plot $\Delta t'_s$ (H–X) nematic against the interplanar angle θ, a series of curves will be obtained, the individual slopes and positions of these depending on x the unknown factor. Some representative plots are show in Fig. X.4.

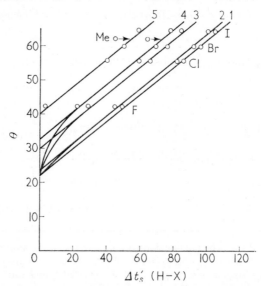

FIG. X.4. The relationship between the decrease in the nematic thermal stability of a 4-p-n-alkoxybenzylideneaminobiphenyl brought about by the steric effect of a 2-substituent, and the interplanar angle calculated for the 2-substituted biphenyl.

For the 3-substituted monoanils, Δt (H–Cl) nematic, the decrease in nematic thermal stability caused by the chloro- substituent, is 70°. On this basis, Δt (H–F) nematic $= x$ would be $45\cdot8°$. This is the value of x used in obtaining curve 5 in Fig. X.4. If this curve is extrapolated to $\Delta t'_s$ (H–X) $= 0$, i.e. when the 2-substituent is hydrogen, the interplanar angle θ is about 40°. Thus, the interplanar angle predicted for the nematic mesophase of an unsubstituted monoanil derived from 4-amino-biphenyl is about 40°, rather a smaller angle than that observed (45°), experimentally for the molecule of biphenyl in the gas phase or in solution. However, the 3-substituted monoanils appear to be anomalous systems, and as discussed later, may well involve a steric effect which accounts for the high Δt (H–Cl) nematic value of 70°. Therefore, x

should probably be given a lower value than 45·8°. Taking the extreme case where $x = 0°$, an almost straight line relationship (curve 1) between θ and $\Delta t'_s$ (H–X) nematic is obtained, and the line may be extrapolated to an interplanar angle of 23–24° for the unsubstituted biphenyl nucleus. It is of interest to note that the angle θ calculated for the unsubstituted biphenyl molecule is 23·2°. However, we can hardly postulate that a 2-fluoro- substituent in the biphenyl monoanils has no effect on the mesomorphic thermal stability of the system as a result of its molecular broadening effect. In fact this would be equivalent to saying that the fluoro- substituent does not broaden the molecule, and this is clearly unreasonable. We must therefore decide upon a reasonable value for x. For the 3'-substituted 4'-n-alkoxybiphenyl-4-carboxylic acids, Δt (H–F) nematic is 9°, and for the 3-substituted p-n-alkoxybenzoic acids, Δt (H–F) nematic is 26·5°. The molecules of the substituted monoanils are more similar in size to the dimeric molecules of the benzoic acids, and it would seem realistic to propose that a value of 26·5° be used for x. Curve 4 has been drawn using this value for x, and for comparison, curves 2 and 3 have been included using values of $x = 4°$ and 20°, respectively. If we assume that the approximate straight line relationships shown by the curves between the points for X = fluoro- and X = iodo- continue to hold for values of $\Delta t'_s$ (H–X) nematic less than for X = F, then curves 2, 3, and 4 may be extrapolated respectively to interplanar angles = 23·5, 30, and 33° for $\Delta t'_s$ (H–X) nematic = 0. Again therefore, as in the case of $x = 0$, interplanar angles considerably lower than the angle of 45° for biphenyl in the gas phase or in solution are indicated for the nematic melt.

We should now consider whether a straight line relationship between θ and $\Delta t'_s$ (H–X) nematic is likely. We might expect that a fixed change in the interplanar angle θ at small values of θ would have less effect on the mesomorphic thermal stability than a similar change in θ at large interplanar angles. On this basis, we would postulate that the curve obtained on plotting θ against $\Delta t'_s$ (H–X) nematic would become steeper at low values of θ and $\Delta t'_s$ (H–X) nematic. Indeed, each of the curves 2, 3, and 4 may readily be extrapolated to values of $\theta = 23·2°$ at $\Delta t'_s$ (H–X) nematic = 0. Curves 1, 2, 3, and 4 could in fact be extrapolated to even lower values of θ, even to $\theta = 0°$, at $\Delta t'_s$ (H–X) nematic = 0.

Now, the calculations made by Branch[17] show that, if an unsubstituted molecule of biphenyl is to adopt a planar conformation, then the van der Waal's radius of the hydrogen atom must not exceed 0·94 Å. This radius for hydrogen is rather small, and we must assume that the planar molecule which exists in crystalline biphenyl arises through steric compression of the system by crystal forces. The residual crystal forces which exist in the partially ordered structure of the nematic mesophase

may also constrain the biphenyl ring system into a more planar arrangement, and it is possible that the interplanar angle for the nematic mesophase is less than the calculated angle of 23·2°. In this way we may
justify the steeper extrapolations of curves 1, 2, 3, and 4 in Fig. X.4 to
angles lower than $\theta = 23·2°$.

On the other hand, if the covalent radius of 1·08 Å used by Branch[17]
for the hydrogen atom is too high, then the angles θ calculated for all
the substituents will be too high. All the curves in Fig. X.4 would
therefore be displaced downwards, so making extrapolations to values
of θ less than 23·2° more reasonable. It is not therefore out of the
question that the non-sterically affected biphenyl ring system is coplanar in the nematic melt. Inconclusive as the results are in this
respect, two points do emerge quite clearly from these studies:

(1) The interplanar angle for the biphenyl ring system in the nematic
mesophases of biphenyl derivatives, is considerably less than 45°, the
interplanar angle for biphenyl in the gas phase or in solution.

(2) In the nematic melt, no free rotation of the phenyl rings of the
biphenyl nucleus occurs about the 1,1'-bond. If such free rotation did
occur, all the monoanils would be similarly affected, irrespective of the
nature of the substituent, and the mesomorphic thermal stability would
not be a function of the interplanar angle θ. That is, the steric effects
would, in all cases, be non-existent, and the mesomorphic thermal
stabilities would decrease solely because of the increase in molecular
breadth occasioned by the substituent. As a relationship exists between
$\Delta t'_s$ (H–X) nematic and θ, this demonstrates that such free rotation
does not occur. We must assume therefore that the biphenyl ring
system is fairly rigid in the nematic melt, and that some angle θ is
adopted such that (a) the strain on the 1,1'-bond is minimal, and (b)
the molecules may pack together as closely as possible.

It will be noted from Fig. X.4 that the points for X = Me do not lie
on the various lines drawn through the points for the halogens, using
different values for x. In all cases, the points for Me lie above and to the
left of the curves, suggesting that the methyl group causes a smaller
twisting of the phenyl rings about the 1,1'-bond than the calculated
value for θ would suggest. Now, the calculated angle θ for a 2-methyl
substituent was obtained by regarding the methyl group as a sphere of
van der Waal's radius 2·0 Å (see Table X.7). This is not, however, a
strictly accurate model of the methyl group, for interstices do exist
between the surfaces of the three hydrogen atoms, and if the hydrogen
atom in the 2'-position can lock itself between the surfaces of the hydrogen atoms of two of the C—H links of the methyl group, a smaller interplanar angle than the calculated angle of 62·4° would result. As shown
in Fig. X.4, an angle of about 58·5° would allow the points for X = Me
to lie on the curves, and molecular models show that a decrease of

some 4° from the calculated angle is not unreasonable if this straddling of the 2'-hydrogen atom by the methyl group does occur. The 2'-substituted monoanils (XXVI)[6] do not help to verify or extend the ideas concerning the steric effect of an angular substituent in the bi-phenyl nucleus on the mesomorphic thermal stability, except in the most general way. Certainly, a 2'-substituent gives rise to very low

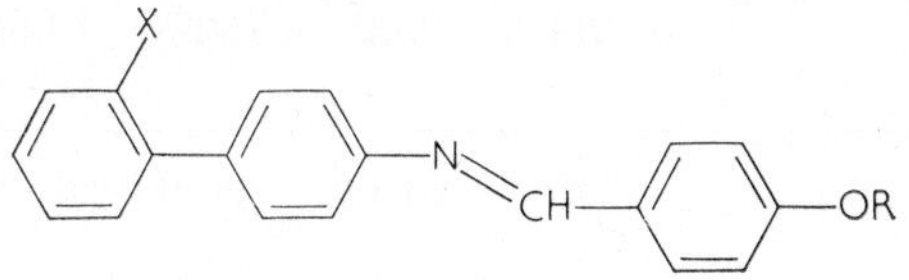

XXVI

mesomorphic thermal stabilities, and this confirms the view that a steric effect is again operating in the mesomorphic states of these com-pounds. However, it has not so far been possible to obtain the pure 2'-fluoro- monoanils, and without these, the extrapolations involved in any plots similar to those made for the 2-substituted monoanils (Fig. X.4) are very long, and the deductions concerning the angle θ for the unsubstituted system are consequently unreliable.

It should be noted, too, that neither the 2- nor the 2'-substituted monoanils give any useful information concerning the steric influences of substituents on the smectic thermal stabilities—no smectic meso-phases are given by the monoanils containing larger substituents, such as bromo-.

To verify the above results obtained for the 2-substituted monoanils, a study was made of the dianils (XXVII) derived from 2-substituted benzidines.

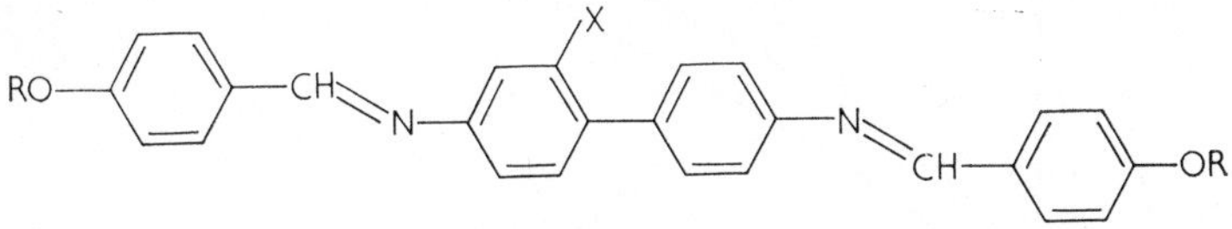

XXVII

These 2-substituted 4,4'-di-(p-n-alkoxybenzylideneamino) biphenyls[3, 12] have the advantage that their mesomorphic thermal stabilities are higher, and that smectic mesophases occur even when X = iodo-. The mesomorphic transition temperatures for a series of such dianils are recorded in Table X.8.

We may now apply the method used to analyse the nematic thermal stabilities of the 2-substituted monoanils, to an assessment of the steric effects of 2-substituents on the nematic *and* smectic thermal stabilities of the compounds XXVII.

The $\Delta t'_s$ (H–X) nematic values are for X = F, (29·4–x); Cl, (59·85–

TABLE X.8

2-Substituted (X) 4,4'-Di-(p-n-alkoxybenzylideneamino)biphenyls[3, 12]
Average transition temperature (°)

Substituent (X)	H	F	Cl	Br	I	Me
Smectic-nematic transition temp. (C_{10} only)	311·5	253	153·8	123·5	91	166·8
Nematic-isotropic transition temp. (C_7–C_{10})	345	315·6	260·9	245·8	222·4	259·6
Δt (H–X) smectic		58·5	157·7	188	220·5	144·7
Δt (H–X) nematic		29·4	84·1	99·2	122·6	85·4

x); Br, $(66·7-x)$; I, $(79·6-x)$; Me, $(63·15-x)°$, and the $\Delta t'_s$ (H–X) smectic values are for X = F, $(58·5-x)$; Cl, $(129·95-x)$; Br, $(149-x)$; I, $(161·75-x)$; Me, $(94·2-x)°$. The $\Delta t'_s$ (H–X) smectic values are obtained using the average Δt (X_1-X_2) smectic values listed below, c.f. Table X.3: F–Cl, 27·75; Cl–Br, 11·25; Br–I, 19·75; H–Me, 50·5°.

The $\Delta t'_s$ (H–X) nematic and smectic values are plotted against the calculated angles θ in Figs. X.5 (a) and (b) respectively.

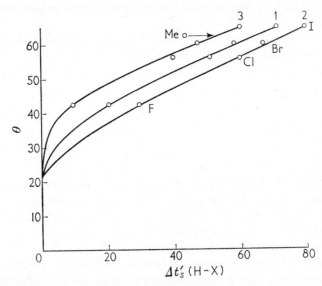

FIG. X.5(a). The relationship between the decrease in the nematic thermal stability of a 4,4'-di-(p-n-alkoxybenzylideneamino)biphenyl brought about by the steric effect of a 2- substituent, and the interplanar angle calculated for the 2-substituted biphenyl.

Let us consider first the steric effect of the substituents on the nematic thermal stabilities (Fig. X.5 (a)). For the 3′–substituted 4′-n-alkoxybiphenyl-4-carboxylic acids, Δt (H–F) nematic is 9°, and curve 1 in Fig. X.5 (a) has been constructed using $x = 9°$. Curves 2 and 3 are drawn for arbitrary values of $x = 0$ and 20° respectively. It will be noted that the points for X = Me again lie well above the lines, but, as in the case of the 2-substituted monoanils, an angle $\theta = 58\cdot5°$ would bring these points very close to the lines. Almost straight line relationships are shown to exist in Fig. X.5 (a) for the points for fluoro-, chloro-

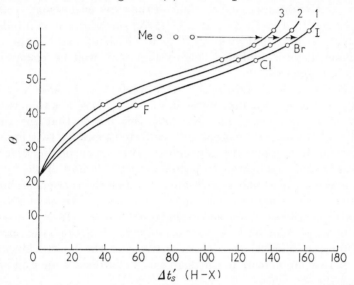

Fig. X.5(b). The relationship between the decrease in the smectic thermal stability of a 4,4′-di-(p-n-alkoxybenzylideneamino)biphenyl brought about by the steric effect of a 2- substituent, and the interplanar angle calculated for the 2-substituted biphenyl.

bromo-, and iodo-, but, as discussed earlier, all the lines have been extrapolated to $\theta = 23$–24°, at $\Delta t'_s$ (H–X) nematic = 0. The increased gradients of the lines for values of $\Delta t'_s$ (H–X) nematic which are less than that for fluoro- are, however, quite gentle, and indeed the most reasonable extrapolation is shown in curve 1, for which the realistic value of $x = 9°$ has been employed. Curve 2 is solely of theoretical interest, because x has been taken as 0°.

Turning again to the 2-substituted monoanils, we have now considerably more justification for extrapolating the lines in Fig. X.4 with increasing gradients for points with $\Delta t'_s$ (H–X) nematic lower than for fluoro-.

The data for the 2-substituted dianils therefore reinforce the view that the interplanar angle for the unsubstituted biphenyl nucleus, in the nematic mesophase, is much less than 45°, and may be even lower than the calculated angle of 23·2°.

Turning now to the smectic mesophases of the dianils, the curves in Fig. X.5 (b) have been drawn using the $\Delta t'_s$ (H–X) smectic values given above, and values of $x = 0.5$, 10·5, and 20·5° respectively for curves 1, 2, and 3. In this connection, we should remember that Δt (H–F) smectic for the 3′-substituted 4′-n-alkoxybiphenyl-4-carboxylic acids is very low (0·5°). The gradients of the three curves between X = F and Cl are very low, and once again a relationship between $\Delta t'_s$ (H–X) smectic and θ appears to exist. Each of the three curves may readily be extrapolated to $\theta = 23$–24°, at $\Delta t'_s$ (H–X) smectic = 0, and indeed to lower values of θ, and even to $\theta = 0°$, without making the curves unrealistic, i.e. the biphenyl ring system may well be planar in the smectic mesophase.

Since the gradients for the curves between the points for X = F and X = Cl for the smectic mesophase in Fig. X.5 (b) are less than those for the nematic mesophase (Fig. X.5 (a)), this means that the thermal stability of the smectic mesophase is affected more by twisting of the phenyl rings from a planar arrangement. It is not surprising that this is the case, because a deviation from coplanarity will most markedly affect the lateral intermolecular attractions, on which the thermal stability of the smectic mesophase is much more dependent. We have noted too that extrapolations to interplanar angles of 0° at $\Delta t'_s$ (H–X) values = 0, whilst being possible for *both* smectic and nematic mesophases, are more likely for the smectic mesophase, because of the lower values of x. Since there is an increase in the degree of molecular disorder on passing through the sequence

solid——→smectic——→nematic——→isotropic liquid, vapour, or solution,

a gradual change in the interplanar angle may occur on passing from the solid state ($\theta = 0°$) to the isotropic liquid ($\theta = 45°$). Moreover, the residual crystal forces should be greater in the smectic mesophase than in the nematic mesophase. The interplanar angle for the biphenyl ring system may therefore be as low as 0° in the smectic mesophase, and should certainly be no larger than that for the nematic mesophase, for which it is quite reasonable to suggest an angle $\theta = 23$–24°, or even less.

We should also note that the gradients of the individual curves in Fig. X.5 (b) change as the angle θ is increased, i.e. the curves are drawn so that the gradients decrease, rapidly at first and then more gradually, from $\Delta t'_s$ (H–X) smectic = 0 to the point for chloro-, and then increase again to the points for bromo- and iodo-. The polarizability of an aromatic ring system should be a maximum in the plane of the ring system, i.e. at right angles to the long axes of the deformable π-orbitals, and we can assume that lateral intermolecular attractions between the sides of aromatic molecules will contribute more to the intermolecular cohesions than will attractions between the planes of the molecules. Therefore, if a steric effect rotates one of the phenyl rings out of the plane (XX') of the rest of the molecule, into a new position (YY'), the polarizability of the system in the plane XX' should decrease as θ increases, see Fig. X.6. The component of the polarizability of the ring which has been rotated out of the plane XX', in the plane XX', will be a function of $\cos\theta$, so that the decrease in intermolecular attraction should be a function of $\cos\theta$. This means that when θ is small, the effect of a given change, $\Delta\theta$, on the polarizability in the plane XX' will be less significant than when θ is large. The gradient of the curve relating the steric influence on the mesomorphic thermal stability, i.e. $\Delta t'_s$ (H–X), to the angle θ should therefore decrease as θ increases.

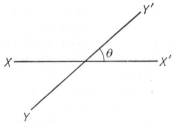

FIG. X.6. The lines X–X' and Y-Y' represent the planes of the two aromatic rings in biphenyl, inclined at an angle (θ) to one another.

However, if the plane of the ring (YY') is rotated still further away from the plane XX', the polarizability of the rotated ring will begin to enhance the attractions between the planes of the molecules. The increase in these attractive forces will be a function of $\sin\theta$, and will therefore become more important as θ increases. A combination of these effects could explain (a) the very approximate straight line relationship of the $\Delta t'_s$ (H–X) smectic against θ curves for the points for fluoro-, chloro-, and bromo-, (b) the sharper rise to the points for iodo-, and (c) the steeper fall for $\Delta t'_s$ (H–X) smectic values lower than those for fluoro-.

This increase in the gradient of the $\Delta t'_s$ (H–X) curves for larger substituents was not observed for the nematic mesophase, and it can only be suggested that, since the thermal stability of this mesophase is not so critically dependent on the lateral intermolecular attractions, it will not be so sensitive to the influence of the angle θ on these attractive forces.

Returning to Fig. X.5 (b), the points for X = Me are displaced well to the left of the curves, and even if the angle of 58·5° is used, the points do not approach the curves very closely. It is possible that this large discrepancy for the methyl derivatives arises from the stronger residual crystal forces in the smectic mesophases. These crystal forces may be able to compress a 2-methylbiphenyl so that it adopts a more nearly planar conformation. As shown by molecular models, there is no doubt that the polyatomic methyl group makes it far less difficult for the phenyl rings to pass through a planar arrangement than does a monatomic substituent of similar size, i.e. chloro-. To give a fit with the curves in Fig. X.5 (*b*), an angle as low as 50° would appear to be necessary for the 2-methyl dianils in the smectic mesophase. However, one cannot be too dogmatic about this point, if only for the reason that the average Δt (H–Me) smectic value used to obtain the $\Delta t'_s$ (H–Me) smectic values, is open to some doubt, the figure being based on all too few values from non-sterically affected series of compounds.

As a result of these studies of 2-substituted biphenyl derivatives which are mesomorphic, it appears quite certain that free rotation about the 1,1'-bond of the biphenyl nucleus does not occur in the mesomorphic melts. The molecule appears to have a fairly rigid structure, and the interplanar angle which is adopted increases with increasing size of the substituent in the 2-position. The conformation of a non-sterically affected biphenyl nucleus in the mesophase is still in some doubt. The ring system could well be planar, but the experimental evidence merely shows that the angle is considerably less than 45°. However, the over-all picture suggests strongly that a non-sterically affected biphenyl nucleus will not give free rotation about the 1,1'-bond, and that the residual crystal forces constrain the ring system with as low an interplanar angle as possible, in order that the molecules may pack together with as much economy as possible. Thus, while we cannot say whether non-sterically affected biphenyl systems adopt planar arrangements of the rings, or arrangements which involve some relatively small interplanar angle θ, it does seem likely that all non-sterically affected biphenyl systems will adopt approximately the same angle θ, whether this angle be 0° or not. The result is that the arguments used in the discussion of the mesomorphic thermal stabilities of the 3'-substituted 4'-n-alkoxybiphenyl-4-carboxylic acids in terms of their molecular breadths still stand, and that any variations in the interplanar angles from one derivative to another should be so small that they would not be expected to affect the mesomorphic thermal stabilities.

It is of interest now to examine plots of mesomorphic transition temperatures against the breadths of molecules which do involve steric effects, i.e. for the 2-substituted 4-*p*-n-alkoxybenzylideneaminobiphenyls and 4,4'-di-(*p*-n-alkoxybenzylideneamino)biphenyls. For these systems, we did not necessarily expect a simple relationship of the kind found for the nematic melts of the 3'-substituted 4'-n-alkoxybiphenyl-4-carboxylic acids, for the steric effects of the substituents will lower the mesomorphic thermal stabilities, and not necessarily in direct proportion to the molecular breadth-increasing effects of the substituents.

Bearing in mind that the 2-substituted monoanils exhibit smectic mesophases over only a limited range of substituents, the orders of increasing effect of the substituents on the mesomorphic thermal stabilities are:

(a) *Smectic mesophase*

Monoanils $H < F < Cl < (Br)$—no smectic mesophase.

Dianils $H < F < Me < NO_2 < Cl < Br < I$

(b) *Nematic mesophase*

Monoanils $H < F < Cl$ slightly $< Me < Br < I*$

Dianils $H < F < Cl$ slightly $< Me < Br < NO_2 < I$

* the 2-nitro- monoanils have not been examined.

The same general conclusions are reached by a consideration of either the monoanils or the dianils, but since more data are available for

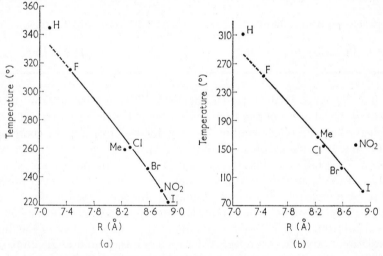

FIG. X.7. The molecular breadths of the 2-substituted 4,4'-di-(p-n-alkoxy-benzylideneamino)biphenyls plotted against (a) their nematic-isotropic transition temperatures and (b) their smectic-nematic transition temperatures.

the dianils, we will discuss only these compounds. In Figs. X.7 (a) and (b), the mesomorphic transition temperatures (t) for the dianils have been plotted against the breadths of the molecules (R—from molecular models), assuming in all cases that the benzylideneamino- groups adopt a *trans-: trans-* arrangement.

For the nematic-isotropic transition temperatures of the dianils (Fig. X.7 (a)), the points fall reasonably smoothly with increasing molecular breadth, and it would seem that the order

$$H < F < Cl \text{ slightly} < Me < Br < NO_2 < I$$

is at least largely determined by the separation of the molecular axes, whether this separation increases because of the broadening effect of the substituent, because of the steric effect of the substituent, or because of both these factors. The decreases in nematic thermal stability are of course much greater than would be obtained with the same substituents in a non-sterically affected system of comparable size, and there is a particularly marked decrease in transition temperature on passing from unsubstituted to 2-fluoro- dianil, c.f. Table. X.9.

TABLE X.9

Decreases in Nematic-Isotropic Transition Temperature $(°)$

	H–F	F–Cl	Cl–Br	Br–I	NO$_2$–I
No steric effect: Biphenyl acids	9	22·5	9	10	0
Steric effect: 2-sub. dianils	29·4	54·7	15·1	23·4	8
Steric effect: 2-sub. monoanils	48·7	61·1	18·4	18·8	—

The decrease in nematic thermal stability on passing from unsubstituted dianil or monoanil to 2-fluoro- derivative is very marked, and it is clear that the effect cannot be explained simply by the increase in molecular breadth which is small $(0·27°\text{Å})$. However, since the curve in Fig. X.7 (a) falls reasonably smoothly through the points for X = F, Cl, Br, I, NO$_2$, and Me, it appears that the gradient of this curve reflects both the increasing breadth effect and the increasing steric effect caused by the 2-substituent. This would lead us to believe therefore, that the steep fall from X = H to F is explained by the steric effect of the fluoro-substituent, and there is a larger increase in interplanar angle on passing from X = H to F than would normally be anticipated. That is, the interplanar angles which would be obtained for non-sterically affected biphenyl ring systems by a straightforward back extrapolation of the $\Delta t'_s$ (H–X) nematic against θ curves are too high, and in this way we obtain some vindication of the extrapolations which have been made in these plots using increasing gradients for points with values of $\Delta t'_s$ (H–X) nematic lower than for fluoro-. Such extrapolations of the $\Delta t'_s$ (H–X) nematic against θ curves have been made to interplanar angles of about 23°, equivalent to the angle of 23·2° calculated by Branch. If such an angle exists in the non-sterically affected biphenyl nucleus, then on passing from unsubstituted to 2-fluoro- dianil, $\Delta\theta = 19·1°$, $\Delta R = 0·27°$Å, and $\Delta t = 29·4°$. It is of course impossible to say whether a change of 19–20° in θ explains quantitatively the large decrease in nematic thermal stability which accompanies the small breadth increase of 0·27°Å. We have argued that, for low values of θ, a change in θ will have a relatively small effect on the nematic thermal stability, and if $\Delta\theta = 19·1°$ is insufficient to explain the large fall in nematic thermal stability, one could postulate that the non-sterically affected parent compounds are planar, such that $\Delta\theta$ (H–F) may be as high as 42·3°, c.f. the extrapolations to values of θ less than 23·2° suggested for the $\Delta t'_s$ (H–X) nematic curves.

As mentioned earlier, for substituents larger than fluoro-, both the molecular breadths and the interplanar angles increase more or less in parallel, and a relatively smooth decrease in nematic thermal stability is to be expected. Only the points for the 2-methyl derivatives lie *slightly* off the curves—for the dianils, some 5–6° below the line, and for the monoanils, 6–7° below. Once more, this suggests that the effects of a chloro- substituent and of a methyl group on the nematic thermal stabilities are about the same. Since dipole moments do not influence the effect of a substituent on the nematic thermal stability, we must infer that the over-all size effects, i.e. the molecular broadening effects and the steric effects of the 2-methyl and 2-chloro- substituents are about the same. However, the angle θ calculated by Branch for 2-methylbiphenyl was 62·4°, and the angle for 2-chlorobiphenyl, 55·9°. Once more, then, the evidence points to the view that the angle of 62·4° for a 2-methylbiphenyl may be too high, and that the angle should be nearer 58° for the nematic mesophase, and perhaps even lower for the smectic mesophase.

Figure X.7 (b) illustrates the plot of the smectic-nematic transition temperatures against the molecular breadths of the dianils. A sudden fall in transition temperature again occurs on passing from X = H to F, and applying the arguments used above, a relatively larger increase in the interplanar angle θ must occur on passing from X = H to F than would be expected on the basis of other larger substituents. The point for X = NO_2 lies above the curve by some 55°, and this displacement reminds us of the displacement of the smectic-isotropic point for 3′-nitro-4′-n-octyloxybiphenyl-4-carboxylic acid from the plot of the smectic-nematic transition temperatures against the molecular breadths of the 3′-halogeno-acids. The higher smectic thermal stability of the 2-nitro- dianil may again be explained by the large ring-NO_2 dipole moment which enhances the intermolecular lateral attractions. It is also possible that the interplanar angle for a 2-nitro-biphenyl is lower relative to other 2-substituted biphenyls carrying substituents such as bromo- and iodo-, which are similar in size to the nitro- groups. The lower angle would arise if the nitro- group were rotated out of the plane of the ring system, about the ring-NO_2 bond, and would result in a high average transition temperature for the 2-nitro- dianils relative to the other 2-substituted dianils. However, since the displacement of the point for $X = NO_2$ occurs only for the smectic-nematic transition temperatures (Fig X.7 (*b*)), and not for the nematic-isotropic transition temperatures (Fig. X.7 (*a*)) of the 2-nitro- dianils, it seems more likely that the effect is explained by the magnitude of the ring-NO_2 dipole moment.

The other interesting point connected with Fig. X.7 (*b*) is the fact that the point for the average smectic-nematic transition temperature for the 2-methyl dianils lies on the curve—it would have been expected that the low Me-ring dipole moment would lead to a low thermal stability for the smectic mesophases, c.f. the explanation of the low, predicted smectic-nematic transition temperature for 3'-methyl-4'-n-octyloxybiphenyl-4-carboxylic acid. In fact, the average smectic-nematic transition temperature for the 2-methyl dianils is higher than that for the 2-chloro- dianils by 13°, i.e. the average smectic thermal stability for the methyl derivatives is about 33° higher than would be expected. It is interesting to note that the 2'-methyl monoanils behave similarly, and Δt (Me–Cl) smectic for these compounds is 17°. The 2-methyl monoanils do not exhibit smectic mesophases, and a *decrease* in smectic thermal stability must therefore occur on passing from chloro- to methyl substituted monoanil. It was first thought that conjugation of the methyl group with the benzylideneamino- group occurred in the 2'-methyl monoanils and 2-methyl dianils (XXVIII). This conjugation would enhance the Me-ring dipole moment, but would decrease the ring-halogen dipole moment. This conjugation could not, however, occur in the 2-methyl monoanils, in which the methyl group and the benzylideneamino- group are effectively *meta*- to one another. For the

XXVIII

2'-methyl monoanils and the 2-methyl dianils, the smectic thermal stabilities might therefore be expected to be higher than those of the isomeric chloro- compounds, and the observed results would be explained qualitatively. However, recent studies[18] of the extent to which conjugation may occur from a 2-substituent to groups such as —CO$_2$H and —NH$_2$ in the 4'-position of biphenyl, indicate that this conjugative effect is unlikely to have any significant effect on the mesomorphic properties. No really satisfactory explanation can therefore be offered for the enhanced smectic thermal stabilities exhibited by 2'-methyl monoanils and 2-methyl dianils.

As mentioned earlier, the range of substituents studied in the case of the 2'-substituted monoanils was incomplete, as the 2'-fluoro- monoanils were not obtained pure. A satisfactory attempt to relate the changes in the mesomorphic transition temperatures of these compounds to the changes in the molecular breadths cannot therefore be made. In so far as the nematic-isotropic transition temperatures of the methyl, chloro-, bromo-, and iodo- compounds are concerned, the temperatures appear to change with molecular breadth as would be expected by analogy with the 2-substituted systems. Moreover, the large separation of the transition temperatures for X = H and X = Cl or Me again suggest that a large decrease in mesomorphic thermal stability must occur on passing from the unsubstituted to the 2'-fluoro- monoanil. However, this cannot be verified.

Finally, it should be mentioned that differences do occur between the mesomorphic transition temperatures of isomeric 2- and 2'-substituted monoanils—the decrease in smectic thermal stability which occurs on passing from a 2'-methyl to a 2-methyl monoanil has already been mentioned. On the other hand, the *smectic* thermal stability in-

XXIX

creases from 2'- to 2-chloro- monoanil (4·5°), and the *nematic* thermal stability decreases from 2'- to 2-methyl monoanil (14·4°), from 2'- to 2-chloro monoanil (6·9°), from 2'- to 2-bromo- monoanil (10·4°), and from 2'- to 2-iodo- monoanil (6·2°). The effects are quite small, but it is not easy to assess the reasons for the thermal stability changes. Although the interplanar angle should be the same for isomeric 2- and 2'- substituted systems, in the case of the 2'-substituted monoanils (XXIX), we must imagine that the substituted phenyl ring is rotated from the plane of the rest of the molecule. One cannot expect that the breadth-increasing effect of the 2'-substituent on the *interplanar* attractions, as distinct from its twisting effect, will be the same as that of a 2-substituent on the interactions between the *sides* of the molecules. Indeed, the 2'-substituent would be expected to have the smaller effect on the mesomorphic thermal stability, since rotation of the phenyl ring *and* the substituent from the plane of the molecule will lessen the breadth-increasing effect on the lateral attractions. However, the fairly *large decrease* in smectic thermal stability which must occur from 2′- to 2-methyl isomer, and the fact that the 2-chloro- monoanils have the *more* thermally stable smectic mesophases suggest that other factors must influence the relative mesomorphic thermal stabilities of pairs of isomers.

In the light of the above discussions, it is clear that steric effects can have a most marked effect on the mesomorphic thermal stabilities. The 2-substituted mono- and di-anils derived from 4-aminobiphenyl and benzidine were studied primarily to obtain information regarding the interplanar angle (θ) for the non-sterically affected biphenyl ring system in the mesomorphic states of compounds. However, the work led to further studies, which may be divided into two sections:

(*a*) The influence of substituents *ortho*- to the benzylideneamino-groups of mono- and di-anils derived from 4-aminobiphenyl and benzidine.

(*b*) The steric effects which are involved with more than one angular substituent in the biphenyl ring system.

The results of these studies are summarized in the remainder of this chapter.

1. THE MESOMORPHIC PROPERTIES OF 3-SUBSTITUTED
4-*p*-n-ALKOXYBENZYLIDENEAMINOBIPHENYLS AND
4,4′-DI-(*p*-n-ALKOXYBENZYLIDENEAMINO)BIPHENYLS—XXX AND XXXI

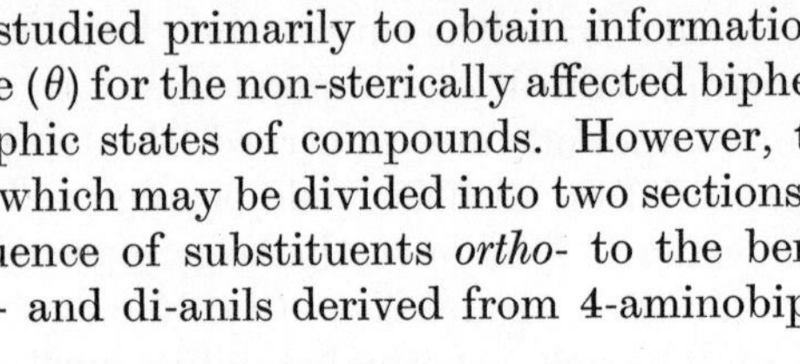

XXX

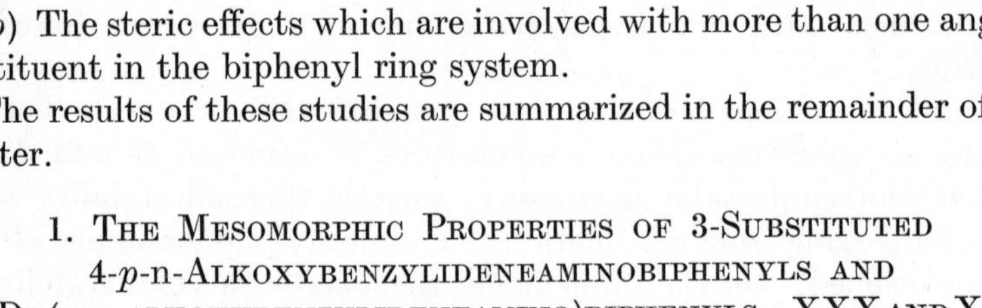

XXXI

Compounds of the type XXX were first examined in the hope that their mesomorphic properties could be used as a guide to the effect of a substituent X on the mesomorphic thermal stability, in the absence of any steric effect. However, the compounds XXX do not exhibit smectic mesophases, and the decreases (Δt (H—X) nematic) in mesomorphic thermal stability resulting from the introduction of the 3-substituents are large, c.f. Table X.5, Δt (H–Me) $= 62 \cdot 2°$, Δt (H–Cl)$= 70°$, Δt (H–Br)

$= 78°$. These effects may be explained in two different ways: (a) If the 3-substituent and the —N=CH— link lie *trans-* to one another as shown in XXX, the molecular breadth is considerable, and the nematic, and in particular the smectic thermal stability should be low.

(b) If the 3-substituent and the —N=CH— link lie *cis-* to one another, as shown in XXXII, the molecular breadth is comparable with other monosubstituted monoanils, but a steric effect between the substituent and the hydrogen of the —N=CH— unit will prevent the molecule from being coplanar. Furthermore, the dipole moments of

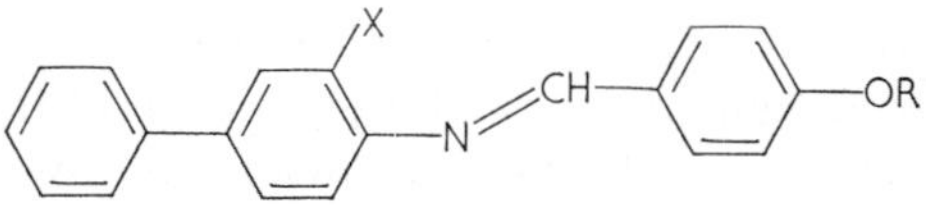

XXXII

the ring-X and —N=CH— bonds will partially oppose one another. Both effects would lower the mesomorphic thermal stabilities.

Certain 3-substituted dianils (XXXI) were therefore prepared in order to throw more light on this problem, and in the hope that the influence of 3-substituents on smectic thermal stabilities would be ascertained. Table X.10 summarizes the relevant data.

TABLE X.10

3-Substituted 4,4'-Di-(p-n-alkoxybenzylideneamino)biphenyls

Nematic mesophases	Δt (H–Cl) =	48·4° (70°)	Δt (Cl–Br) =	9·8° (8°)
	Δt (H–Br) =	58·2 (78)	Δt (Me–Cl) =	0·3 (7·8)
Smectic mesophases	Δt (H–Cl) =	97·6	Δt (Cl–Br) =	24·6
	Δt (H–Br) =	122·2	Δt (Me–Cl) =	−22·5

The values in parenthesis are the decreases in nematic thermal stability for the 3-substituted monoanils.

The decreases in nematic thermal stability on passing from parent dianil to 3-substituted derivative are smaller than the corresponding decreases from parent monoanil to 3-substituted monoanil. This is understandable, since the molecules of the dianils are larger than those of the monoanils. The Δt (Cl–Br) and Δt (Me–Cl) nematic values are quite normal, average values, and suggest that the 3-substituent causes no steric effect, i.e. that the molecules are planar, adopting the *trans-*

configuration (XXXI). Therefore, as far as the nematic properties are concerned, the 3-substituted mono- and di-anils are similar.

For the smectic mesophases, the Δt (H–Cl) and Δt (Me–Cl) values also suggest that the molecules adopt the planar, *trans*- configuration (XXXI). However, the Δt (Cl–Br) smectic value is rather larger than would be expected for substituents which do not cause a steric effect, yet it is unlikely that the bromo- compound adopts a *cis*- arrangement, and the chloro- and methyl compounds a *trans*- arrangement. Molecular models show, however, that a 3-bromo-substituent causes a slight steric strain even when the benzylideneamino- group is in the *trans*-configuration. This strain may be relieved by a certain amount of bending of the ring-N bond, thus forcing the molecule away from its over-all linear arrangement. Now the separation of the molecular axes is larger in the nematic melt than in the smectic mesophase, and provided that the degree of bond bending is not great, the smectic thermal stability should be more affected than the nematic thermal stability by this steric strain. It is unlikely that conjugative interactions between substituent and benzylideneamino- group play any part in affecting the mesomorphic thermal stabilities, c.f. the normal Δt (Me–Cl) smectic value of $-22 \cdot 5°$, and the data for the 3-substituted dianils are best interpreted in terms of planar molecules with the benzylideneamino-groups lying *trans*- to the 3-substituent. A knowledge of the influence of steric factors on the Δt (X$_1$–X$_2$) smectic and nematic values is therefore of assistance in interpreting the behaviours of these 3-substituted anils.

We will now consider briefly the 3,3′-disubstituted dianils of benzidine (XXXIII)—see also p. 293.

XXXIII

(1) Δt (Me–Cl) nematic $= 3 \cdot 6°$, Δt (Cl–Br) nematic $= 18 \cdot 2°$, and Δt (H–Cl) nematic $= 9 \cdot 42°$. The first two of the above decreases are approximately double the average decreases observed in other monosubstituted series for the same changes of substituent, and the last decrease is approximately double the Δt (H–Cl) nematic value for the 3-substituted dianils. It seems reasonable to conclude therefore that the two 3-substituents lie *trans*- to one another. X-ray crystallography by Toussaint[19] has shown that the chloro- substituents are *trans*- to one another for the planar molecule of 3,3′-dichlorobenzidene.

(2) Δt (Cl–Br) smectic $= 22 \cdot 8°$ and Δt (H–Cl) smectic $= 181°$. Again these two decreases are respectively, approximately double

the average Δt (Cl–Br) smectic value for other systems and the Δt (H–Cl) smectic value for the 3-substituted dianils. However, the Δt (Cl–Br) smectic value is not double Δt (Cl–Br) smectic for the 3-substituted dianils, and is in fact lower—22·8° compared with 24·6°. That is, all the decreases for the 3,3'-disubstituted dianils are quite normal, and no steric effect such as that postulated between the 3-bromo- substituent and the nitrogen of the benzylideneamino- linkage of the 3-bromo-dianils appears to occur. There is no satisfactory explanation of this apparent anomaly. It is possible that slightly different bond lengths in the disubstituted dianils lead to an avoidance of the steric effect with the 3-bromo- substituent, for as mentioned above, models show that the steric effect is only slight. On the other hand, it is possible that the effect of the bond bending in the 3,3'-disubstituted dianils would cancel out, since the steric strain would occur at both ends of the molecule, leading to equal and opposite displacements of the molecule (XXXIII) from linearity. That is, the molecule would still be symmetrical, and have an average linear configuration. Structures XXXIV and XXXV for the 3- and 3,3'-substituted dianils, respectively, illustrate exaggerated configurations for the molecules to illustrate this point.

The above studies of the 3-substituted mono- and di-anils and of the 3,3'-disubstituted dianils illustrate quite clearly that the 3-substituent and the benzylideneamino- group adopt a *trans-* configuration. This again suggests that, in the mesomorphic states, the molecules adopt the configuration which involves the minimum strain, that free rotation of the groups is restricted, and that the molecular structure is reasonably rigid.

2. THE MESOMORPHIC PROPERTIES OF DI-, TRI-, AND TETRA-SUBSTITUTED 4,4'-DI-(p-n-ALKOXYBENZYLIDENEAMINO)-BIPHENYLS (Alkyl groups R = C_7H_{15}–$C_{10}H_{21}$)

Disubstituted compounds. The dianils studied carried substituents in the 2,2'-, 2,3'-, 2,5- and 2,6-positions, i.e. all have at least one substituent *ortho*- to the central 1,1'-bond, c.f. structure XXXVI.

XXXVI

Synthetical difficulties prevented our studying a wide range of disubstituted dianils, but the 2,2'-, 2,3'-, 2,5-, and 2,6-dichloro- dianils, the 2,2'-, 2,5-, and 2,6-dibromo- dianils, and the 2,2'-, 2,3'-, and 2,5-dimethyl dianils have been obtained pure. None of the compounds exhibits smectic properties.

2,5-Disubstituted dianils. The absence of smectic properties for these compounds is hardly surprising, for the two substituents must lie on opposite sides of the molecule, thus preventing the close approach of neighbouring molecules on either side. As would be expected then, the Δt (H–X) nematic values are large— Δt (H–Cl) = 134·6° and Δt (H–Br) = 157·7°. The 2-substituent will decrease the nematic thermal stability by both breadth and steric effects, and the 5-substituent will decrease the nematic thermal stability by a breadth effect alone. Now the average Δt (Cl–Br) nematic value for the 2- and 2'- substituted monoanils and the 2-substituted dianils is 16·3°, and the average Δt (Cl–Br) nematic value is 8·25° when a breadth effect alone operates. One would predict therefore that Δt (Cl–Br) nematic would be 24·55° for the 2,5-disubstituted dianils, and it is interesting to note that the actual decrease observed is 23·1°. It would therefore appear that when the substituents are changed, the over-all decrease in nematic thermal stability is the approximate sum of the usual decreases obtained with each substituent separately, i.e. an additive effect seems to operate, and this fact will be referred to again later.

Δt (Me–Cl) nematic is only 3·1°, and the close similarity of nematic-isotropic transition temperatures for isomeric methyl and chloro- substituted compounds again reminds us that the breadth and steric effects of these two substituents must be closely similar, i.e. the interplanar angle calculated for 2-methylbiphenyl is probably too large.

2,3'-Disubstituted dianils. For these compounds, Δt (Me–Cl) nematic is again very small, only −0·7°. The nematic mesophases of the 2,3'-

dimethyl and dichloro-dianils are slightly more thermally stable than those of the corresponding 2,5-disubstituted compounds—by 4·4 and 8·2° respectively. This relatively small difference between the pairs suggests that the 2,3'-disubstituted compounds adopt a *trans-* configuration (XXXVII). The 2,3'- and 2,5-disubstituted systems are therefore related as 2'- and 2-substituted systems. It will be remembered that the 2'-substituted monoanils have slightly more thermally stable nematic mesophases than the 2-substituted analogues, and the slightly higher

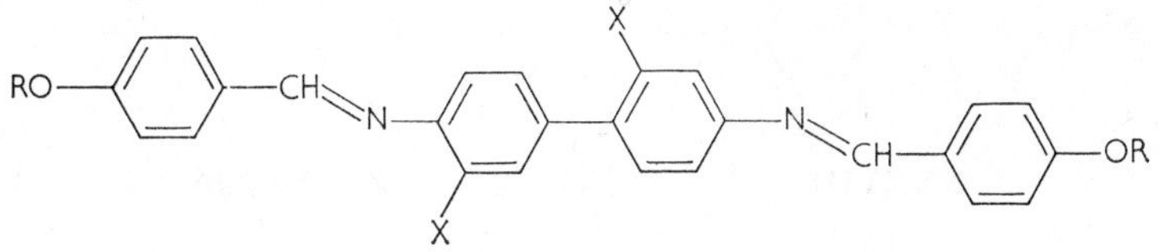

XXXVII

nematic thermal stabilities of the 2,3'-disubstituted compounds probably stem from the same effects. Unfortunately, the 2,3'-dibromo-dianils are not available to check that Δt (Cl–Br) nematic is normal.

2,6-Disubstituted Dianils. Two main points should be noted: (1) Δt (Cl–Br) nematic = 26·3°—even greater than Δt (Cl–Br) nematic = 23·1° for the 2,5-disubstituted dianils; and (2) the nematic thermal stabilities for the 2,6-disubstituted compounds are lower by some 18–22° than those for the 2,5-disubstituted dianils.

In the 2,6-disubstituted dianils, the 2-substituent may be considered to cause the twisting of the phenyl groups from the plane, and this being so, the 6-substituent should act merely by increasing the breadth of the molecule. Looked at in this light, the 2,5- and 2,6-disubstituted dianils should be closely similar in behaviour. It could be argued that the molecules of the 2,6- and 2,5- isomers may pack differently in the meso-phases, but this would not account for differences between the Δt (Cl–Br) nematic values.

However, it is clear from molecular models that the second chloro-substituent in the 6-position does in fact *strain* the 1,1'-bond unless the interplanar angle is allowed to increase. It has also been demonstrated by Beaven[20] that the changes in intensity and wavelength of the con-jugation band for biphenyl correspond to a decrease in the extent of conjugation and an increase in the interplanar angle on passing from 2-methyl- to 2,6-dimethyl-biphenyl. It would be expected then that similar changes would occur with other substituents. If a larger inter-planar angle does exist in the 2,6-disubstituted dianils, the lower nematic thermal stabilities of the compounds would be explained. Moreover, a 6-bromo- substituent will increase the interplanar angle more than a 6-chloro- substituent, and the increase in Δt (Cl–Br) nematic on passing

from the 2,5- to the 2,6-disubstituted dianils would therefore be explained.

2,2'-Disubstituted dianils. (see also p. 293) For these compounds,
Δt (Cl–Br) nematic is 27·6° and Δt (Me–Cl) nematic is 0°. These dianils
may be considered to adopt either a *cis-* (XXXVIII) or a *trans-*
(XXXIX) configuration with respect to the 2- and 2'- substituents.

XXXVIII   XXXIX

If the *trans-* configuration is adopted, one substituent will exert its
normal breadth-increasing effect on the system, and the other, due to
rotation of the substituted phenyl ring out of the plane of the paper,
will exert a smaller breadth increasing effect. Therefore, the 2,2'-disub-
stituted dianils should have higher nematic thermal stabilities than the
2,5- or 2,6-disubstituted dianils, for the same reasons that the 2,3'-
disubstituted dianils have more thermally stable nematic mesophases
than the 2,5-disubstituted dianils. The *trans-* arrangement does not
therefore account for the fact that the nematic mesophases of the 2,2'-
disubstituted dianils are less stable, by some 7–8°, than those of the
2,6- isomers, or for the fact that Δt (Cl–Br) nematic is 1·3° higher than
for the 2,6-disubstituted compounds.

For this reason, one must consider the apparently less likely *cis-*
configuration for the molecule. The interplanar angle for structure
XXXVIII will be greater than for the 2-substituted dianils or the 2,5-
disubstituted dianils, but molecular models do not help to decide
whether the interplanar angle for a 2,2'-disubstituted dianil is greater
than for a 2,6-disubstituted dianil. However, Beaven[20] has shown that
the biphenyl conjugation is less marked, as measured by ultra violet
absorption, for 2,2'-dimethylbiphenyl, and one would infer then that the
interplanar angle would be larger than for 2,6-dimethylbiphenyl. The
more twisted structure of the molecule would certainly account for the
lower thermal stabilities of the mesophases of the 2,2'-disubstituted
dianils compared with the 2,6-disubstituted dianils.

The fact that Δt (Cl–Br) nematic is 1·3° greater for the 2,2'-disub-
stituted dianils than for the 2,6-disubstituted dianils suggests that the
interplanar angle increases more in the 2,2'-disubstituted systems on
passing from chloro- to bromo- substituted compound. This is understandable, because the increased interplanar angle of the 2,6-disub-
stituted dianils over that of the 2-substituted compounds arises through

steric interaction of the 6-substituent with the other ring, whilst for the 2,2'-disubstituted dianils, the increased angle arises from steric interactions between the two substituents. Therefore, as the sizes of both substituents increase, the interplanar angles for the 2,2'-disubstituted systems will increase faster than for the 2,6-disubstituted compounds, for which the size of the phenyl ring remains the same, irrespective of the substituents.

There is in fact a considerable accumulation of evidence confirming the view that 2- and 2'-substituents in biphenyl lie *cis*- to one another. Thus, Beaven,[20,21] has concluded that the 2,2'-dihalogenobiphenyls have *cis*- configurations, and electron diffraction work by Bastiansen[15] on the four isomeric 2,2'-dihalogenobiphenyls has shown that the inter-halogen distances are approximately twice the van der Waal's radii of the halogen atoms, i.e. the halogeno- substituents are in a *cis*- disposition. Smare,[22] and Foweather and Hargreaves[13] have used X-ray crystallography to demonstrate the *cis*- configurations of 2,2'-dichlorobenzidine and *m*-tolidine hydrochloride. The potential energy curves for *cis*- and *trans*- configurations of 2,2'-disubstituted biphenyls have also been discussed recently.[23]

We have seen then that the positional order of decreasing nematic thermal stability for the disubstituted dianils is

$$2,3'->2,5->2,6->2,2'-$$

From a study of these compounds, further evidence has been obtained to show that the greater the interplanar angle for the biphenyl nucleus, the lower the nematic thermal stability of the system. This again suggests that free rotation does not occur about the 1,1'-bond of the biphenyl nucleus in the nematic states of compounds. Again, it is noticeable that the nematic isotropic transition temperatures for isomeric methyl and chloro- derivatives are closely similar, and this emphasizes that the methyl group probably exerts a steric effect which is less marked than that which would occur if the group behaved as a spherical unit of van der Waal's radius = 2·0 Å.

2,2',6-Trisubstituted dianils. Only the trichloro- derivatives have been obtained pure, and as would be expected, the compounds exhibit only nematic properties. The nematic thermal stability of these trichloro- derivatives (XL) is markedly reduced (62°) compared with

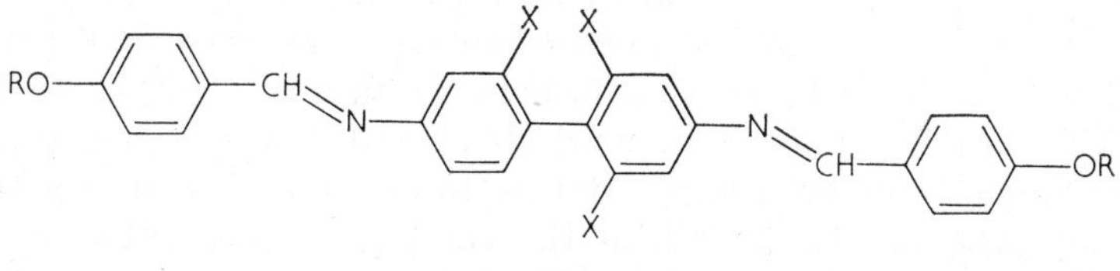

XL

the 2,2'-dichloro- dianils, and indeed, in the case of the decyl ether, the nematic mesophase has become monotropic. The corresponding tribromo- derivatives were prepared, but satisfactory purifications could not be effected on them. The compounds did exhibit monotropic nematic mesophases, for which the average (C_7–C_{10}) nematic-isotropic transition temperature was about 85°. This would give a Δt (Cl–Br) nematic value of 37–38°, which is probably slightly high, since the tribromo- compounds were impure. We may predict Δt (Cl–Br) nematic for these trihalogeno- dianils by taking Δt (Cl–Br) for the 2,2'-disubstituted dianil, and adding the normal Δt (Cl–Br) value of 8·25°, to allow for the effect of the 6-substituent. This leads to a calculated decrease of 27·6 + 8·25 = 35·85°, which is in agreement with the approximate experimental value. The isotropic liquids of the tribromodianils yield the nematic mesophases only when they are cooled 10–30° below the melting points, and it is very unlikely that the tri-iodo- or other heavily trisubstituted dianils of this type will be mesomorphic. The trifluoro- and trimethyl derivatives should, however, exhibit mesophases.

2,2',6,6'-Tetrasubstituted dianils (XLI). The even greater synthetical difficulties encountered with these compounds have meant that the effect of tetrachloro- substitution alone has been studied, and only enough of the parent benzidine was obtained to make one dianil— 4,4'-di-(*p*-n-heptyloxybenzylideneamino)-2,2',6,6'-tetrachlorobiphenyl.

RO—⟨benzene⟩—CH=N—⟨benzene, X X / X X⟩—⟨benzene, X X / X X⟩—N=CH—⟨benzene⟩—OR

XLI

The compound was not mesomorphic, and this was expected, because another substantial decrease in nematic thermal stability from that of the analogous trichloro- compound will occur. The melting point of the tetrachloro- dianil is 89°, and therefore Δt (H–Cl) nematic is >256°. The tetrafluoro- derivatives may be mesomorphic, but this is extremely doubtful.

As long ago as 1951, Wiegand[24] made a brief investigation of the effects of di- and tetra- substitution on the mesomorphic properties of 4,4'-di-(*p*-methoxybenzylideneamino)biphenyl. In agreement with the above findings on the longer chain heptyl ether, he demonstrated that the 2,2',6,6'-tetrachloro- and methyl- substituted systems were not mesomorphic, and he attributed this to the non-coplanarity of the molecule—the melting points of the compounds were 217–219° and 212–213°, respectively. He also studied the 2,2'- and 3,3'-dichloro- and dimethyl derivatives, and pointed out that the chloro- and methyl substituents may in each case be arranged either *cis-* or *trans-* in the biphenyl ring system, c.f. structures XXXIII, XXXVIII, and XXXIX. In the case of the 2,2'-disubstituted systems he assumed that the *trans-*configuration would be planar, and that only the *cis-* configuration would result in any twisting about the 1,1'-bond, i.e. he assumed that the steric effect stems from interference between the two chloro- or methyl substituents, and that a steric effect between say the 2-substituent and the 6'-hydrogen does not arise. Simply because the 2,2'-disubstituted derivatives were mesomorphic, he concluded that the molecules must adopt the *trans-* configuration, which he considered to be planar. It is unfortunate that he chose to study the methyl ethers, because, as is evident from Table X.11, the nematic-isotropic transition temperature of 4,4'-di-(p-methoxybenzylideneamino)biphenyl cannot be obtained, and the large decrease in nematic thermal stability from parent compound to the 2,2'-dichloro- or dimethyl derivative, which is observed for the longer chain ethers, is masked. Wiegand also points out that both the *cis-* and *trans-* configurations of the 3,3'-disubstituted compounds are planar, and he reaches no decision between the two possible configurations for the molecules.

TABLE X.11

4,4'-Di-(p-methoxybenzylideneamino)biphenyls[24]

Substituent	solid-nematic (°)	nematic-isotropic (°)
—	252–253	>345
3,3'-dichloro-	148–149	>340
2,2'-dichloro-	215–216	320–321
3,3'-dimethyl	180–181	353
2,2'-dimethyl	172–173	307–308

It is interesting to record that 3,3',5,5'-tetrachlorobenzidine is quite readily available but the diamine does not react with an aldehyde to give a Schiff's base. 3-Nitrobenzidine (XLII) is also anomalous, reacting with aldehydes to give *mono*anils, and leaving the amino- group *ortho-* to the nitro- group unattacked, under normal conditions.

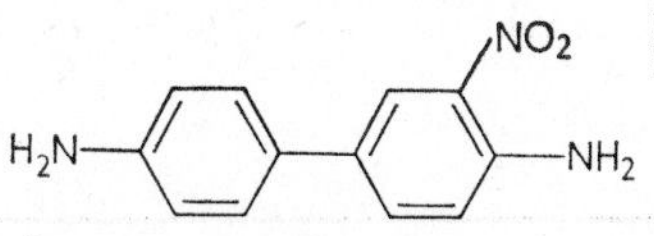

XLII

3. THE ADDITIVITY OF THE EFFECTS OF SUBSTITUENTS ON THE MESOMORPHIC THERMAL STABILITIES OF DI-, TRI-, AND TETRA-SUBSTITUTED DIANILS

In discussing the *di*substituted dianils, we have noticed that the decreases in nematic thermal stability (Δt (X_1–X_2) nematic) on passing from, say, chloro- to bromo- may be obtained in certain cases by adding the decreases in thermal stability which are known to occur for each substituent separately. In only one instance has this additive effect been mentioned when $X_1 = H$, i.e. in the case of the 3,3'-disubstituted dianils, for which Δt (H–Cl) nematic is approximately double Δt (H–Cl) nematic for the 3-substituted dianils. It is therefore of some interest to examine whether such an additivity principle is more generally applicable throughout the series of disubstituted dianils, and also to systems carrying more than two substituents. To test this idea, the nematic-isotropic transition temperatures of the heptyl–decyl ethers, and the smectic-nematic transition temperatures of the decyl ethers of the various chloro- substituted dianils are recorded in Table X.12. In fact, so few of the systems give smectic mesophases, that no general con-

TABLE X.12

Chloro- substituted 4,4'-Di-(p-n-alkoxybenzylideneamino)biphenyls

	Average transition temperature (°)			
	smectic-nematic (C_{10})	Δt (H–Cl) smectic	nematic-isotropic (C_7–C_{10})	Δt (H–Cl) nematic
H	311·5		345	
3-Cl	279	42·5	296·6	48·4
2-Cl	153·8	157·7	260·9	84·1
3,3'-di-Cl	155·2	156·3	250·8	94·2
2,3'-di-Cl			218·6	126·4
2,5-di-Cl			210·4	134·6
2,6-di-Cl			192·1	152·9
2,2'-di-Cl			185	160
2,2',6-tri-Cl			122·9	222·1
2,2',6,6'-tetra-Cl*			<89	>256

* C_7 only

clusions can be reached about the applicability of an additivity rule to smectic thermal stabilities, and the discussion is therefore restricted to the nematic properties of the compounds.

(1) *3,3'-Dichloro- dianils.* Δt (H–Cl) = 94·2°, i.e. approximately double the observed Δt (H–Cl) value of 48·4° for the 3-chloro dianils. It will be remembered that this relationship indicates a *trans*-arrangement of the 3,3'-dichloro- substituents.

(2) *2,5-Dichloro- dianils.* Δt (H–Cl) may be considered as the sum of the decreases in nematic thermal stability arising from the molecular broadening effect of the 5-chloro- substituent, and the breadth and steric effects of the 2-chloro- substituent. If we add Δt (H–Cl) = 48·4° (3-Cl dianils) and Δt (H–Cl) = 84·1° (2-Cl dianils), we obtain Δt (H–Cl) for the 2,5-dichloro- dianils = 132·5°, agreeing well with the observed decrease of 134·6°.

(3) *2,2'-, 2,3'-,* and *2,6-Dichloro- dianils.* The nematic thermal stabilities of these compounds have already been discussed in detail. In the case of the 2,2'- and 2,6-dichloro- compounds, the additivity principle would not be expected to apply, because the interplanar angles involved are probably larger than those for the simple monosubstituted systems which would be used to supply the data for the summations. Similarly, even if the substituents in the 2,3'-dianils are *trans-*, a deviation from additivity is again likely, because the substituent in the ring which is rotated from the plane of the rest of the molecule will affect the interplanar cohesions, and not the side to side cohesions which will be involved in the case of the monosubstituted system used to obtain the calculated decrease in thermal stability. However, a summation of the Δt (H–Cl) values for the 2- and 3-substituted dianils gives a reasonable approximation (132·5°) to the Δt (H–Cl) value of 126·4° for the 2,3'-dichloro- dianils.

(4) *2,2',6-Trichloro- dianils.* If we take the decrease in nematic thermal stability due to the 6-chloro- substituent as the difference between the Δt (H–Cl) values for the 2-chloro- and 2,6-dichloro- dianils, we obtain a figure of 68·8°, and if this is added to Δt (H–Cl) = 160° for the 2,2'-dichloro- dianils, we obtain a predicted Δt (H–Cl) value of 228·8° for the trichloro- dianils, in very good agreement with the observed decrease in nematic thermal stability of 222·1°. It is possible that the increase in interplanar angle due to the 6-chloro- substituent is greater in the 2,6-dichloro- dianils than in the 2,2',6-trichloro- dianils, and this may account for the discrepancy of 6·7°.

(5) *2,2',6,6'-Tetrachloro- dianils.* Beaven[20] has shown that the biphenyl conjugation decreases on passing from 2,2',6-trimethyl- to 2,2',6,6'-tetramethyl-biphenyl. It appears then that a 6'-substituent increases the interplanar angle, and should therefore decrease the nematic thermal stability of a system by both a breadth effect and some

degree of steric effect. If we assume that Δt (H–Cl) due to the $6'$-substituent is $60°$, i.e. about the same as the decrease given by the 6-chloro-substituent in the $2,2'6$-trichloro- dianils, and if we add to this Δt (H–Cl) $= 222\cdot1°$ for the $2,2',6$-trichloro- dianils, we obtain Δt (H–Cl) $= 282\cdot1°$ for the $2,2',6,6'$-tetrachloro- dianils. Therefore, the average $(C_7–C_{10})$ nematic-isotropic transition temperature for these dianils would be $63\cdot9°$. The heptyl ether in fact solidified to a glass at about $89°$, and it is therefore apparent why this type of compound is not mesomorphic.

It seems therefore that in these cases in which it is reasonable to apply an additivity principle, each chloro- substituent acts separately in lowering the nematic thermal stability, and that the over-all decrease in nematic thermal stability is the sum of the decreases due to each chloro-substituent. Since it has been noted that the nematic-isotropic transition temperatures for isomeric chloro- and methyl substituted biphenyls are always closely similar, it follows that the additivity principle applies to methyl substituents. A comparison of the data for the methyl substituted dianils in Table X.13 with those in Table X.12 for the chloro-compounds shows how close the agreement is.

TABLE X.13

Methyl substituted 4,4'-Di-(p-n-alkoxybenzylideneamino)biphenyls

Substituent	Average transition temperature Nematic-isotropic $(C_7–C_{10})$	Δt (H–Me) nem.
H*	$345°$	
2-Me*	$259\cdot6$	$85\cdot4°$
3,3'-di-Me	$254\cdot5$	$90\cdot6$
2,3'-di-Me	$217\cdot9$	$127\cdot1$
2,5-di-Me	$213\cdot5$	$131\cdot5$
2,2'-di-Me	$184\cdot8$	$160\cdot2$

* These compounds do exhibit smectic mesophases.

Finally we should consider whether bromo- substituents have additive effects on the nematic thermal stabilities. If this is so, then Δt (H–Br) nematic for the 3-bromo- dianils should be half Δt (H–Br) nematic $= 112\cdot4°$ for the $3,3'$-dibromo- dianils. The calculated decrease $(\Delta t$ (H–Br) nematic) of $56\cdot2°$ for the 3-bromo- dianils in fact agrees closely with the observed decrease of $58\cdot2°$.

In the case of the 2-bromo- dianils, Δt (H–Br) nematic is $99\cdot2°$, and, as seen above, we may take Δt (H–Br) nematic for a 5- (equivalent to a 3-) substituent as $56 \cdot 2°$. The sum of these decreases gives Δt (H–Br) nematic $= 155 \cdot 4°$ for the 2,5-dibromo- dianils. The observed decrease is $157 \cdot 7°$.

The 2,2′,6-tribromo- dianils were not obtained absolutely pure, but the average (C_7–C_{10}) nematic-isotropic transition temperature observed was $84 \cdot 8°$, equivalent to a Δt (H–Br) nematic value of $260 \cdot 2°$. For the 2,2′-dibromo- dianils, Δt (H–Br) is $187 \cdot 6°$, and the difference between the Δt (H–Br) values for the 2,6-dibromo- and the 2-bromo- dianils is $80°$. On adding these two temperatures, we obtain Δt (H–Br) $= 267 \cdot 6°$ for the 2,2′,6-tribromo- dianils. This increase would give an average nematic-isotropic transition temperature of $77 \cdot 4°$ for these tribromo-dianils, but this is $7 \cdot 4°$ lower than the recorded average transition temperature. However, we should remember that the predicted average transition temperature for the trichloro- dianils was $6 \cdot 7°$ low, and it was tentatively suggested that the 6-chloro- substituent has a larger effect on the interplanar angle in the 2,6-disubstituted dianils, than it has in the 2,2′,6-trichloro- dianils. If the discrepancy of $6 \cdot 7°$ in the case of the trichloro- dianils is explained in these terms, then the slightly larger discrepancy of $7 \cdot 6°$ is not unexpected in the case of the tribromo-dianils. This would suggest that the nematic-isotropic transition temperatures for the 2,2′,6-tribromo- dianils are approximately correct, despite the fact that the compounds were considered to be somewhat impure.

These studies of the di-, tri-, and tetra-substituted dianils have therefore high-lighted the additivity of the effects of substituents on nematic thermal stabilities. Presumably, similar additivity effects would operate in systems other than those of the dianil type, but it has not been possible to ascertain whether this is the case, because a sufficient number of suitably substituted compounds has not been prepared.

From the discussions of the effects of changes in molecular constitution on the mesomorphic thermal stabilities of compounds, it is clear that mesomorphic transition temperatures exhibit trends which may be related, in a qualitative way at least, to the particular changes in structure and type of the molecules. The approximate constancy of certain Δt (X_1–X_2) mesomorphic values for substituted systems, and the success of applying additivity principles to the di- and poly-substituted dianils serve to underline the fact that mesomorphic transition temperatures are related to the *structures* of the *molecules* in a way in which melting points are not, presumably because solid-mesomorphic or -isotropic liquid transitions are complicated by variations in the crystal lattice type and crystal lattice energy, and the way in which these factors affect the temperature of melting. The success of applying qualitative arguments to discussions of the relative mesomorphic behaviours of so many different substituted and unsubstituted systems naturally leads one to consider whether quantitative relationships could be established between the absolute temperature of a given mesomorphic change (smectic-nematic, smectic-isotropic, nematic-isotropic, etc.) and relevant molecular quantities such as the dipole moments of the molecules, the molecular polarizabilities, the intermolecular separations, etc. Although the achievement of quantitative relations of this kind represents the ultimate aim of all work on the subject of mesomorphism and chemical constitution, their realization is not easy, because the *detailed* aspects of the molecular organization in the mesomorphic states remain unknown. However, thanks to the recent work of Maier and Saupe, a very notable advance has been made towards obtaining quantitative relationships for the nematic-isotropic transition temperatures of substances. In 1958, these authors first published[25] a simple molecular theory of the nematic liquid crystalline state, by which it was shown that the nematic-isotropic transition temperature may be determined by calculation of the free enthalpies of the phases involved at the transition.

The change in inner energy at the nematic-isotropic transition is given as

$$\Delta U = U_n - U_i = -\tfrac{1}{2}(N_L/m)(A/V_n^2)S^2$$

where

N_L = the Avogadro number,
V = the molecular volume,
S = the degree of order of the molecules arranged with their long axes parallel to one another,
m = an amount related to the degree of steric hindrance of the molecules,
A = a characteristic constant for the substance, independent of temperature and volume.

Substituting for A and m, values for S were calculated for different temperatures, for p-azoxyanisole, and the calculated values were found to agree well with the experimentally* determined degrees of molecular order at these temperatures. In the following year, Maier and Saupe[26] carried their work a stage further by formulating a molecular statistical theory of the nematic liquid crystalline state. A formula was derived for the average inner field acting on a single molecule in a nematic molecular order. It is interesting to note that the calculations were limited to the dipole-dipole constituent of pure dispersion forces, i.e.

---

* By measurement of the infra red dichroism.

quadruple-quadruple interactions were ignored, and that interactions of a dipole-dipole or induced dipole nature involving the permanent dipole moments of the molecules were not considered to make significant contributions. Maier's reasons for neglecting such interactions were based on his infra red studies[27] of the nematic and isotropic liquid states of various substances. For a given substance, the spectra of the two states were always closely similar, and this led him to believe that no specific interactions existed between the molecules in the nematic melt. This view has now been confirmed by the author's work on the 3'-substituted 4'-n-alkoxybiphenyl-4-carboxylic acids and other systems, by which it has been shown that dipole moments do not appear to influence the nematic-isotropic transition temperatures. That is, unlike smectic-nematic transition temperatures, nematic-isotropic transition temperatures are a function of the dispersion forces, which depend on the polarizability of the system, and are inversely proportional to some power of the molecular separation—hence the existence of a relationship between the nematic-isotropic transition temperatures and the breadths of the molecules.

Maier and Saupe have demonstrated mathematically that the inner field should produce a nematic molecular order within a given temperature range, and that this order should transform at a certain temperature into an isotropic molecular order. The reader is referred to the original paper for the detailed mathematical treatment, but it should be mentioned here that the analysis predicts, as required by experiment, that the nematic-isotropic transition shall be discontinuous and occur with energy uptake, i.e. that it shall be a first order transition.

More recently still (1960), Maier and Saupe[29] have improved their theory by the introduction of close range order parameters, and have calculated constituents of thermodynamic energy functions corresponding to the nematic molecular order. A correlation is obtained between the volume discontinuity at the transition to the isotropic liquid and the degree of order (S_K) of the nematic mesophase in the neighbourhood of the transition point.

$$\frac{\Delta V_K}{V_{n,K}} = - \frac{kV_{n,K}^2 T_K}{AS_K^2} \left[\frac{AS_K(S_K + 1)}{kT_K V_{n,K}^2} - 2l_n I \frac{AS_K}{kT_K V_{n,K}^2} \right]$$

The reader is again referred to the original paper for the derivation of this equation and a full definition of the symbols, and we need only note that T_K is the temperature of the nematic-isotropic transition. This relationship permits an empirical determination of the parameter A which is characteristic of the substance. This parameter A (expressed in 10^{-9} erg. cm^6) has been obtained for thirteen substances including p-methoxycinnamic acid, 2,4-nonadienoic acid, ethyl p-(4-ethoxy-benzylidenamino)-α-methylcinnamate, and eight 4,4'-di-n-alkoxy-azoxy- and -azo-benzenes. For this range of compounds, three rules have been established.

(1) All nematic melts give a value of S_K approximately equal to 0·44 in the vicinity of the nematic-isotropic transition.

(2) In the neighbourhood of the clearing point, the quantity $A/kT_K V_{n,K}^2$ also has an almost constant value of 4·55.

(3) By plotting values of S, the degree of molecular order, for a range of temperatures (T) against $T V_n^2/T_K V_{n,K}^2$ one obtains a curve which is of the same type for all the nematic substances.

Whilst it is clear that quantitative theories concerning the thermal stabilities of mesomorphic states have still a long way to progress, the value of the work by Maier and Saupe is obvious, and it is hoped that their theories will be extended and applied to a much wider range of compounds, so that more of the many problems involved in the study of chemical constitution and mesomorphic behaviour may be more thoroughly comprehended.

REFERENCES

1. Gray, G. W. and Jones, B. (1954). *J. Chem. Soc.* 2556.
2. Gray, G. W. and Jones, B. (1955). *J. Chem. Soc.* 236.
3. Byron, D. J., Gray, G. W., Ibbotson, A. and Worrall, B. M. Unpublished work.
4. Gray, G. W. and Jones, B. (1954). *J. Chem. Soc.* 683.
5. Iball, J. and Burns, D. M. (1954). *Nature* **173**, 635.
6. Gray, G. W., Hartley, J. B., Ibbotson, A. and Jones, B. (1955). *J. Chem. Soc.* 4359.
7. Gray, G. W. and Ibbotson, A. (1957). *J. Chem. Soc.* 3228.
8. Gray, G. W. and Worrall, B. M. (1959). *J. Chem. Soc.* 1545.
9. Gray, G. W. and Jones, B. (1954). *J. Chem. Soc.* 1467.
10. Gray, G. W., Jones, B. and Marson, F. (1956). *J. Chem. Soc.* 1417.
11. Gray, G. W., Jones, B. and Marson, F. (1957). *J. Chem. Soc.* 393.
12. Gray, G. W. (1958). " Steric Effects in Conjugated Systems ", Butterworths, London, p. 160 (Editor: G. W. Gray).
13. Foweather, F. and Hargreaves, A. (1948). *Acta Cryst.* **1**, 81.
14. Firag, M. S. and Kader, N. A. (1960). *J. Chem. U.A.R.* **3**, 1.
15. Bastiansen, O. (1949). *Acta. Chem. Scand.* **3**, 408; (1950). **4**, 926; (1954). **8**, 1593.
16. Beaven, G. H. and Hall, D. M. (1956). *J. Chem. Soc.* 4637.
17. Branch, S. J. and Gray, G. W. Unpublished work.
18. Byron, D. J. and Gray, G. W. Unpublished work.
19. Toussaint, J. (1948). *Acta Cryst.* **1**, 43.
20. Beaven, G. H. (1958). " Steric Effects in Conjugated Systems ", Butterworths, London, p. 23 (Editor: G. W. Gray).
21. Beaven, G. H. (1958). " Steric Effects in Conjugated Systems ", Butterworths, London, p. 170 (Editor: G. W. Gray).
22. Smare, D. L. (1948). *Acta Cryst.* **1**, 150.
23. Smith, J. W. (1958). " Steric Effects in Conjugated Systems ", Butterworths, London, p. 172 (Editor: G. W. Gray).

24. Wiegand, C. (1951). *Z. Naturforsch.* **6b**, 240.
25. Maier, W. and Saupe, A. (1958). *Z. Naturforsch.* **13a**, 564.
26. Maier, W. and Saupe, A. (1959). *Z. Naturforsch.* **14a**, 882.
27. Maier, W. and Englert, G. (1957). *Z. phys. Chem. (Frankfurt)* **12**, 123.
28. Maier, W. and Englert, G. (1960). *Z. Elektrochem.* **64**, 689.
29. Maier, W. and Saupe, A. (1960). *Z. Naturforsch.* **15a**, 287.

AUTHOR INDEX

Numbers in parentheses are reference numbers and are included to assist in locating references when the authors' names are not mentioned in the text. Numbers in italics refer to the page on which the reference is listed.

A

Aaron, C., 131 (18), *138*, 174 (15), 183 (15), *196*
Andrew, E. R., 94 (38), *96*

B

Balaban, I. E., 13 (14), *16*
Barth, G., 107, 109 (28), *124*
Bastiansen, O., 260 (15), 289, *298*
Bauer, E., 112, *124*
Baumgartner, G., 208 (16), 215, *238*
Beaven, G. H., 260 (16), 287, 288, 289, 293, *298*
Becherer, G., 97, *123*
Beevers, R. B., 14 (36), *16*, 51 (22), *54*
Beneschevich, D., 73, *79*
Bennett, G. M., 58 (2), *65*
Benton, D. P., 94 (35), *96*
Bernal, J. D., 66, 74, 77, *78*, *79*, 81, 84, 87, 94, *95*, 109, *124*, 144, 176, 186, 189, *196*
Bernamont, J., 112, *124*
Beveridge, J. M. R., 190, *196*
Bhide, B. V., 108, *124*
Bhide, R. D., 108, *124*
Bingham, E. C., 102 (11), *123*
Bircon, N., 184, *196*
Birstein, V., 36 (12), 38 (12), *54*, 74, *79*
Björnstähl, Y., 104, *123*
Bogojawlensky, A., 126, 127, 129, *138*
Bose, E., 67, *78*, 102, *123*
Bouma, P. J., 107, *124*
Bragg, Sir W., 28, 29, 35, 36, *54*
Branch, S. J., 266 (17), 269, 270, *298*
Branner, F., 14 (24), *16*
Broome, F. K., 14 (29), *16*
Brown, G. H., 82, 87, *95*, 104, 107, *123*, *124*
Browning, J., 14 (31), *16*
Bryan, R. F., 141, 145, *196*, 217 (15), *238*

Burns, D. M., 241 (5), *298*
Bury, C. R., 14 (31), *16*
Byron, D. J., 131 (17, 18), 134, *138*, 170 (13), 171 (13), 172 (14), 173 (14), 174 (15), 183 (15), *196*, 203 (13), 204 (15), 205 (13), *238*, 241 (3), 250 (3), 265 (3), 271 (3), 272 (3), 280 (18), *298*

C

Carr, E. F., 110, *124*
Chatelain, P., 33, 40, 49, *54*, 77, 78, *79*, 116, 117, 118, 120 (47, 48), *124*
Conrat, F., 102, *123*
Crowfoot, D., 66, *78*, 81, 84, 86, 87, 94, *95*, 109, *124*, 144, 176, 186, 189, *196*
Culling, P., 130 (16), *138*, 161 (9), 162 (9), 167 (9), *196*

D

Dave, J. S., 127, 129, 133 (12), 134, *138*, 183 (19), *196*
de Brettville, A., 88, *95*
de Broglie, M., 80, *95*
de Kock, A. C., 127, 134, *138*
Dewar, M. J. S., 127, 129, 133, 134, *138*, 183, *196*
Dreyer, J. F., 14 (25), *16*, 33 (11), *54*
Dunell, B. A., 94, *96*
Du Pont, G., 134, *138*

E

Eaborn, C., 195, *196*
Eichwold, E., 97, *123*
Englert, G., 89, 90, *95*, 297 (27), *299*
Ewing, R., 93, *96*

F

Falgueirettes, J., 117, 120, *124*
Ferguson, A., 121, *124*

301

304 AUTHOR INDEX

Stewart, G. W., 69, *78*, 82, 83, *95*
Stuart, A., 20, *54*
Stumpf, F., 47, *54*
Svedberg, T., 137, *138*

T

Tamman, G., 4, *15*, 127, *138*
Taschek, R., 89, *95*
Taylor, A. M., 89, *95*
Thomas, S. B., 114 (37), *124*
Tolstoi, N. A., 109, 111, *124*
Toussaint, J., 284, *298*
Tropper, H., 78, *79*
Tzvetkov, V., 67, 74, 75, 78, *78*, *79*, 104, 106, 107, 111, *123*, *124*

U

Ungar, C., 36 (12), 38 (12), *54*

V

Van Wyk, A., 72 (12), *79*
Vold, M. J., 13 (18), *16*, 94 (36), *96*
Vold, R. D., 13 (17–21), 14 (28), *16*, 94 (36, 37), *96*, 114, *124*

Vorländer, D., 89, 94, *95*, *96*, 99, 100, *123*, 127, 134 (21), *138*
Vries, Hl. de, 48, 50, *54*

W

Walter, R., 126, 127, *138*
Ward, J. C., 14 (36), *16*, 51 (22), *54*
Weygand, C., 151 (6), 176 (16), 184, 185, *196*
White, G. F., 102 (11), *123*
Wiegand, C., 187 (27), 191, *196*, 290 (24), 291, *299*
Wiehl, H. E., 107, 109 (28), *124*
Williams, D., 89, *95*
Windsor, P. A., 14 (32), *16*
Winogradow, N., 126, 127, 129, *138*
Worrall, B. M., 64 (6), *65*, 170 (13), 171 (13), 178 (18), *196*, 203 (13), 204 (13), 205 (13), *238*, 241 (3), 246 (8), 250 (3), 265 (3), 271 (3), 272 (3), *298*

Z

Zernicke, F., 67, 70, *78*
Zocher, H., 36, 38, *54*, 74, 76, 77, 78, *79*, 83, *95*
Zolina, V., 75, *79*

SUBJECT INDEX

For homologous *series* of *ethers* containing the n-alkoxy group and for the 4-n-alkylbenzoic acids, individual members of the series have *not* been listed in the index under methoxy, ethoxy, methyl, ethyl, etc., but are grouped under the chemical name of the particular *series* of compounds, e.g. 4-n-alkoxybenzoic acids and n-propyl 7-n-alkoxyfluorene-2-carboxylic acids. However, when reference is made in the text to a specific ether or 4-n-alkylbenzoic acid, rather than to the behaviour of the series as a whole, the page number in the index carries an asterisk.